Florida Freshwater Plants

Alison Fox

University of Florida
Institute of Food and Agricultural Sciences

Florida Freshwater Plants
A Handbook of Common Aquatic Plants in Florida Lakes

Mark V. Hoyer

Daniel E. Canfield, Jr.

Christine A. Horsburgh

Karen Brown

- by the same authors

The Handbook of Common Freshwater Fish in Florida Lakes, by Mark V. Hoyer and Daniel E. Canfield, Jr., presents research results of 40 species of fish found in Florida lakes. Like **Florida Freshwater Plants**, complete biological description, with photographs and diagrams, is provided for each species. Additional information: population statistics, demographics, and water chemistries. SP160. ISBN 0-916287-10-6.

- of related interest

Aquatic Macrophytes and Their Relation to the Limnology of Florida Lakes presents a thorough treatment of the role of aquatic plants in Florida lakes. SP115.

Identification Manual for Wetland Plant Species of Florida, by Robert L. Dressler, David W. Hall, Kent D. Perkins, and Norris H. Williams. Basic information about 250 plant species found in Florida's wetlands are covered in this book. Basic botanical descriptions, preferred habitats, and keys to recognition are accompanied by diagrams showing flowering season and geographical distribution. Color photos and black-and-white drawings throughout. Publication SP35.

Aquatic Plant Identification Deck, by Victor Ramey. Seventy-two laminated cards provide color photographs of aquatic plants on one side and basic information about them on the other. The set is pocket-sized and post-bound at one corner, ideal for field use. Publication SM50.

Aquatic Plant Identification Poster. This beautiful four-color poster illustrates many important aquatic plants. A color drawing of each plant shows its primary features and is accompanied by its common and scientific names. Publication SM51.

Resources Catalog. Many books, manuals, videos, CD-ROMS, flash cards, and other media related to natural science and food resources are available from the University of Florida's Institute of Food and Agricultural Sciences. Publication SP1. Price:$1.00.

The above books may be ordered by contacting:

    C.M. Hinton

    Publications Distribution Center

    University of Florida

    P.O. Box 11011

    Gainesville, Florida 32611-0011

    1-800-226-1764

Cover Design by Charles M. Brown

Cover Photos by Kerry Dressler, Alison Fox, and Jess Van Dyke

Table of Contents

Appendix

Foreword

Aquatic plants may either enhance or diminish the many industrial, navigational, and recreational uses of the state's freshwaters, depending on how skillfully they are managed. Understanding the biology of aquatic plants is fundamental to controlling their abundance and meeting management objectives. In response to this need, the Department of Fisheries and Aquatic Sciences of the University of Florida and the Center for Aquatic Plants have pooled their resources to develop a unique reference book, Florida Freshwater Plants: A Handbook of Common Aquatic Plants in Florida Lakes.

A special contribution came from Karen Brown, the Coordinator of Educational Media at the Center for Aquatic Plants. She provided the book with a particularly useful dimension by furnishing a literature search on all plant species in the Handbook, giving the reader a synopsis of all scientific work that has been conducted on each plant species to date.

The Handbook's authors, Mark Hoyer, Daniel Canfield, and Christy Horsburgh, are research scientists who have worked for the Department of Fisheries and Aquatic Sciences (formerly the Department of Fisheries and Aquaculture) since the department's formation in 1984. The Handbook fulfills the mission statement of the department, "... to advance our basic and applied knowledge of the biological structure and the productivity of Florida's freshwater, estuarine, and marine ecosystems." It was the authors' goal that this book (1) help aquatic plant management personnel understand the ranges of environmental conditions where an aquatic plant naturally occurs, and (2) provide an identification guide for a larger non-professional audience.

Thanks to the cooperative effort between the Center for Aquatic Plants and the Department of Fisheries and Aquatic Sciences, everyone who wishes to have a better understanding of common aquatic plants in Florida will benefit by having this historic, definitive management tool.

WALLIS H. CLARK, JR.

Department Chairman
Department of Fisheries and Aquatic Sciences
Institute of Food and Agricultural Sciences
University of Florida

RANDALL K. STOCKER

Center Director and Professor
Center for Aquatic Plants
Institute of Food and Agricultural Sciences
University of Florida

Introduction

An understanding of aquatic plant biology is important to the development of aquatic plant management strategies. The efficacy of mechanical, biological, and chemical controls; the success of aquascaping; and the effects of macrophyte management on water quality and fish and wildlife populations all depend on the ecological aspects of aquatic plants.

In this book, our major objective is to examine the relation of water chemistry in Florida lakes to the presence and distribution of 103 common aquatic plants. Most of these species occur in many other places across North America and the world, making these data valuable to aquatic biologists and interested citizens who manage the world's vast aquatic resources.

The designation of "common aquatic plant" was arrived at by arbitrarily setting 10 as the minimum number of lakes in which a species had to occur to be considered "common." Of the more than 170 species of aquatic plants identified in the 322 Florida lakes (Appendix–Table 1) used in this book, only 103 occurred in more than 10 lakes.

Much research has been conducted on many species of aquatic plants, especially nuisance species such as Eurasian watermilfoil (*Myriophyllum heterophyllum*), hydrilla (*Hydrilla verticillata*), and water hyacinth (*Eichhornia crassipes*). The most important environmental factors affecting macrophyte presence and distribution in lakes have been identified as lake trophic status (Hutchinson 1975), substrate characteristics (Pearsall 1920), light availability (Spence 1975; Chambers and Kalff 1985; Canfield et al. 1985), lake morphology (Pearsall 1917; Spence 1982; Duarte and Kalff 1986), and general water chemistry (Beal 1977; Hellquist 1982; Kandono 1982).

There are a few good books on Florida aquatic plants already available (Dressler et al. 1987 and 1991; Tarver et al. 1986; Godfrey and Wooten, 1979 and 1981), but they are mainly for identification purposes. This handbook is a summary of plant and water chemistry data collected on 322 Florida lakes (Appendix–Table 2) that cover the entire state (Figure 1). It includes water chemistry data to show the ranges of environmental conditions where an aquatic plant naturally occurs. The lakes are extremely diverse, ranging from acidic to alkaline, oligotrophic to hypereutrophic, and 2 to 180,000 hectares in size (Appendix–Table 3). The data were collected during several research and monitoring projects conducted over the last 15 years.

This book is organized similarly to the *Handbook of Common Freshwater Fish in Florida Lakes* (Hoyer and Canfield 1994): The introduction is followed by a methods section describing where and how the data were collected, then individual listings for the 103 plant species are arranged alphabetically by genus and species. Each species listing has a photograph of the plant and a Florida map showing the lakes found to contain that species, as well as all lakes in the data set. This illustrates any geographical pattern of that species in Florida. A table on the range of environmental variables for that species is presented. (Data from all lakes broken out by variable are found in Tables 4.1-4.16 in the appendix.) The listing is completed by sections on the species' description and distribution, biology, and Florida data. The photographs are used by permission from the Aquatic Plant Information Retrieval System at the University of Florida Center for Aquatic Plants; others who wish to use them are invited to contact that office at 352-392-1799.

A section that synthesized the available primary literature on each plant species was originally planned, similar to the way Carlander (1969, 1977) handled his two books on fish species. However, computer searches conducted by the Aquatic Plant Information Retrieval System (APIRS) yielded more than 200 references each for many of the species, which would have made this book excessively long. Thus, we listed only selected references to the basic ecology of the species and noted the total number of references to the plant in the APIRS database. Interested readers are urged to contact APIRS (University of Florida, Center for Aquatic Plants, 7922 N.W. 71 St., Gainesville, Fla. 32653-3071; http://aquat1.ifas.ufl.edu/) for further reference information on individual species.

Finally, we chose not to include a lengthy discussion of each species and water chemistry variable, incorporating the primary literature, and therefore present these data with many interpretations and uses left up to the reader.

Figure 1. Outline map of Florida, showing the locations of the 322 lakes from which data on aquatic weeds were collected for this book.

Methods

The data used for this book are compiled from several research and monitoring projects conducted over the last 15 years (Canfield 1981; Greis 1985; Canfield and Joyce 1985; Canfield and Hoyer 1992; Canfield et al. 1993; Florida Aquatic Plant Survey 1982 to 1992; Unpublished data, University of Florida). Lakes for which water chemistry data were available (n≈600) were compared to those lakes in which aquatic plant species had been identified (n≈450). This yielded a common data set of 322 lakes.

For both water chemistry and aquatic plant data, some lakes were sampled in multiple years and through different research projects. In these cases, all water chemistry data were averaged by year and then overall, and an aquatic plant species list for a lake was the sum of all species ever identified in that lake. All water chemistry variables were not sampled in every lake (Appendix–Table 2) because of lost or destroyed samples or different sampling protocols between studies. We were able, nevertheless, to estimate most water chemistry variables in the majority of lakes.

For statistical comparisons, pH was normally distributed, but the remaining variables were logarithmically transformed to meet the requirements of parametric statistics. The mean for each variable from the lakes with an individual species was compared to the mean for each variable of all lakes in the data set using Dunnett's test (SAS Institute, Inc., 1989). This yields a conservative comparison because the subset of lakes with an individual species is also in the group of all lakes. Thus statistical differences shown in this book should represent real trends in Florida lakes.

Literature Cited

Beal, E.O. 1977. A manual of marsh and aquatic vascular plants of North Carolina with habitat data. Technical Bulletin No. 247. North Carolina Agricultural Research Service, Raleigh.

Bureau of Aquatic Plant Management. 1982–1992. Florida Aquatic Plant Survey. Department of Environmental Protection, Tallahassee, Florida.

Canfield, D.E., Jr. 1981. Chemical and trophic state characteristics of Florida lakes in relation to regional geology. Florida Cooperative Fish and Wildlife Unit, Final Report, University of Florida, Gainesville.

Canfield, D.E., Jr., K.A. Langeland, S.B. Linda, and W.T. Haller. 1985. Relations between water transparency and maximum depth of macrophyte colonization in lakes. Journal of Aquatic Plant Management 23:25-28.

Canfield, D.E., Jr. and J.C. Joyce. 1985. Aquatic macrophytes of 55 Ocala National Forest lakes. Final Report (Contract #43-4283-5-369). Report on National Forests in Florida, U.S. Department of Agriculture, Tallahassee, Fla.

Canfield, D.E., Jr. and M.V. Hoyer. 1992. Aquatic macrophytes and their relation to the limnology of Florida lakes. Final report. Bureau of Aquatic Plant Management, Florida Department of Natural Resources, Tallahassee.

Canfield, D.E., Jr., S. Fisher, M.V. Hoyer, C.A. Horsburgh, M. Stonecipher, and D. Willis. 1993. Florida LAKEWATCH. Department of Fisheries and Aquatic Sciences, University of Florida, Gainesville.

Carlander, K.D., 1969. Handbook of Freshwater Fishery Biology, Volume 1. Iowa State University Press, Ames, Iowa.

Carlander, K.D., 1977. Handbook of Freshwater Fishery Biology, Volume 2. Iowa State University Press, Ames, Iowa.

Chambers, P.A. and J. Kalff. 1985. Depth distribution and biomass of submersed macrophyte communities in relation to Secchi depth. Canadian Journal of Fisheries and Aquatic Science 42: 701-709.

Cofrancesco, A.F., Jr. 1984. Alligatorweed and its biocontrol agents. Information Exchange. Bulletin A-84-3. U.S. Army Corps of Engineers, Vicksburg, Miss.

Dressler, R.L., D.W. Hall, K.D. Perkins, and N.H. Williams. 1987 and 1991. Identification manual for wetland plant species of Florida. Publication SP-35. Institute of Food and Agricultural Sciences, University of Florida, Gainesville.

Duarte, C.M. and J. Kalff. 1986. Littoral slope as a predictor of the maximum biomass of submerged macrophyte communities. Limnology and Oceanography 31:1072-1080.

Godfrey, R.K. and J.W. Wooten. 1979. Aquatic and Wetland Plants of the Southeastern United States–Monocotyledons. University of Georgia Press, Athens, Georgia. 712 pp.

Godfrey, R.K. and J.W. Wooten. 1981. Aquatic and Wetland Plants of the Southeastern United States–Dicotyledons. University of Georgia Press, Athens, Georgia. 933 pp.

Greis, J.G. 1985. A characterization of Ocala National Forest lakes. National Forests in Florida, U.S. Forest Service, Tallahassee, Florida.

Hellquist, C.B. 1980. Correlation of alkalinity and the distribution of *Potamogeton* in New England. Rhodora 82:331-344.

Hoyer, M.V. and D.E. Canfield, Jr. Handbook of Common Freshwater Fish in Florida Lakes. University of Florida, Gainesville. 178 pp.

Hutchinson, G.E. 1975. A treatise on limnology. Vol. III. Limnological Botany. John Wiley and Sons, New York. 660 pp.

Kadono, Y. 1982. Occurrence of aquatic macrophytes in relation to pH, alkalinity, Ca^{++}, Cl^- and conductivity. Japanese Journal of Ecology 32:39-44.

Maddox, D.M., L.A. Andres, R.D. Hennessey, R.D. Blackburn, and N.R. Spencer. 1971. Insects to control alligatorweed, an invader of aquatic ecosystems in the U.S. BioScience 21:985-991.

Pearsall, W.H. 1920. The aquatic vegetation of the English lakes. Journal of Ecology 8:163-201.

Literature Cited, cont.

Pearsall, W.H. 1917. The aquatic and marsh vegetation of Esthwaite water. Journal of Ecology 5:180-201.

Spence, D.H.N. 1975. Light and plant response in freshwater. Pp. 93-133 in Light as an ecological factor, II,G.C. Evans, R. Bainbridge, and O. Rackman, editors. Blackwell Scientific Publications, London.

Spence, D.H.N. 1982. The zonation of plants in freshwater lakes. Advances in Ecological Research 12:37-125.

Tarver, D.P., J.A. Rodgers, M.J. Mahler, and R.L. Lazor. 1986. Aquatic and wetland plants of Florida. Bureau of Aquatic Plant Research and Control, Florida Department of Natural Resources, Tallahassee.

Species Descriptions

Alternanthera philoxeroides (alligator-weed)

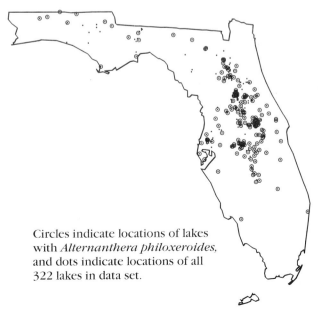

Circles indicate locations of lakes with *Alternanthera philoxeroides,* and dots indicate locations of all 322 lakes in data set.

Description and distribution

Alligator-weed is a sprawling, perennial, herbaceous plant that can root at the nodes and often forms dense mats of vegetation. The stems are hollow and either simple or branched. The leaves are opposite, entire, elliptical, 50–130 mm long, and 5–20 mm wide and have a distinct midrib on both sides. Some hairs may be found in the leaf axils. Flowers occur on long branches that are at least 55 mm long in a solitary head up to 13 mm in diameter and consist of a cluster of 6–20 white florets and five stamens. Alligator-weed, which is native to South America, is now naturalized in the southern United States and found in the Coastal Plain from Virginia to Florida, westward to Texas (Godfrey and Wooten 1981). The Florida distribution map shows that alligator-weed was found in lakes across the whole state, with no apparent geographical pattern.

Biology

Alligator-weed flowers primarily from April to October but probably can be found flowering throughout the year in Florida (Dressler et al. 1987). Mature seeds have not been found in the United States, suggesting all reproduction in Florida is by vegetative means. Growth can be extremely rapid with roots free-floating in water or rooted in soil-extracting nutrients. The rapid growth allows the plant to form large tangled mats that can cause problems in many aquatic systems. These weed problems have led to one of the few successful uses of aquatic insects as biocontrol agents. Three species of insect (*Agasicles hygrophila*, *Amynothrips andersoni*, and *Vogtia malloi*) were identified in Argentina as possible control agents for alligator-weed. After appropriate quarantine studies were conducted (Maddox et al. 1971), the alligator-weed flea beetle (*Agasicles*) was released into the United States in 1964, followed by *Amynothrips* in 1967, and the alligator-weed stem-borer (*Vogtia*) in 1971. The results were described by Cofrancesco (1984), leaving no doubt that these insects were successful biocontrol agents.

1

In Texas and Louisiana, alligator-weed is used as browse for deer and cattle. It is of little value to other forms of wildlife.

Florida data

Alligator-weed was identified in 180 lakes. The 10th and 90th percentiles for pH, alkalinity, total phosphorus, and total nitrogen values in these lakes show that 80% of the lakes with alligator-weed had levels between 5.3 and 8.8, 1.6 and 77.1 (mg/L as $CaCO_3$), 11 and 125 (μg/L), and 360 and 1930 (μg/L), respectively. These 180 lakes also collectively averaged significantly higher pH, alkalinity, total phosphorus, calcium, and magnesium values than all 322 lakes. Thus while alligator-weed can occur in a range of lake types, it tends to occur in alkaline, hardwater, eutrophic lakes.

Selected references from a total of 818 alligator-weed citations in the APIRS database:

Bowmer, K.H., G. McCorkelle, and P.I. Eberbach, 1991. Alligator weed control project 86/85. Final Report, National Water Research Program, Division Water Resources, CSIRO, Australia, 88 pp.

Brunson, M.W. No date. Aquatic weed identification and control—alligator weed and *Hydrilla verticillata*. Information Sheet 1034, Mississippi State University, Cooperative Extension Service, 2 pp.

Chester, E.W. 1988. Alligatorweed, *Alternanthera philoxeroides* (Mart.) Griseb. in Kentucky. Transactions of the Kentucky Academy of Science 49:140–142.

Cofrancesco, A.F. 1984. Ten year update of the status of alligatorweed in the Southeast. Proceedings of the 18th Annual Meeting, Aquatic Plant Control Research Program, 14–17 Nov. 1983, Raleigh, N.C. U.S. Army Corps of Engineers, Vicksburg, Miss. Misc. Paper A-84-4.

Cofrancesco, A.F. 1984. Alligatorweed and its biocontrol agents. U.S. Army Corps of Engineers, Waterways Experiment Station, Aquatic Plant Control Research Program. Information Exchange Bulletin, A-84-3.

Evans, L.S. 1948. Alligator weed—a new menace for Florida. Proceedings of the Annual Meeting Soil Science Society of Florida, 12-13 Oct. 1948, Clewiston, Fla. Volume 9:29–31.

Hellweg, M.R. 1993. Red hygro or alligator weed. Aquatic Gardener 6(5):159–160.

Julien, M.H., J.E. Broadbent, and K.L.S. Harley. 1979. The current status of biological control of *Alternanthera philoxeroides* in Australia. Proceedings of the Asian-Pacific Weed Science Society Conference 7:231–235.

Langeland, K.A., C.A. Nalepa, and K.G. Wilson. 1984. Status of alligatorweed control in North Carolina. Proceedings of the 18th Annual Meeting, Aquatic Plant Control Research Program, 14-17 Nov. 1983, Raleigh, N.C. U.S. Army Corps of Engineers. Vicksburg, Miss., Misc. Paper A-84-4, pp. 172–178.

Maddox, D.M. and R.N. Hambrick, 1970. A current examination of the alligatorweed flea beetle in Texas. 24th Southern Weed Science Society Annual Meeting, Memphis, Tenn. Pp. 343-348.

Quimby, P.C., G.B. Vogt, and S.H. Kay. 1983. Biocontrol of alligatorweed with insects. Proceedings of the Mississippi Entomological Association. Annual Meeting II (1):27-29.

Roberts, L.I.N., C.J. Winks, O.R.W. Sutherland, and R.A. Galbreath. 1984. Progress of biological control of alligatorweed in New Zealand. Proceedings of the New Zealand Weed and Pest Control Conference 37:50-54.

Schaefer, S. 1993. Other experience with *Alternanthera*. Aquatic Gardener 6(5):162.

Alternanthera philoxeroides

Variables	Mean all lakes (n=322)	Number of lakes	Mean	10th percentile	Median	90th percentile
pH*	6.7	180	7.1	5.3	7.2	8.8
Alkalinity (mg/L as CaCO$_3$)*	23.9	180	31.1	1.6	19.6	77.1
Conductance (µS/cm @ 25°C)	149	180	182	43	130	346
Color (Pt-Co units)	52	180	61	7	34	137
Total phosphorus (µg/L)*	45	180	61	11	28	125
Total nitrogen (µg/L)	866	180	998	360	819	1930
Chlorophyll a (µg/L)	20	180	25	2	11	67
Secchi (m)	1.8	159	1.4	0.4	1.1	3.0
Calcium (mg/L)*	17.6	180	25.4	2.5	14.0	70.5
Magnesium (mg/L)*	8.2	180	11.8	1.2	7.2	32.4
Sodium (mg/L)	13.2	170	17.0	3.9	8.8	31.9
Potassium (mg/L)	2.6	180	2.9	0.2	2.0	8.0
Sulfate (mg/L)	15.2	170	17.5	4.0	11.3	44.7
Chloride (mg/L)	23.4	180	30.0	8.0	15.9	44.0
Iron (mg/L)	0.2	140	0.2	0.0	0.1	0.4
Silicon (mg/L)	1.5	140	1.8	0.1	0.9	4.4

* Denotes a significant difference (p<0.05) from mean of all lakes.

Azolla caroliniana (azolla)

Alison Fox

Kerry Dressler

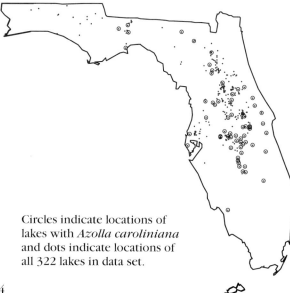

Circles indicate locations of lakes with *Azolla caroliniana* and dots indicate locations of all 322 lakes in data set.

Description and distribution

Azolla is a small (<15 mm), free-floating fern commonly found in extensive colonies covering ponds and lakes. The stems are branching, and the leaves are tiny, bilobed, and scale-like. The leaves can appear from green to dark brown. The roots are unbranched and inconspicuous from the underside of the plant. Azolla is found throughout the eastern and southern United States. The Florida distribution map shows that azolla was primarily found in lakes from north-central to southern Florida but not frequently in northwestern Florida. Lakes are progressively more alkaline and nutrient rich as one moves from northwestern to southern Florida (Canfield and Hoyer 1988). Thus the distribution of azolla in Florida suggests that it may tend to occur in alkaline, hardwater, nutrient-rich lakes.

Biology

Azolla is a fern with its two spore types encased in special capsules called sporocaps, which are actually outgrowths of several fertile leaves. Azolla grows equally well suspended on water or rooted in mud. When it floats on a pond or lake, vegetative propagating can be rapid, completely covering the system. Young plants are green and, as the plant matures change, to red and finally dark brown (usually in the fall and winter). When azolla completely covers a pond or lake, it can impair navigation and recreational uses. Wildlife use is minimal; however, it can be habitat for some aquatic invertebrates.

Florida data

Azolla was identified in 62 lakes. The 10th and 90th percentiles for pH, alkalinity, total phosphorus, and total nitrogen values in these lakes showed that 80% of the lakes with azolla had levels that fell between 5.7 and 8.7, 2.2 and 65.7 (mg/L as $CaCO_3$), 15 and 119 (µg/L), and 440 and 1800 (µg/L), respectively. These 62 lakes also collectively averaged significantly higher color, total phosphorus, chlorophyll *a*, calcium, and magnesium levels than all 322 lakes. Thus while azolla can occur in a range of lakes types, it tends to occur in alkaline, hardwater, nutrient-rich lakes.

Selected references from a total of 1,302 azolla citations in the APIRS database:

Buckingham, G. and M. Buckingham. 1981. A laboratory biology of *Pseudolampsis guttata* (Leconte) (Coleoptera: Chrysomelidae) on waterfern, *Azolla caroliniana* Willd. (Pteridonphyta: Azollaceae). Coleopterists Bulletin 35(2):181–188.

Cody, W.J. and F.W. Schueler. 1988. A second record of the mosquito fern, *Azolla caroliniana*, in Ontario. Canadian Field-Naturalist 102 (3):545–546.

Lumpkin, T.A. and D.L. Plucknett. 1982. Azolla as a green manure: Use and management in crop production. Westview Tropical Agriculture Series. No. 5. Westview Press, Boulder, Colorado.

Martin, A.R.H. 1976. Some structures in Azolla megaspores, and an anomalous form. Review of Palaeobotany 21:141–69.

Moore, A.W. 1969. Azolla: Biology and agronomic significance. Botanical Review 35:17–34.

Perkins, S.K., G.A. Peters, T.A. Lumpkin, and H.E. Calvert. 1985. Scanning electron microscopy of perine architecture as a taxonomic tool in the genus *Azolla* Lamark. Scanning Electron Microscopy 4:1719–1734.

Peters, G.A. 1991. Azolla and other plant-cyanobacteria symbioses: Aspects of form and function. Plant and Soil 137:25–36.

Peters, G.A. and H.E. Calvert. 1983. The *Azolla-Anabaena azollae* symbiosis. Pp. 109–145 in Algal symbiosis, L. J. Goff, editor. Cambridge University Press, London.

Rao, H.S. 1935. The structure and life-history of *Azolla pinnata* R. Brown with remarks on the fossil history of the Hydropteridae. Proceedings of the Indian Academy of Science, Section B:2(2):175–200.

Sutton, D.L. 1981. Azolla. Aquatics 3(2):4.

Azolla caroliniana

Variables	Mean all lakes (n=322)	Number of lakes	Mean	10th percentile	Median	90th percentile
pH	6.7	62	7.3	5.7	7.3	8.7
Alkalinity (mg/L as $CaCO_3$)	23.9	62	28.1	2.2	20.8	65.7
Conductance (µS/cm @ 25°C)	149	62	204	69	113	550
Color (Pt-Co units)*	52	62	80	20	56	160
Total phosphorus (µg/L)*	45	62	66	15	44	119
Total nitrogen (µg/L)	870	62	990	440	930	1800
Chlorophyll a (µg/L)*	20	62	20	3	11	47
Secchi (m)*	1.8	56	1.1	0.5	0.8	2.4
Calcium (mg/L)*	17.6	62	30.8	5.3	18.0	91.3
Magnesium (mg/L)*	8.2	62	14.3	3.7	10.3	34.4
Sodium (mg/L)	13.2	60	21.8	5.2	9.0	84.7
Potassium (mg/L)	2.6	62	2.7	0.3	2.1	5.9
Sulfate (mg/L)	15.2	60	20.3	4.3	12.2	51.1
Chloride (mg/L)	23.4	62	39.2	8.9	16.7	149.3
Iron (mg/L)	0.2	54	0.3	0.0	0.2	0.6
Silicon (mg/L)*	1.5	54	2.6	0.4	1.9	6.5

* Denotes a significant difference ($p<0.05$) from mean of all lakes.

Baccharis spp. (salt bush)

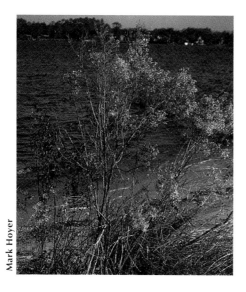

Mark Hoyer

Mark Hoyer

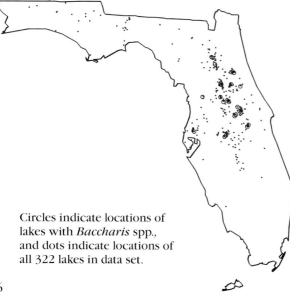

Circles indicate locations of
lakes with *Baccharis* spp.,
and dots indicate locations of
all 322 lakes in data set.

Description and distribution

Members of the *Baccharis* genus are shrubs averaging three meters tall. Four species occur in Florida: *B. dioica, B. halimifolia, B. glomeruliflora,* and *B. angustifolia* (Tarver et al. 1986). The stems of salt bush are highly branched. The leaves are alternate, fleshy, and spatulate, except for *B. angustifolia,* which has linear leaves. Leaf blades of *B. dioica* are entire, whereas the other three species' are serrated or deeply toothed. The flower heads are sessile or peduncled and clustered in groups of three to five. Flowers are unisexual and without florets and consist of a yellow or greenish corolla and a white hair-like pappus that aids in seed dispersal. The fruit is a small nutlet, 1.4 mm long with feathery or cottony hairs. *B. halimifolia* is distributed from Florida to Texas and as far north as Massachusetts. *B. dioica* and *B. glomeruliflora* occur primarily in south Florida and the West Indies. *B. angustifolia* can be found within the Coastal Plain states from Texas to North Carolina. The Florida distribution map shows that salt bush occurred mostly in central Florida with no apparent geographical pattern.

Biology

Baccharis species flower during late summer and early fall in Florida (Dressler et al. 1987). *Baccharis* species can be found in hammocks throughout Florida, around shore-hammocks, sea-beaches, salt marshes, brackish water marshes, and freshwater swamps. Salt bush provides little food for wildlife but may be valuable cover and nesting habitat for several species of birds.

Florida data

Salt bush was identified in 24 lakes. The 10th and 90th percentiles for pH, alkalinity, and total phosphorus, and total nitrogen values in these lakes show that 80% of the lakes with salt bush had levels between 5.6 and 8.9, 0.7 and 122.5 (mg/L as $CaCO_3$), 5 and 50 (µg/L), and 320 and

2660 (µg/L), respectively. The water chemistry averages of the 24 lakes showed no significant differences from those of all 322 lakes. This suggests that salt bush can occur in a wide range of aquatic systems.

Selected references from a total of 51 salt bush citations in the APIRS database:

Chapman, V.J. 1974. Salt marshes and salt deserts of the world. Pp. 3–19 in Ecology of Halophytes, R.J. Reimold and W.H. Queen, editors. Academic Press, New York.

Dardeau, M.R., R.F. Modlin, W.W. Schroeder, and J.P. Stout. 1992. Estuaries. Pp. 615–746 in Biodiversity of the southeastern United States–Aquatic communities, C. T. Hackney, editor. John Wiley and Sons, Inc. New York.

Davis, S.M., L.H. Gunderson, W.A. Park, J.R. Richardson, and J.E. Mattson. 1994. Landscape dimension, composition, and function in a changing Everglades ecosystem. Pp. 419–444 in Everglades: The ecosystem and its restoration, S. M. Davis and J. C. Ogden, editors. St. Lucie Press, Delray Beach, Fla.

Demort, C.L. 1991. The St. Johns River system. Pp. 97–120 in The rivers of Florida, R. J. Livingston, editor. Springer-Verlag, Inc., New York.

Hays, S.M. 1989. Scientists fight brush with imported insects. Agricultural Research 37(4):16–17.

Montague, C.L. and R.G. Wiegert. 1990. Salt marshes. Pp 481–516 in Ecosystems of Florida. R.L. Myers and J.J. Ewel, editors. University of Central Florida Press, Orlando, Fla.

Palmer, W.A. and W.H. Haseler. 1992. The host specificity and biology of *Trirhabda bacharidis* (Weber) (Coleoptera: Chrysomelidae), a species introduced into Australia for the biological control of *Baccharis halimifolia* L. Coleopterists Bulletin 46(1):61–66.

Stutzenbaker, C.D. and M.W. Weller. 1989. The Texas coast. Pp. 385–405 in Habitat management for migrating and wintering waterfowl in North America, L.M. Smith, R.L. Pederson, and R.M. Kaminski, editors. Texas Tech University Press, Lubbock, Tex.

Baccharis spp.

Variables	Mean all lakes (n=322)	Number of lakes	Mean	10th percentile	Median	90th percentile
pH	6.7	24	7.1	5.6	6.9	8.9
Alkalinity (mg/L as CaCO$_3$)	23.9	24	32.4	0.7	12.2	122.5
Conductance (µS/cm @ 25°C)	149	24	188	68	133	412
Color (Pt-Co units)	52	24	28	6	18	76
Total phosphorus (µg/L)	45	23	25	5	14	50
Total nitrogen (µg/L)	870	23	1000	320	710	2660
Chlorophyll (µg/L)	20	24	26	2	8	119
Secchi (m)	1.8	13	1.4	0.3	1.3	2.7
Calcium (mg/L)	17.6	24	15.0	2.7	7.7	44.6
Magnesium (mg/L)	8.2	24	6.9	1.5	3.4	16.9
Sodium (mg/L)	13.2	24	13.6	7.0	10.0	17.0
Potassium (mg/L)	2.6	24	3.8	0.4	2.5	11.7
Sulfate (mg/L)	15.2	24	16.9	2.5	15.0	35.3
Chloride (mg/L)	23.4	24	27.1	12.0	20.0	41.3
Iron (mg/L)	0.2	12	0.10	0.0	0.10	0.3
Silicon (mg/L)	1.5	12	2.2	0.1	0.6	9.4

* Denotes a significant difference (p<0.05) from mean of all lakes.

Bacopa caroliniana (lemon bacopa)

Kerry Dressler

Description and distribution

Lemon bacopa is a small, erect, aquatic herb that may be found submersed or emerged. The leaves are succulent and smell of lemons when crushed. The leaves are opposite, ovate, 10–30 mm long, and 7–15 mm wide and have three to seven veins. They range from reddish-brown to lime-green. Solitary flowers sit on short stems 3–15 mm long and have two green linear bracts located below the blue flowers. The fruit is a capsule with many tiny seeds that is covered by the sepals. *Bacopa caroliniana* can be distinguished from *B. monnieri* in two ways: *B. caroliniana* has hairy stems and blue flowers, while *B. monnieri* has smooth stems and white flowers. Lemon bacopa occurs from the coastal plains of southeast Virginia, south to southern Florida and west to eastern Texas (Godfrey and Wooten 1981). The Florida distribution map shows that lemon bacopa was found in lakes across the whole state, with no apparent geographical pattern.

Biology

Lemon bacopa flowers throughout the year in Florida (Dressler et al. 1987). Reproduction occurs by both seed germination and vegetatively. The plants can merge and form large mats of vegetation in ponds and lakes. However, these mats seldom cause a serious problem to navigation or recreational activities. Lemon bacopa provides good habitat and refuge for invertebrates and fish. Because of its attractive structure and color, it is also used as an aquarium plant.

Florida data

Lemon bacopa was identified in 102 lakes. The 10th and 90th percentiles for pH, alkalinity, total phosphorus, and total nitrogen values in these lakes showed that 80% of the lakes with lemon bacopa had levels that fell between 4.9 and 8.4, 1.4 and 49.6 (mg/L as $CaCO_3$), 9 and 50 (µg/L), and 300 and 1280 (µg/L), respectively. The water chemistry averages of the 102 lakes with lemon bacopa showed no significant differences from those of all 322 lakes. This suggests that lemon bacopa is able to occur in many of Florida's diverse aquatic habitats.

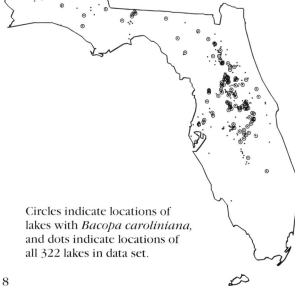

Circles indicate locations of lakes with *Bacopa caroliniana,* and dots indicate locations of all 322 lakes in data set.

Selected references from a total of 39 lemon bacopa citations in the APIRS database:

Booth, G. and K. Booth. 1994. Update at 1½ years—comparing technologies. Aquatic Gardener 7(4):119-127.

Gunderson, L.H. 1994. Vegetation of the Everglades: Determinants of community composition. Pp. 323-340 In Everglades: The ecosystem and its restoration, S.M. Davis and J.C. Ogden, editors. St. Lucie Press, Delray Beach, Fla.

Kutty, V. 1994. The quest. Aquatic Gardener 6(6):173-176.

Kutty, V. 1994. The quest, part 3 (I found what I was looking for). Aquatic Gardener 7(2):37-42.

Lodge, T.E. 1994. The Everglades handbook: Understanding the ecosystem. St. Lucie Press, Delray Beach, Fla.

Nall, L.E. and J.D. Schardt. 1978. Large-scale operations management test of use of the white amur for control of problem aquatic plants. In Vol. 1, The aquatic macrophytes of Lake Conway, Florida. U.S. Army Corps of Engineers, Technical Report # A-78-2. Vicksburg, Miss.

Rader, R.B. and C.J. Richardson. 1992. The effect of nutrient enrichment on algae and macroinvertebrates in the Everglades. Wetlands 12:121-135.

Van Dijk, G. 1985. A bit about bacopa. Aquatics 7:13-14.

Williams, V.P., E.J. Moyer, and D. Moxley. 1992. Lake restoration for aquatic habitat and fisheries improvement in Florida. North American Lake Management 1:49-63.

Bacopa caroliniana

Variables	Mean all lakes (n=322)	Number of lakes	Mean	10th percentile	Median	90th percentile
pH	6.7	102	6.6	4.9	6.6	8.4
Alkalinity (mg/L as $CaCO_3$)	23.9	102	18.8	1.4	6.4	49.6
Conductance (µS/cm @ 25°C)	149	102	142	32	93	260
Color (Pt-Co units)	52	102	44	5	25	111
Total phosphorus (µg/L)	45	102	23	9	14	50
Total nitrogen (µg/L)	870	102	740	300	610	1280
Chlorophyll a (µg/L)	20	102	10	1	4	26
Secchi (m)	1.8	91	2.0	0.6	1.7	4.1
Calcium (mg/L)	17.6	101	17.9	1.1	8.7	47.3
Magnesium (mg/L)	8.2	101	9.4	0.8	5.8	20.9
Sodium (mg/L)	13.2	98	14.2	2.8	7.8	20.1
Potassium (mg/L)	2.6	101	2.3	0.2	1.2	6.7
Sulfate (mg/L)	15.2	98	16.1	3.0	7.9	44.3
Chloride (mg/L)	23.4	101	25.2	4.8	14.1	34.4
Iron (mg/L)	0.2	79	0.2	0.0	0.10	0.6
Silicon (mg/L)	1.5	79	1.4	0.1	0.5	3.8

Bacopa monnieri (bacopa)

Kerry Dressler

Description and distribution

Bacopa is a creeping perennial with sporadic branching and stems up to 30 cm long. The leaves are opposite, 7-15 mm long, and 3-7 mm wide and usually contain a single midrib. White flowers with five green sepals exist on stems 13-20 mm long. *Bacopa caroliniana* can be distinguished from *B. monnieri* in two ways: *B. caroliniana* has hairy stems and blue flowers, while *B. monnieri* has smooth stems and white flowers. Bacopa occurs in the Coastal Plains states from Texas to Florida and as far north as Maryland (Godfrey and Wooten 1981). The Florida distribution map shows that bacopa was found primarily in lakes from central to southern Florida, but not frequently in northwestern Florida. Lakes are progressively more alkaline and nutrient-rich as one moves from northwestern to southern Florida (Canfield and Hoyer 1988). Thus, the distribution of bacopa in Florida suggests that it may prefer alkaline, hardwater, nutrient-rich lakes.

Biology

Bacopa flowers throughout the year in Florida (Dressler et al. 1987). Reproduction occurs by both seed germination and vegetative means. The plants can merge and form large mats of vegetation in ponds and lakes. However, these mats seldom cause a serious problem to navigation or recreational uses. Bacopa provides good habitat and refuge for invertebrates and fish. Because of its attractive structure and color, it is also used as an aquarium plant. It is also occasionally used as food by waterfowl.

Florida data

Bacopa was identified in 57 lakes. The 10th and 90th percentiles for pH, alkalinity, total phosphorus, and total nitrogen values in these lakes showed that 80% of the lakes with bacopa had levels that fell between 6.1 and 8.7, 2.3 and 92.4 (mg/L as $CaCO_3$), 12 and 84 (μg/L), and

Circles indicate locations of lakes with *Bacopa monnieri,* and dots indicate locations of all 322 lakes in data set.

410 and 11900 (µg/L), respectively. These 57 lakes also collectively had significantly higher alkalinity, specific conductance, calcium, magnesium, and potassium levels than all 322 lakes. Thus while bacopa can occur in a range of lakes types, it tends to occur in alkaline, hardwater, nutrient-rich lakes.

Selected references from a total of 60 bacopa citations in the APIRS database:

Booth, G. and K. Booth. 1993. Some assembly required (Part 8) from 6 weeks to 4 months. Aquatic Gardener 6:109-115.

Chabreck, R.H., T. Joanen, and S.L. Paulus. 1989. Southern coastal marshes and lakes. Pp. 249-277 in Habitat management for migrating and wintering waterfowl in North America, L.M. Smith, R.L. Pederson, and R.M. Kaminski, editors. Texas Tech University Press, Lubbock, Tex.

Demort, C.L. 1991. The St. Johns River system. Pp. 97-120 in The rivers of Florida, R.J. Livingston, editor. Springer-Verlag, Inc., New York.

Dutta T. and U.P. Basu. 1963. Terpenoids, Pt. II—Isolation of a new triterpene saponin, from Bacopa monnieri Wettst. Indian Journal of Chemistry 1:408-409.

Felley, J.D. 1992. Medium-low-gradient streams of the gulf coastal plain. Pp. 233-270 in Biodiversity of the southeastern United States aquatic communities, C. T. Hackney, editor. John Wiley and Sons, Inc., New York.

Jain, P. and D.K. Kulshreshtha. 1993. Bacoside A1, minor saponin from Bacopa monnieri. Phytochemistry 33:449-451.

Nall, L.E. and J.D. Schardt. 1978. Large-scale operations management test of use of the white amur for control of problem aquatic plants. In Vol. 1, The aquatic macrophytes of Lake Conway, Florida. U.S. Army Corps of Engineers, Technical Report # A-78-2. Vicksburg, Miss.

Rastogi, R.P. and M.L. Dhar. 1960. Chemical examination of Bacopa monnieri Wettst. Journal of Scientific Indian Research 12:455-456.

Sinha, S. and P. Chandra. Removal of Cu and Cd from water by Bacopa monnieri L. Water, Air, and Soil Pollution 51:271-276.

Van Dijk, G. 1985. A bit about bacopa. Aquatics 7:13-14.

Bacopa monnieri

Variables	Mean all lakes (n=322)	Number of lakes	Mean	10th percentile	Median	90th percentile
pH*	6.7	57	7.4	6.1	7.6	8.7
Alkalinity (mg/L as $CaCO_3$)*	23.9	57	37.5	2.3	30.8	92.4
Conductance (µS/cm @ 25°C)*	149	57	233	59	173	627
Color (Pt-Co units)	52	57	41	6	25	111
Total phosphorus (µg/L)	45	57	43	12	28	84
Total nitrogen (µg/L)	870	57	940	410	750	1900
Chlorophyll a (µg/L)	20	57	21	3	13	52
Secchi (m)	1.8	52	1.5	0.4	1.2	3.5
Calcium (mg/L)*	17.6	57	33.4	4.4	20.0	89.6
Magnesium (mg/L)*	8.2	57	15.0	2.5	8.8	46.5
Sodium (mg/L)	13.2	51	24.3	5.5	11.4	90.8
Potassium (mg/L)*	2.6	57	3.5	0.8	2.4	8.2
Sulfate (mg/L)	15.2	51	22.7	4.5	13.0	60.4
Chloride (mg/L)	23.4	57	41.3	8.7	19.7	148.1
Iron (mg/L)	0.2	45	0.1	0.0	0.1	0.3
Silicon (mg/L)	1.5	45	1.6	0.2	0.8	4.1

* Denotes a significant difference ($p < 0.05$) from mean of all lakes.

Bidens spp. (bur marigold)

Kerry Dressler

Kerry Dressler

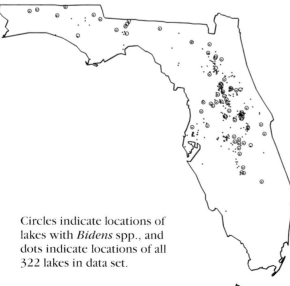

Circles indicate locations of lakes with *Bidens* spp., and dots indicate locations of all 322 lakes in data set.

Description and distribution

There are several species in the genus *Bidens* that occur in Florida. *Bidens mitis* is commonly found in open marshes, ponds, and lakes and will be described here. For descriptions of the remaining species, see Godfrey and Wooten (1981). Bur marigold is an annual herb growing to 120 cm tall that has little or much branching. The leaves are opposite, highly variable, usually stalked, lanceolate or narrowly lanceolate, and more or less toothed to deeply lobed. The flower-like heads are formed from two rows of bracts; the outer bracts are usually shorter and green, while the inner bracts are long and yellow. The fruit is a nutlet 2–6 mm long, flattened, with tiny bristles or hairs on the upper edges. This is where it gets the common term of beggar-tick. There are many species of *Bidens* that occur in most parts of the United States (Beal 1977; Godfrey and Wooten 1981). The Florida distribution map shows that *Bidens* spp. were found in lakes across the whole state, with no apparent geographical pattern.

Biology

Bidens species flower throughout the year in Florida (Dressler et al. 1987). Reproduction occurs by seed germination. The plants can merge and form large mats of vegetation along the shores of ponds and lakes. However, these mats seldom cause a serious problem to navigation or recreation. *Bidens* spp. provide good habitat and refuge for invertebrates and fish. Several species of birds and mammals use the seeds for food.

Florida data

Bur marigold was identified in 70 lakes. The 10th and 90th percentiles for pH, alkalinity, total phosphorus, and total nitrogen values in these lakes showed that 80% of the lakes with bur marigold had levels between 5.0 and 8.6, 1.0 and 97.0 (mg/L as $CaCO_3$), 9 and 108(μg/L), and 230 and 1920 (μg/L), respectively. The water chemistry averages of the 70 lakes with bur marigold showed no significant differences from those of all 322 lakes. This suggests that bur marigold may be able to occur in many of Florida's diverse aquatic habitats.

Selected references from a total of 211 bur marigold citations in the APIRS database:

Gilman, B. 1991. Restoring the lake. Conservationist 45:20–23.

Heckman, C.W. 1981. The mechanics of penetration by fruit of *Bidens cernua* L. (Compositae) into the cephalic region of cyprinids. Int. Rev. Ges. Hydrobiol. 66.127–132.

Holloway, M. 1994. Nurturing nature. Scientific American 270:98–108.

Lillie, R.A. 1990. A quantitative survey of the submersed macrophytes in Devil's Lake, Sauk County, with a historical review of the invasion of Eurasian watermilfoil, *Myriophyllum spicatum* L. Wisconsin Academy of Science, Arts and Letters 78:1–20.

Loftin, J.P. 1994. On the waterfront. Florida Water Magazine 3:14–24.

Lowcock, L.A. and R.W. Murphy. 1990. Seed dispersal via amphibian vectors: Passive transport of bur-marigold, *Bidens cernua*, achenes by migrating salamanders, genus *Ambystoma*. Canadian Field-Naturalist 104:298–300.

Mitsch, W.J. and J.G. Gosselink. 1993. Tidal freshwater marshes. Pp. 265–291 in Wetlands, 2nd ed. Van Nostrand Reinhold, New York.

Odum, W.E. 1988. Comparative ecology of tidal freshwater and salt marshes. Annual Review of Ecological Systems 19:147–176.

Prince, H.H., P.I. Padding, and R.W. Knapton. 1992. Waterfowl use of the Laurentian Great Lakes. Journal of Great Lakes Research 18:673–699.

Vanhoek, C. 1992 Inventorying McKethan Lake Recreation Area. Palmetto 12:10–11.

Bidens spp.

Variables	Mean all lakes (n=322)	Number of lakes	Mean	10th percentile	Median	90th percentile
pH	6.7	70	6.9	5.0	7.0	8.6
Alkalinity (mg/L as CaCO$_3$)	23.9	70	30.0	1.0	12.4	97.0
Conductance (µS/cm @ 25°C)	149	70	162	23	105	420
Color (Pt-Co units)	52	70	62	4	31	161
Total phosphorus (µg/L)	45	70	53	9	22	108
Total nitrogen (µg/L)	870	70	870	230	670	1920
Chlorophyll a (µg/L)	20	70	19	2	7	60
Secchi (m)	1.8	62	1.7	0.5	1.4	3.7
Calcium (mg/L)	17.6	70	28.7	1.3	15.4	91.7
Magnesium (mg/L)	8.2	70	12.6	1.0	7.1	34.9
Sodium (mg/L)	13.2	70	15.0	2.0	7.7	42.6
Potassium (mg/L)	2.6	70	1.8	0.2	1.2	4.8
Sulfate (mg/L)	15.2	70	14.7	3.3	9.2	43.3
Chloride (mg/L)	23.4	70	27.0	3.3	13.8	67.4
Iron (mg/L)	0.2	59	0.2	0.0	0.1	0.6
Silicon (mg/L)	1.5	59	2.3	0.1	1.3	6.4

Brachiaria mutica (paragrass)

Mark Hoyer

Description and distribution

Paragrass is a stout, perennial grass with horizontal creeping stolons from which flowering vertical branches arise. The stolons can be up to several meters long. An important characteristic is the presence of dense shaggy hairs at the leaf nodes. The leaves are flat, 110–330 mm long, and 12–15 mm wide with very fine short hairs on the upper surface of the blade; the undersides are smooth. The inflorescence is a long panicle, 130–250 mm long, consisting of numerous spikelets, 3 mm long, throughout its ascending or spreading branches. Paragrass is native to Africa but was introduced into the United States as a forage grass (Godfrey and Wooten 1979), primarily in wet areas of Florida and Texas. Paragrass can be considered a naturalized citizen. The Florida distribution map shows that paragrass was found primarily in lakes from north-central to southern Florida but not frequently in northwestern Florida. Lakes are progressively more alkaline and nutrient rich as one moves from northwestern to southern Florida (Canfield and Hoyer 1988). Thus the distribution of paragrass in Florida suggests that it may prefer alkaline, hardwater, nutrient-rich lakes.

Biology

As with other grasses, paragrass reproduces primarily by seed germination. Vegetative reproduction from the rapidly growing rhizomes, however, can be substantial. Paragrass grows well in cultivated or disturbed areas with moist soil. Growth usually begins along the bank and then spreads horizontally into the water where dense stands form floating mats. These floating mats can impede navigation and recreational activities in streams, ponds, and lakes. In many developed countries, paragrass is commonly cultivated and used as forage grass for cattle. Many aquatic birds use it as nesting habitat and eat the seeds. It also provides good habitat and refuge for invertebrates and fish. Dense growths, however, cause problems in drainage and irrigation ditches by severely reducing water flow.

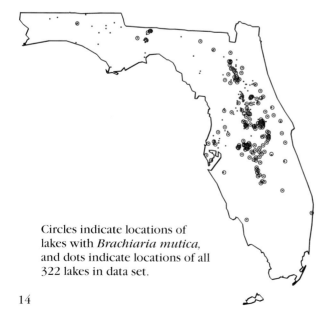

Circles indicate locations of lakes with *Brachiaria mutica*, and dots indicate locations of all 322 lakes in data set.

Florida data

Paragrass was identified in 161 lakes. The 10th and 90th percentiles for pH, alkalinity, total phosphorus, and total nitrogen values in these lakes showed that 80% of the lakes with paragrass had levels that fell between 5.3 and 8.7, 1.2 and 87.9 (mg/L as $CaCO_3$), 12 and 113 (μg/L), and 390 and 1850 (μg/L), respectively. The 161 lakes collectively averaged significantly higher pH, specific conductance, total phosphorus, calcium, and magnesium levels than all 322 lakes. Thus while paragrass can occur in a range of lake types, it tends to occur in alkaline, hardwater, nutrient-rich lakes.

Selected references from a total of 52 paragrass citations in the APIRS database:

Ampong-Nyarko, K. and S.K. De Datta. 1991. Principal rice herbicides. Pp. 65–72 in A handbook for weed control in rice. International Rice Research Institute, Manila, Philippines.

Canfield, D.E., Jr. and M.V. Hoyer. 1988. The nutrient assimilation capacity of the Little Wekiva River. Final Report. City of Altamonte Springs, Altamonte Springs, Fla.

Doren, R.F., L.D. Whiteaker, and A.M. Larosa. 1991. Evaluation of fire as a management tool for controlling *Schinus terebinthifolius* as secondary successional growth on abandoned agricultural land. Environmental Management 15:121–129.

Lantz, P.S. 1993. Florida's most invasive species. Palmetto 13:6–7.

Miller, I.L. and W.M. Lonsdale. 1992. Ecological management of *Mimosa pigra*: Use of fire and competitive pastures. Pp. 104–106 in A guide to the management of *Mimosa pigra*, K.L.S. Harley, editor. CSIRO, Australia.

Mitchell, D.S. and K.H. Bowmer. 1990. Aquatic weed problems and management in Australasia. Pp. 355–370 in Aquatic weeds: The ecology and management of nuisance aquatic vegetation, A.H. Pieterse and K.J. Murphy, editors. Oxford Scientific Publications, Oxford University Press, New York.

Schmitz, D.C. 1990. The invasion of exotic aquatic and wetland plants in Florida: History and efforts to prevent new introductions. Aquatics 12:6–13.

Schmitz, D.C., B.V. Nelson, L.E. Nall, and J.D. Schart. 1991. Exotic aquatic plants in Florida: Historical perspectives and review of the present aquatic plant regulation program. Proceedings of the symposium on exotic pest plants, Technical Report NPS/NREVER/NRTR-91/06, Nov. 2–4, 1988. University of Miami, Coral Gables, Fla.

Steward, K.K. 1981. Improving technology for chemical control of aquatic weeds. U.S. Army Corps of Engineers, Waterways Experiment Station, Technical Report A-81-2. Vicksburg, Miss.

Brachiaria mutica

Variables	Mean all lakes (n=322)	Number of lakes	Mean	10th percentile	Median	90th percentile
pH*	6.7	161	7.1	5.3	7.3	8.7
Alkalinity (mg/L as $CaCO_3$)	23.9	161	32.1	1.2	19.4	87.9
Conductance (μS/cm @ 25°C)*	149	161	189	55	135	365
Color (Pt-Co units)	52	161	51	7	31	126
Total phosphorus (μg/L)*	45	161	51	12	26	113
Total nitrogen (μg/L)	870	161	950	390	710	1850
Chlorophyll a (μg/L)	20	161	24	3	10	66
Secchi (m)	1.8	142	1.4	0.4	1.1	2.9
Calcium (mg/L)*	17.6	161	26.3	2.5	14.8	71.6
Magnesium (mg/L)*	8.2	161	12.8	1.5	7.8	34.7
Sodium (mg/L)	13.2	148	17.3	4.9	8.8	35.5
Potassium (mg/L)	2.6	161	3.2	0.2	2.3	8.2
Sulfate (mg/L)	15.2	148	19.5	4.4	12.7	47.8
Chloride (mg/L)	23.4	160	30.3	8.7	15.9	44.4
Iron (mg/L)	0.2	125	0.2	0.0	0.1	0.4
Silicon (mg/L)	1.5	125	1.7	0.2	1.0	3.8

* Denotes a significant difference (p<0.05) from mean of all lakes.

Brasenia schreberi (water shield)

Kerry Dressler

Kerry Dressler

Description and distribution

Water shield is an herb with floating leaves attached to long stalks growing vertically from horizontal rhizomes, which are rooted in the substrate. The stalks are attached to the center of the leaf bottom. The floating leaves are oval to elliptical, generally 50-120 mm long and 30-60 mm wide, green above and purple below. A gelatinous material covers the stalks and the undersides of the leaves to form an extremely slimy covering. Small purple flowers, 10-15 mm in diameter, open at the water surface. These flowers consist of three to four sepals and petals with 18 to 30 stamens and four to 18 pistils. Four to seven club-shaped, leathery fruits come from each flower, and one or two small black seeds are in each fruit. Water shield is found primarily in the eastern United States and north to Ontario, but it has also been found along the Pacific Coast in Oregon and California (Godfrey and Wooten 1981). The Florida distribution map shows that water shield occurs from extreme northwestern to central Florida, but not extreme south Florida. Lakes are progressively more alkaline and nutrient rich as one moves from northwestern to southern Florida (Canfield and Hoyer 1988). Thus the distribution of water shield in Florida suggests that it may prefer acid, softwater, nutrient-poor lakes.

Biology

Water shield reproduces primarily by seed germination, but young shoots do arise from rootstocks, suggesting that some reproduction is vegetative. It flowers primarily in the spring and early summer (March to June) in Florida (Dressler et al. 1987). Water shield can form dense mats that can impede navigation and recreational use of ponds and lakes. The seeds, leaves, and underwater portions are used extensively by many species of aquatic birds. Water shield also provides habitat for invertebrates and fish.

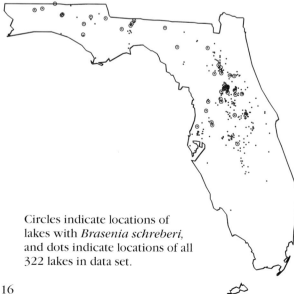

Circles indicate locations of lakes with *Brasenia schreberi,* and dots indicate locations of all 322 lakes in data set.

Florida data

Water shield was identified in 43 lakes. The 10th and 90th percentiles for pH, alkalinity, total phosphorus, and total nitrogen values in these lakes showed that 80% of the lakes with water shield had levels that fell between 4.7 and 7.2, 1.1 and 23.4 (mg/L as $CaCO_3$), 9 and 30 (µg/L), and 210 and 1080 (µg/L), respectively. The 43 lakes collectively averaged significantly lower pH, alkalinity, specific conductance, calcium, magnesium, sodium, potassium, sulfate, and chloride values than all 322 lakes. Thus while water shield can occur in a range of lake types, it tends to occur in acid, softwater lakes with low nutrient concentrations.

Selected references from a total of 214 water shield citations in the APIRS database:

Collinson, M.E. 1980. Recent and tertiary seeds of the Nymphaeaceae *sensu lato* with a revision of *Brasenia ovula* (Brong.) Reid and Chandler. Annals of Botany 46:603–632.

Elakovich, S.D. 1987. An examination of the phytotoxicity of the water shield, *Brasenia schreberi*. Journal of Chemical Ecology 13:1935–1940.

Ito, M. 1986. Studies in the floral morphology and anatomy of Nymphaeales. III. Floral anatomy of *Brasenia schreberi* Gmel. and *Cabomba caroliniana* A. Gray. Bot. Mag. Tokyo 99:169–184.

Kakuta, M. and A. Misaki. 1979. The polysaccharide of "Junsai (*Brasenia schreberi* J. F. Gmel)" mucilage: Fragmentation analysis by successive Smith degradations and partial acid hydrolysis. Agric. Biol Chem 43:1269–1276.

Kunii, H. 1993. Rhizome longevity in two floating-leaved aquatic macrophytes, *Nymphaea tetragona* and *Brasenia schreberi*. Journal of Aquatic Plant Management 31:94–98.

Osborn, J.M. and E.L. Schneider. 1988. Morphological studies of the Nymphaeaceae *sensu lato*. XVI. The floral biology of *Brasenia schreberi*. Annals of the Missouri Botanical Garden 75:778–794.

Raymond, M. and P. Dansereau. 1949. The geographical distribution of the bipolar Nymphaeaceae, *Nymphaea tetragona* and *Brasenia schreberi*. Proceedings of the Pacific Science Congress 7:122–131.

Tokura, A. 1937. On the blooming of *Brasenia schreberi* J.F. Gmel. Journal of Japanese Botany 13:829–839.

Brasenia schreberi

Variables	Mean all lakes (n=322)	Number of lakes	Mean	10th percentile	Median	90th percentile
pH*	6.7	43	5.9	4.7	5.9	7.2
Alkalinity (mg/L as $CaCO_3$)*	23.9	43	7.7	1.1	2.5	23.4
Conductance (µS/cm @ 25°C)*	149	43	55	17	40	116
Color (Pt-Co units)	52	43	36	5	24	82
Total phosphorus (µg/L)	45	43	17	9	13	30
Total nitrogen (µg/L)	870	43	580	210	490	1080
Chlorophyll a (µg/L)	20	43	7	1.0	4	19
Secchi (m)	1.8	41	2.3	1.0	2.1	4.2
Calcium (mg/L)*	17.6	43	6.6	0.7	2.9	21.4
Magnesium (mg/L)*	8.2	43	3.3	0.6	1.9	8.8
Sodium (mg/L)*	13.2	43	4.9	1.8	3.7	8.8
Potassium (mg/L)*	2.6	43	0.9	0.10	0.3	1.9
Sulfate (mg/L)*	15.2	43	6.6	2.8	5.5	10.6
Chloride (mg/L)*	23.4	43	8.9	2.8	7.6	17.8
Iron (mg/L)	0.2	31	0.2	0.0	0.1	0.6
Silicon (mg/L)	1.5	31	0.9	0.10	0.3	3.4

* Denotes a significant difference (p<0.05) from mean of all lakes.

Cabomba caroliniana (fanwort)

Kerry Dressler

Kerry Dressler

Description and distribution

Fanwort is a submersed plant with slender stems, which are numerously branched near the base, and many slender roots. It has two types of green leaves: The submersed leaves are opposite or whorled and finely dissected in the shape of a fan, while the floating leaves, which are few, are alternate and narrowly diamond-shaped. The flowers are white to pink and 12–20 mm in diameter and are on stalks that arise from the tips of the stem. The fruit consists of two to four leathery pods, each containing three small seeds 2–3 mm long. Fanwort occurs chiefly in the Coastal Plain from Virginia to south Florida and west to east Texas (Godfrey and Wooten 1981). It has, however, been naturalized in many northern states. The Florida distribution map shows that fanwort was found in lakes across the whole state, with no apparent geographical pattern.

Biology

Fanwort flowers from April to November in Florida (Dressler et al. 1987). Reproduction is primarily through seed germination, but fragmentation can be a major method of reproduction. Fanwort is generally rooted in water 1–3 meters deep, but it may continue to grow even after it is uprooted from the substrate. It is a popular aquarium plant, which is why it has become naturalized in many northern states. The growth of fanwort can be considerable, allowing it to clog canals, streams, ponds, and lakes, even impairing uses of aquatic systems. Fanwort provides good habitat and refuge for invertebrates and fish. The seeds are sometimes consumed by waterfowl.

Florida data

Fanwort was identified in 49 lakes. The 10th and 90th percentiles for pH, alkalinity, total phosphorus, and total nitrogen values in these lakes show that 80% of the lakes with fanwort had levels between 5.3 and 8.3, 1.6 and 40.0 (mg/L as CaCO$_3$), 10 and 44 (µg/L), and 320 and 1280 (µg/L), respectively. The water chemistry averages of the 49 lakes were

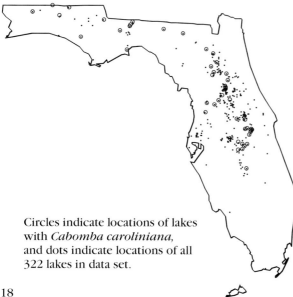

Circles indicate locations of lakes with *Cabomba caroliniana,* and dots indicate locations of all 322 lakes in data set.

not significantly different from those of all 322 lakes. This suggests that fanwort may be able to occur in many of Florida's diverse aquatic habitats.

Selected references from a total of 210 fanwort citations in the APIRS database:

Fassett, N.C. 1953. A monograph of Cabomba. Castanea 18:116-128.

Hanlon, C. 1990. The Florida native—Cabomba (fanwort). Aquatics 12(4):4-6.

Martin, D.F. and R.P. Wain. 1991. The *Cabomba* color problem. Aquatics 13(1):17.

Orgaard, M. 1991. The genus *Cabomba* (Cabombaceae)—a taxonomic study. Nordic Journal of Botany 11(2):179-203.

Osborn, J.M., T.N. Taylor, and E.L. Schneider. 1991. Pollen morphology and ultrastructure of the Cabombaceae: Correlations with pollination biology. American Journal of Botany 78(10):1367-1378.

Riemer, D.N. and J.R. Trout. 1979. Effects of low concentrations of Terbutryn on *Myriophyllum* and *Cabomba*. Journal of Aquatic Plant Management 18:6-9.

Sanders, D.R. 1979. The ecology of *Cabomba caroliniana*. Pp. 133-146 in Weed control methods for public health applications, E.O. Gangstad, editor. CRC Press, Boca Raton, Fla.

Schneider, E.L. and J.M. Jeter. 1982. Morphological studies of the Nymphaeaceae. XII. The floral biology of *Cabomba caroliniana*. American Journal of Botany 69(9):1410-1419.

Tarver, D.P. and D.R. Sanders, Sr. 1977. Selected life cycle of fanwort. Journal of Aquatic Plant Management 5:18-22.

Wain, R.P., W.T. Haller, and D.F. Martin. 1983. Genetic relationship among three forms of *Cabomba*. Journal of Aquatic Plant Management 21(2):96-98.

Cabomba caroliniana

Variables	Mean all lakes (n=322)	Number of lakes	Mean	10th percentile	Median	90th percentile
pH	6.7	49	6.6	5.3	6.5	8.3
Alkalinity (mg/L as CaCO$_3$)	23.9	49	16.0	1.6	7.3	40.0
Conductance (µS/cm @ 25°C)	149	49	94	19	83	204
Color (Pt-Co units)	52	49	48	8	32	101
Total phosphorus (µg/L)	45	49	23	10	16	44
Total nitrogen (µg/L)	870	49	740	320	600	1280
Chlorophyll a (µg/L)	20	49	11	2	6	30
Secchi (m)	1.8	44	1.9	0.7	1.6	3.6
Calcium (mg/L)	17.6	49	13.3	1.5	8.2	26.8
Magnesium (mg/L)	8.2	49	7.5	0.9	5.6	14.8
Sodium (mg/L)	13.2	47	7.5	1.8	6.4	14.5
Potassium (mg/L)	2.6	49	1.5	0.2	0.8	4.5
Sulfate (mg/L)	15.2	47	9.6	2.9	6.4	20.8
Chloride (mg/L)	23.4	49	13.8	2.9	12.5	27.6
Iron (mg/L)	0.2	40	0.3	0.0	0.2	0.7
Silicon (mg/L)	1.5	40	1.3	0.10	0.5	3.6

Canna spp. (golden canna)

Karen Brown

Kerry Dressler

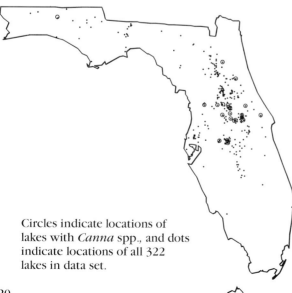

Circles indicate locations of lakes with *Canna* spp., and dots indicate locations of all 322 lakes in data set.

Description and distribution

Canna spp. are tall perennial herbs, about 1.3 m tall. The stems are stout and grow from rhizomes. The leaves are large, 200–600 mm long and 50–150 mm wide, alternate, with large sheathing petioles; there can be several leaves on a stem. The flowers are bisexual, extremely showy, terminal, and in spikes, racemes, or panicles. The three sepals are greenish and bract-like, and the three golden petals are mostly narrow, pointed, and larger than the sepals. The fruit is a three-parted, rough, football-shaped capsule, 25–50 mm long with brown or black seeds. *Canna flaccida* is native to Florida (Godfrey and Wooten 1981), and two other species, *C. indica* and *C. generalis*, are cultivars that infrequently escape to roadside ditches or other aquatic habitats in Florida. These species occur in the Coastal Plain from South Carolina to Florida and Texas. The Florida distribution map shows that *Canna* spp. were found primarily in central Florida.

Biology

Canna spp. flower from January to September in Florida (Dressler et al. 1987). *Canna* spp. are much sought after as ornamental plants and support a substantial aquascaping business. They are not reported as beneficial to wildlife in Florida.

Florida data

Canna spp. were identified in 24 lakes. The 10th and 90th percentiles for pH, alkalinity, total phosphorus, and total nitrogen values in these lakes show that 80% of the lakes with *Canna* spp. had levels between 5.5 and 8.9, 1.5 and 121.4 (mg/L as $CaCO_3$), 10 and 122 (µg/L), and 280 and 3500 (µg/L), respectively. These 24 lakes also collectively averaged significantly higher pH, alkalinity, specific conductance, calcium, magnesium, and potassium values than all 322 lakes. Thus while *Canna* spp. can occur in a range of lake types, they tend to occur in alkaline, hardwater, nutrient-rich lakes.

Selected references from a total of 14 golden canna citations, in the APIRS database:

Bergner, I. and U. Jensen. 1989. Phytoserological contribution to the systematic placement of the Typhales. Nordic Journal of Botany 8(5):447-456.

Brix, H. and B.K. Sorrell. Internal pressurization and connective gas flow in some emergent freshwater macrophytes. Limnology and Oceanography 37(7):1420-1433.

Guntenspergen, G.R., F. Stearns, and J.A. Kadlec. 1989. Wetland vegetation. Pp. 73-88 in Constructed wetlands for wastewater treatment: Municipal, industrial and agricultural, D.A. Hammer, editor. Lewis Publishers, Chelsea, Mich.

Loftin, J.P. 1994. On the waterfront. Florida Water Magazine 3(2):14-24.

Mitchell, D.S. and P.A. Thomas. 1972. Ecology of water weeds in the neotropics: An ecological survey of the aquatic weeds *Eichhornia crassipes* and *Salvinia* species, and their natural enemies in the neotropics. UNESCO, Paris.

Pote, J.W. and T.P. Cathcart. 1989. Project description: Use of constructed wetlands to treat wastewater from confined animal operations in Mississippi. Mississippi Agricultural and Forestry Experiment Station, Mississippi State University, Mississippi State, Miss. 26 pp.

Ramey, V. 1991. Aquatic plant identification: Emersed plants, part I. Aquatic Plant Management Series, Center for Aquatic Plants, Information Office, IFAS, University of Florida, Gainesville, 38 mins. (Video).

Reddy, K.R., E.M. D'Angelo, and T.A. Debusk. 1989. Oxygen transport through aquatic plant macrophytes: The role in wastewater treatment. Journal of Environmental Quality 19:261-267.

Wolverton, B.C. 1989. Aquatic plant/microbial filters for treating septic tank effluent. Pp. 173-178 in Constructed wetlands for wastewater treatment: Municipal, industrial and agricultural, D.A. Hammer, editor. Lewis Publishers, Chelsea, Mich.

Canna spp.

Variables	Mean all lakes (n=322)	Number of lakes	Mean	10th percentile	Median	90th percentile
pH*	6.7	24	7.7	5.5	7.8	8.9
Alkalinity (mg/L as CaCO$_3$)*	23.9	24	53.0	1.5	46.8	121.4
Conductance (μS/cm @ 25°C)*	149	24	289	79	246	705
Color (Pt-Co units)	52	24	30	4	23	88
Total phosphorus (μg/L)	45	24	48	10	39	122
Total nitrogen (μg/L)	870	24	1420	280	1190	3500
Chlorophyll a (μg/L)	20	24	44	2	30	156
Secchi (m)	1.8	21	1.8	0.4	1.2	5.6
Calcium (mg/L)*	17.6	24	38.3	2.5	26.7	94.7
Magnesium (mg/L)*	8.2	24	22.0	2.0	16.5	57.9
Sodium (mg/L)	13.2	22	25.9	5.2	14.4	111.2
Potassium (mg/L)*	2.6	24	5.9	0.2	5.1	12.5
Sulfate (mg/L)	15.2	22	27.4	4.3	23.0	64.2
Chloride (mg/L)	23.4	24	46.0	9.4	26.3	183.0
Iron (mg/L)	0.2	18	0.1	0.0	0.10	0.4
Silicon (mg/L)	1.5	18	2.1	0.10	1.3	5.5

* Denotes a significant difference (p<0.05) from mean of all lakes.

Cephalanthus occidentalis (buttonbush)

Kerry Dressler

Kerry Dressler

Description and distribution

Buttonbush is a small to medium size shrub, up to 3 m tall and sometimes reaching tree size. When it becomes large, the bark is rough, ridged, and furrowed or bumpy. The leaves are opposite, deciduous, stalked, elliptic to ovate, and 50–200 mm long and come to a point. The numerous flowers are densely clustered in greenish-white spherical heads, 25–35 mm in diameter, that from a distance resemble buttons. Each fruit contains 2–4 nutlets, and many are tightly packed into a dense ball. Buttonbush is native to most central to eastern states and from Florida west to California (Godfrey and Wooten 1981). The Florida distribution map shows that buttonbush was found in lakes across the whole state with no apparent geographical pattern.

Biology

Buttonbush flowers from February to September in Florida (Dressler et al. 1987). Reproduction is primarily through nutlets stored for long periods in a hard dry fruit. It grows primarily on the shores of lakes but can live for extended periods in the water after lake levels rise. The nutlets, however, do not germinate underwater. Today buttonbush is of little economic value, but in the early 1900s it was used to make fine grades of charcoal. It is now highly valued for wildlife habitat. Some waterfowl use the nutlets as a high energy food source, and many species of wading birds, waterfowl, and songbirds use buttonbush for cover and nesting habitat.

Florida data

Buttonbush was identified in 193 lakes. The 10th and 90th percentiles for pH, alkalinity, total phosphorus, and total nitrogen values in these lakes show that 80% of the lakes with buttonbush had levels between 4.9 and 8.6, 1.0 and 74.0 (mg/L as $CaCO_3$), 10 and 83 (µg/L), and 310 and 1750 (µg/L), respectively. The water chemistry averages of the 193 lakes showed no significant differences from

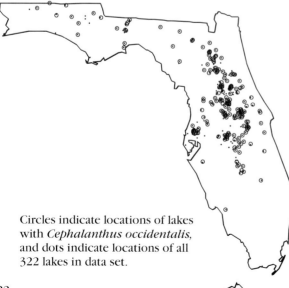

Circles indicate locations of lakes with *Cephalanthus occidentalis,* and dots indicate locations of all 322 lakes in data set.

those of all 322 lakes. That buttonbush occurred in over half of the lakes in the database, across the whole state of Florida, and with water chemistry averages similar to lakes in the database suggests that it can occur in a wide range of lake types.

Selected references from a total of 124 buttonbush citations in the APIRS database:

Donovan, L.A., K.W. McLeod, K.C. Sherrod, and N.J. Stumpff. 1988. Response of woody swamp seedlings to flooding and increased water temperatures. I. Growth, biomass, and survivorship. American Journal of Botany 75(8):1181–1190.

Faber-Langendoen, D. and S.J. Dina. 1987. Growth responses of *Cephalanthus occidentalis* L. buttonbush to varying light levels and flooding. Transactions of the Missouri Academy of Science 21:55–62.

Faber-Langendoen, D. and P.F. Maycock. 1989. Community patterns and environmental gradients of buttonbush, *Cephalanthus occidentalis*, ponds in lowland forests of southern Ontario. Canadian Field-Naturalist 103(4):479–485.

Francis, G. and N. Munro. 1994. A biosphere reserve for Atlantic Coastal Plain flora, southwestern Nova Scotia. Biological Conservation 68:275–279.

Gopal, B. 1988. Wetlands: Management and conservation in India. Water Quality Bulletin 13(1):3–6, 29–30.

Loften, J.P. 1994. On the waterfront. Florida Water Magazine 3(2):14–24.

Mitsch, W.J. and J.G. Gosselink. 1993. Southern deep water swamps. Pp. 412–449 in Wetlands, 2nd ed. Van Nostrand Reinhold, New York.

Sherrod, K.C., T.G. Ciravolo, and K.W. McLeod. 1987. Growth of woody seedlings under varying light conditions. American Journal of Botany 74(5):657–658.

Stanley, R.A., A.T. Tabereaux, and T.F. Hall. 1974. Control of buttonball with picloram. Hyacinth Control Journal 12:38–40.

Toth, L.A. 1993. The ecological basis of the Kissimmee River restoration plan. Florida Scientist 56(1): 25–51.

Cephalanthus occidentalis

Variables	Mean all lakes (n=322)	Number of lakes	Mean	10th percentile	Median	90th percentile
pH	6.7	193	6.8	4.9	6.8	8.6
Alkalinity (mg/L as CaCO₃)	23.9	193	25.4	1.0	10.2	74.0
Conductance (µS/cm @ 25°C)	149	193	158	32	106	309
Color (Pt-Co units)	52	193	54	6	29	131
Total phosphorus (µg/L)	45	192	35	10	19	83
Total nitrogen (µg/L)	870	192	880	310	660	1750
Chlorophyll a (µg/L)	20	193	18	2	7	41
Secchi (m)	1.8	169	1.7	0.4	1.4	3.4
Calcium (mg/L)	17.6	193	20.5	1.6	9.8	57.8
Magnesium (mg/L)	8.2	193	9.5	1.0	5.8	22.8
Sodium (mg/L)	13.2	181	14.2	2.6	8.0	19.6
Potassium (mg/L)	2.6	193	2.6	0.2	1.7	6.9
Sulfate (mg/L)	15.2	181	15.0	3.3	10.0	33.5
Chloride (mg/L)	23.4	193	25.7	5.5	15.3	37.0
Iron (mg/L)	0.2	149	0.2	0.0	0.1	0.4
Silicon (mg/L)	1.5	149	1.7	0.2	0.9	3.8

Ceratophyllum demersum (coontail)

Kerry Dressler

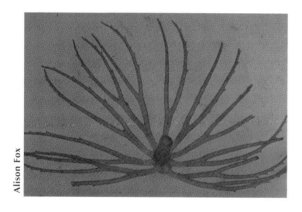

Alison Fox

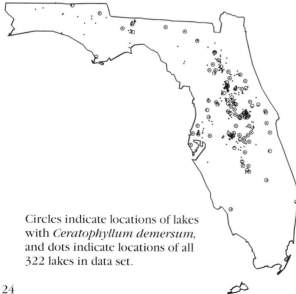

Circles indicate locations of lakes with *Ceratophyllum demersum,* and dots indicate locations of all 322 lakes in data set.

Description and distribution

Coontail is a perennial, submersed aquatic plant having slender elongated stems and whorled leaves. The leaves are finely dissected and 10–30 mm long. Several teeth, found on the midribs, give coontail a rough feel. The plant is olive to dark green. Its flowers are very small and grow at the base of the leaf. The fruit is a one-seeded nutlet. Coontail is a common native plant found throughout the United States. The Florida distribution map shows that it was found throughout the state, but there appears to be a higher percentage of lakes with coontail in central and southern Florida. Lakes are progressively more alkaline and nutrient rich as one moves from northwestern to southern Florida (Canfield and Hoyer 1988). Thus the distribution of coontail in Florida suggests that it may tend to occur in alkaline, hardwater, nutrient-rich lakes.

Biology

Coontail flowers throughout the year in Florida (Dressler et al. 1987). It reproduces by seed germination and fragmentation. It is tolerant of fluctuating water levels and moderate turbidities. This allows it occasionally to grow into large mats in streams, ponds, and lakes, causing impairment of navigational and recreational uses. The seeds and foliage are occasionally eaten by waterfowl. The plant itself serves as habitat and refuge for invertebrates and fish populations. Coontail is also sold as an aquarium plant under the name of hornwort.

Florida data

Coontail was identified in 92 lakes. The 10th and 90th percentiles for pH, alkalinity, total phosphorus, and total nitrogen values in these lakes showed that 80% of the lakes with coontail had levels that fell between 6.0 and 8.6, 2.6 and 100.1 (mg/L as $CaCO_3$), 11 and 129 (μg/L), and 380 and 1870 (μg/L), respectively. These 92 lakes also collectively averaged significantly higher pH, alkalinity, specific conductance, total phosphorus, calcium, magnesium, and sodium levels than all 322 lakes. Thus while coontail can occur in a range of lake types, it tends to occur in alkaline, hardwater, nutrient-rich lakes.

Selected references from a total of 134 coontail citations in the APIRS database:

Batterson, T.R. 1977. The effects of calcium salts on the growth and uptake of phosphorus by coontail. Journal of Aquatic Plant Management 15:36–40.

Best, E.P.H. 1979. Effects of nitrogen on the growth and nitrogenous compounds of *Ceratophyllum demersum*. Aquatic Botany 8:197–206.

Best, E.P.H. 1986. Photosynthetic characteristics of the submerged macrophyte *Ceratophyllum demersum*. Physiologia Plantarum 68(3):502–510.

Best, E.P.H. 1987. Seasonal growth of the submerged macrophyte *Ceratophyllum demersum* L. in mesotrophic Lake Vechten in relation to insulation, temperature and reserve carbohydrates. Hydrobiologia 148(3):213–243.

Gerber, K. 1985. Coontail (*Ceratophyllum demersum* L.). Aquatics 7(2):4,8.

Goulder, R. and D.J. Boatman. 1971. Evidence that nitrogen supply influences the distribution of a freshwater macrophyte, *Ceratophyllum demersum*. Journal of Ecology 59:783–791.

Jones, E.N. 1931. The morphology and biology of *Ceratophyllum demersum*. Botanical Papers, Iowa Studies in National History 13:11–55.

Kulshreshtha, M. and B. Gopal. 1983. Allelopathic influence of *Hydrilla verticillata* (L.F.) Royle on the distribution of *Ceratophyllum* species. Aquatic Botany 16(2):85–87.

Ramaprabhu, T. 1972. Observations on the autecology of *Ceratophyllum demersum* (L.) with notes on its control. Journal of the Asiatic Society 14(2–4):149–162.

Underwood, G.J.C. 1991. Growth enhancement of the macrophytes *Ceratophyllum demersum* in the presence of the snail *Planorbis*: The effect of grazing and chemical conditioning. Freshwater Biology 26:325–334.

Ceratophyllum demersum

Variables	Mean all lakes (n=322)	Number of lakes	Mean	10th percentile	Median	90th percentile
pH*	6.7	92	7.3	6.0	7.4	8.6
Alkalinity (mg/L as $CaCO_3$)*	23.9	92	36.2	2.6	23.5	100.1
Conductance (µS/cm @ 25°C)*	149	92	224	55	170	608
Color (Pt-Co units)	52	92	57	6	37	112
Total phosphorus (µg/L)*	45	92	64	11	27	129
Total nitrogen (µg/L)	870	92	1020	380	830	1870
Chlorophyll a (µg/L)	20	92	23	2	8	66
Secchi (m)	1.8	81	1.5	0.4	1.1	3.5
Calcium (mg/L)*	17.6	92	32.9	6.0	20.6	91.3
Magnesium (mg/L)*	8.2	92	15.3	2.9	10.2	41.5
Sodium (mg/L)*	13.2	90	22.0	4.4	10.4	85.6
Potassium (mg/L)	2.6	92	3.3	0.3	2.2	8.2
Sulfate (mg/L)	15.2	90	21.7	3.3	13.4	54.6
Chloride (mg/L)	23.4	92	39.0	8.2	17.4	155.8
Iron (mg/L)	0.2	80	0.2	0.0	0.1	0.4
Silicon (mg/L)	1.5	80	2.1	0.1	1.1	5.9

* Denotes a significant difference ($p<0.05$) from mean of all lakes.

Ceratopteris thalictroides (water horn fern)

Kerry Dressler

Kerry Dressler

Description and distribution

Water horn fern is an annual water fern with rhizomes that can be rooted or floating. The leaves are highly variable. Fleshy floating leaves are ovate with deeply serrated margins. One of two emersed forms has finely divided, stiff, submersed leaves, and the other has wide leaf segments. The light to dark green leaves are fragile, 100–200 mm long, and 50–100 mm wide and can have short or long petioles. The emersed leaves are divided into fine segments bearing ball-shaped sporangia on the underside in one to two rows lengthwise. Water horn fern is a nonnative species that is common in the tropics. It occurs in the Gulf Coast states, predominately Florida and Louisiana (Tarver et al. 1986). The Florida distribution map shows that water horn fern was found primarily in central and southern Florida. Lakes are progressively more alkaline and nutrient rich as one moves from northwestern to southern Florida (Canfield and Hoyer 1988). Thus the distribution of water horn fern in Florida suggests that it tends to occur in alkaline, hardwater, nutrient-rich lakes.

Biology

Water horn fern reproduces by spores and by buds arising from leaves. It is usually found along the shallow shore of canals, streams, ponds, and lakes. Water horn fern is used to some extent for aquascaping and in large aquariums.

Florida data

Water horn fern was identified in 21 lakes. The 10th and 90th percentiles for pH, alkalinity, total phosphorus, and total nitrogen values in these lakes showed that 80% of the lakes with water horn fern had levels that fell between 6.6 and 8.6, 4.0 and 100.4 (mg/L as $CaCO_3$), 11 and 186 (μg/L), and 330 and 1850 (μg/L), respectively. These 21 lakes also collectively had significantly higher pH, alkalinity, specific conductance, calcium, magnesium, sodium, sulfate, and chloride levels than all 322 lakes. Thus while water horn fern can occur in a range of lake types, it tends to occur in alkaline, hardwater lakes.

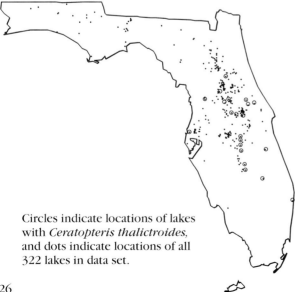

Circles indicate locations of lakes with *Ceratopteris thalictroides,* and dots indicate locations of all 322 lakes in data set.

Selected references from a total of 171 water horn fern citations in the APIRS database:

Benedict, R.C. 1909. The genus *Ceratopteris*: A preliminary review. Bulletin of the Torrey Botanical Club 36:463-476.

Bodle, M.J. 1986. Water sprite. Aquatics 8(1):4-5.

Chasan, R. 1992. *Ceratopteris*: A model plant for the 90s. Plant Cell 4(2):113-115.

Chiang, Y.-L. 1976. On the sex of the prothallia of *Ceratopteris pteridoides* (Hook.) Hieron. Taiwania 21(2):134-137.

De Vol, C.E. 1957. The geographic distribution of *Ceratopteris pteridoides*. American Fern Journal 47:67-72.

Gottlieb, J.E. 1963. Control of marginal leaf meristem growth in *Ceratopteris*. American Journal of Botany 50:614.

Gottlieb, J.E. 1972. Control of marginal leaf meristem growth in the aquatic fern *Ceratopteris*. Botanical Gazette 133(3):299-304.

Hickok, L.G. 1985. Abscisic acid resistant mutants in the fern *Ceratopteris*: Characterization and genetic analysis. Canadian Journal of Botany 63(9):1582-1585.

Hickok, L.G. and R.M. Kiriluk. 1984. Effects of auxins on gametophyte development and sexual differentiation in the fern *Ceratopteris thalictroides* (L.) Brongn. Botanical Gazette 145(1):37-42.

Klekowski, E.J. 1970. Reproductive biology of the Pteridophyta. IV. An experimental study of mating systems in *Ceratopteris thalictroides* (L.) Brongn. Botanical Journal of the Linnean Society 63:153-169.

Ceratopteris thalictroides

Variables	Mean all lakes (n=322)	Number of lakes	Mean	10th percentile	Median	90th percentile
pH*	6.7	21	7.5	6.6	7.4	8.6
Alkalinity (mg/L as CaCO₃)*	23.9	21	36.8	4.0	28.6	100.4
Conductance (µS/cm @ 25°C)*	149	21	294	86	201	773
Color (Pt-Co units)	52	21	59	4	50	112
Total phosphorus (µg/L)	45	21	64	11	44	186
Total nitrogen (µg/L)	870	21	950	330	860	1850
Chlorophyll a (µg/L)	20	21	21	2	8	66
Secchi (m)	1.8	21	1.5	0.4	1.0	3.6
Calcium (mg/L)*	17.6	21	42.8	10.1	31.8	98.0
Magnesium (mg/L)*	8.2	21	24.9	7.3	17.0	54.2
Sodium (mg/L)*	13.2	21	32.8	6.5	13.5	116.0
Potassium (mg/L)	2.6	21	4.5	0.6	3.3	12.5
Sulfate (mg/L)*	15.2	21	31.0	8.1	27.6	60.8
Chloride (mg/L)*	23.4	21	59.1	12.6	24.9	212.7
Iron (mg/L)	0.2	21	0.2	0.0	0.1	0.4
Silicon (mg/L)	1.5	21	2.5	0.1	2.6	5.0

* Denotes a significant difference (p<0.05) from mean of all lakes.

Chara spp. (muskgrass)

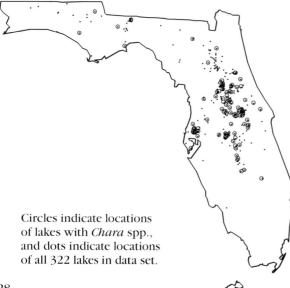

Circles indicate locations
of lakes with *Chara* spp.,
and dots indicate locations
of all 322 lakes in data set.

Description and distribution

Muskgrass superficially resembles seed plants like *Ceratophyllum demersum,* but it is really an algae. The plant has no part larger than three cells thick. There are 35 species of *Chara* that occur in the United States (Tarver et al. 1986). They are coarse and usually have a rough texture because of calcareous deposits. In most species the stems, branches, and branchlets are composed of cortical cells. These columnar-shaped cells develop from specialized node cells and are usually subtended by numerous spine cells. At each node along the main axis and its branches, there is a whorl of 6–16 branchlets. The branchlets are never forked, but consist of 5–15 nodes or joints, which have whorls of minute, spine-like bracts. Male sex organs (antheridias) are borne at the nodes of the branchlets, just below the female sex organs. Muskgrass is usually gray-green, but may have a slightly different appearance due to the calcareous deposits and the accumulation of other sediments. Muskgrass gets its common name from the strong musky odor. The Florida distribution map shows that muskgrass was found primarily in lakes from central to southern Florida. Lakes are progressively more alkaline and nutrient rich as one moves from northwestern to southern Florida (Canfield and Hoyer 1988). Thus the distribution of muskgrass in Florida suggests that it may tend to occur in alkaline, hardwater, nutrient-rich lakes.

Biology

Muskgrass reproduces with the male and female sex organs year round in Florida. Reproduction also occurs through fragmentation. It is capable of dense growths that can impair navigational and recreational activities in canals, streams, ponds, and lakes. Muskgrass is an important food item for some waterfowl and is good habitat and refuge for invertebrates and fish populations.

Florida data

Muskgrass was identified in 106 lakes. The 10th and 90th percentiles for pH, alkalinity, total phosphorus, and total nitrogen values in these lakes showed that 80% of the lakes with muskgrass had levels that fell between 5.5 and 8.5, 1.9 and 96.8 (mg/L as CaCO₃), 10 and 79 (µg/L), and 330 and 1630 (µg/L), respectively. These 106 lakes also collectively averaged significantly higher alkalinity, specific conductance, calcium, magnesium, and potassium levels than all 322 lakes. Thus while muskgrass can occur in a range of lake types, it tends to occur in alkaline, hardwater lakes.

Selected references from a total of 889 muskgrass citations in the APIRS database:

Andrews, M., R. Box, S. McInroy, and J.A. Raven. 1984. Growth of *Chara hispida*. II. Shade adaptation. Journal of Ecology 72(3):885-895.

Blazencic, J. 1980. Contribution to the study of distribution and ecology of species of the genus *Chara* in Serbia. Bulletin du Museum d'Histoire Naturelle de Belgrade (35):103-105.

Crawford, S.A. 1977. Chemical, physical, and biological changes associated with *Chara* succession in farm ponds. Hydrobiologia 55(3):209-217.

Ebinger, J. and R. Vogel. 1977. Distribution of *Chara* species in Illinois. Transactions of the Illinois State Academy of Science 70(1):96-100.

Guha, P. 1987. Studies on the biology, infestation and control measures of *Chara* in water-logged rice fields. Ph.D. Thesis. Indian Institute of Technology, Kharagpur, India.

Kilambi, R.V. and A. Zdinak. 1982. Food intake and growth of hybrid carp (female grass carp *Ctenopharyngodon idella* x male bighead, Aristichthys (*Hypophthalmichthys nobilis*)) fed on zooplankton and *Chara*. Journal of Fish Biology 21:63-67.

Pal, R. and P. Chatterjee. Cytological and spermicidal effects of sulfate on the green alga *Chara*. Indian Journal of Experimental Biology 25:52-54.

Chara spp.

Variables	Mean all lakes (n=322)	Number of lakes	Mean	10th percentile	Median	90th percentile
pH	6.7	106	7.1	5.4	7.2	8.5
Alkalinity (mg/L as CaCO₃)*	23.9	106	32.0	1.9	21.5	96.8
Conductance (µS/cm @ 25°C)*	149	106	201	53	162	354
Color (Pt-Co units)	52	106	41	5	18	101
Total phosphorus (µg/L)	45	105	35	10	19	79
Total nitrogen (µg/L)	870	105	880	330	690	1630
Chlorophyll a (µg/L)	20	106	16	1	7	40
Secchi (m)	1.8	90	1.9	0.5	1.6	3.7
Calcium (mg/L)*	17.6	105	26.5	3.0	14.0	70.3
Magnesium (mg/L)*	8.2	105	12.6	1.7	7.0	35.0
Sodium (mg/L)	13.2	100	18.0	4.1	10.3	22.8
Potassium (mg/L)*	2.6	105	3.7	0.3	2.6	8.9
Sulfate (mg/L)	15.2	100	20.5	5.1	12.3	54.6
Chloride (mg/L)	23.4	106	32.4	7.9	20.0	41.1
Iron (mg/L)	0.2	78	0.1	0.0	0.10	0.4
Silicon (mg/L)	1.5	78	1.8	0.1	0.6	5.2

* Denotes a significant difference (p<0.05) from mean of all lakes.

Cicuta mexicana (water hemlock)

Description and distribution

Water hemlock is a coarse perennial herb that grows to about 2.5 m tall. The stems can be 40–50 mm in diameter, and the surface commonly alternates green and purple stripes, appearing purple from a distance. Lower, larger leaves usually are three-pinnately compound; the overall blades are at least 400 mm long and 600–700 mm broad at the base, their leaflets usually ovate, sometimes lanceolate, commonly asymmetrical. The leaves are prominently veiny, margins irregularly to regularly coarsely toothed. The inflorescence is flat-topped (compound umbels) at the stem tip and leaf axils. The flower is white, with 5 petals and 5 stamens. The fruit is an ellipsoidal, ribbed nutlet 2–3 mm long and 1–2 mm wide. Water hemlock is a native plant occurring from Virginia to south Florida and westward to Texas. The Florida distribution map shows that water hemlock was found primarily in lakes from central to south Florida. Lakes are progressively more alkaline and nutrient rich as one moves from northwestern to southern Florida (Canfield and Hoyer 1988). Thus the distribution of water hemlock in Florida suggests that it may tend to occur in alkaline, hardwater, nutrient-rich lakes.

Biology

Water hemlock flowers from January to August in Florida (Dressler et al. 1987). It grows in floating mats or in deep muck of a shoreline habitat, with the lower branches growing horizontally into the water. All parts of the plant are deadly poisonous to humans and livestock.

Florida data

Water hemlock was identified in 37 lakes. The 10th and 90th percentiles for pH, alkalinity, total phosphorus, and total nitrogen values in these lakes showed that 80% of the lakes with water hemlock had levels that fell between 6.8 and 8.9, 10 and 111.8 (mg/L as $CaCO_3$), 15 and 155 (μg/L),

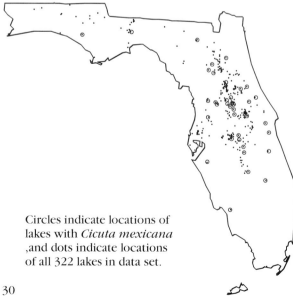

Circles indicate locations of lakes with *Cicuta mexicana* ,and dots indicate locations of all 322 lakes in data set.

and 460 and 2880 (µg/L), respectively. These 37 lakes also collectively had significantly higher pH, alkalinity, specific conductance, total phosphorus, calcium, magnesium, and silica levels than all 322 lakes. Thus while water hemlock can occur in a range of lake types, it tends to occur in alkaline, hardwater, nutrient-rich lakes.

Selected references from a total of 51 water hemlock citations in the APIRS database:

Bell, C.R. and R. Kane. 1981. An anomalous rhizomatous population of *Cicuta maculata* L. at Mountain Lake, Virginia. Castanea 46:4-7.

Dykyjova, D. 1979. Selective uptake of mineral ions and their concentration factors in aquatic higher plants. Folia Geobotanica et Phytotaxonomica 14:267-326.

Grace, J.B. 1993. The adaptive significance of clonal reproduction in angiosperms: An aquatic perspective. Aquatic Botany 44:159-180.

Hestand, R.S., B.E. May, D.P. Schultz, and C.R. Walker. 1973. Ecological implications of water levels on plant growth in a shallow water reservoir. Hyacinth Control Journal 11:54-58.

Kates, A.H., D.E. Davis, and J. McCormack. No date. Poisonous plants of the southern United States. Florida Cooperative Extension Service, Institute of Food and Agricultural Sciences, University of Florida, Gainesville, 31 pp.

Marsh, C.D. and A.B. Clawson. 1914. *Cicuta*, or water hemlock. United States Department of Agricultural Bulletin Number 69, 27 pp.

Mulligan, G.A. 1980. The genus *Cicuta* in North America. Canadian Journal of Botany 58:1755-1767.

Nelson, B. 1983. Water hemlock—*Cicuta mexicana* (Coult.) and Rose. Aquatics 5(1):4, 9.

Perkins, K.D. and W.W. Payne. No date. Guide to the poisonous and irritant plants of Florida. Circular 441. Cooperative Extension Service, Institute of Food and Agricultural Sciences, University of Florida, Gainesville.

Cicuta mexicana

Variables	Mean all lakes (n=322)	Number of lakes	Mean	10th percentile	Median	90th percentile
pH*	6.7	37	7.8	6.8	7.9	8.9
Alkalinity (mg/L as CaCO₃)*	23.9	37	53.9	10.0	44.8	111.8
Conductance (µS/cm @ 25°C)*	149	37	252	66	200	676
Color (Pt-Co units)	52	37	73	14	48	140
Total phosphorus (µg/L)*	45	37	76	15	49	155
Total nitrogen (µg/L)	870	37	1230	460	1060	2880
Chlorophyll a (µg/L)	20	37	33	3	14	128
Secchi (m)*	1.8	35	0.9	0.4	0.8	1.5
Calcium (mg/L)*	17.6	37	47.0	10.1	35.8	98.0
Magnesium (mg/L)*	8.2	37	20.5	5.7	12.0	53.1
Sodium (mg/L)	13.2	36	22.9	5.1	9.7	90.8
Potassium (mg/L)	2.6	37	3.4	0.2	2.6	9.7
Sulfate (mg/L)	15.2	36	20.4	4.0	11.5	54.4
Chloride (mg/L)	23.4	37	41.3	8.7	18.2	174.4
Iron (mg/L)	0.2	35	0.2	0.0	0.2	0.4
Silicon (mg/L)*	1.5	35	3.3	0.4	2.6	7.1

* Denotes a significant difference (p<0.05) from mean of all lakes.

Cladium jamaicense (saw grass)

Description and distribution

Saw grass is a coarse perennial sedge growing up to 3 m tall. It is noted for its spiny, serrated leaf blades with teeth similar to those of a saw. The leaves are 1-1.5 m long and 5-10 mm wide, very stiff, green or brown, and folded at the midvein. The inflorescence can be up to 3 m tall and is much branched with 2-6 spikelets at the branch tip. The fruit is an achene, 2-2.5 mm long, wrinkled, and ovoid to spherical. Saw grass is a native plant that occurs primarily near the coast, from Virginia to Florida and west to Texas (Godfrey and Wooten 1981). The Florida distribution map shows that saw grass was found in lakes across the whole state, with no apparent geographical pattern.

Biology

Saw grass flowers from April to November in Florida (Dressler et al. 1987). It reproduces by seed germination, if water levels are favorable. Asexual reproduction by rhizome growth, however, can be substantial. Saw grass grows well on dry ground or to 2 m deep in fresh or brackish water. Thus it has great growth potential and can form impenetrable stands that can impair water flow, navigation, and recreational uses of some aquatic systems. Waterfowl flying along the coast of Florida use the seeds as a high energy food source. Saw grass is also used as nesting habitat for coots, duck, and several other varieties of aquatic birds.

Florida data

Saw grass was identified in 141 lakes. The 10th and 90th percentiles for pH, alkalinity, total phosphorus, and total nitrogen values in these lakes show that 80% of the lakes with saw grass had levels between 4.9 and 8.6, 1.2 and 100.2 (mg/L as $CaCO_3$), 10 and 73 (µg/L), and 310 and 1810 (µg/L), respectively. The average water chemistry values of the 141 lakes with saw grass showed only one significant difference (iron) from those of all 322 lakes. These data and the distribution map suggest that saw grass can occur in a wide range of Florida lake types.

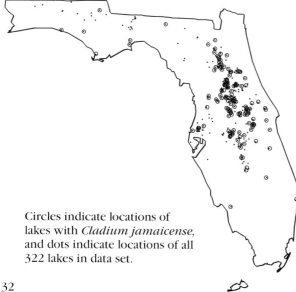

Circles indicate locations of lakes with *Cladium jamaicense,* and dots indicate locations of all 322 lakes in data set.

Selected references from a total of 288 saw grass citations in the APIRS database:

Andrejko, M.J. 1977. Silicate structures and mineralogy of sawgrass (*Cladium jamaicensis* Crantz) and its associated peats from the Florida Everglades. Florida Scientist 40(1):24 (Abstract).

Bachoon, D. and R.D. Jones. 1992. Potential rates of methanogenesis in sawgrass marshes with peat and marl soils in the Everglades. Soil Biology and Biochemistry 24(1):21-27.

Bernard, J.M., F.K. Seischab, and G. Jacoby. 1985. Life history and production of above-and-below-ground structures of *Cladium mariscoides* (Muhl.) Torr. in a western New York fen. Bulletin of the Torrey Botanical Club 112(3):288-294.

Bridges, E.L., S.L. Orzell, and J.R. Burkhalter. 1993. *Cladium mariscoides* (Cyperaceae) in the western Florida panhandle and its phytogeographic significance. Phytologia 74(1):35-42.

Herndon, A., L. Gunderson, and J. Stenberg. 1991. Sawgrass (*Cladium jamaicense*) survival in a regime of fire and flooding. Wetlands 11(1):17-27.

Hofstetter, R.H. 1975. Changes in sawgrass communities in southern Florida. Florida Scientist 38 (Suppl. 1):8 (Abstract).

Hsieh, Y.P. 1988. Dynamics of carbon, nitrogen and phosphorus cycling in a sawgrass tidal marsh with special reference to the aboveground primary production. Journal of Environmental Quality 17(4):676-681.

Koch, M.S. and P.S. Rawlik. 1993. Transpiration and stomatal conductance of two wetland macrophytes (*Cladium jamaicense* and *Typha domingensis*) in the subtropical Everglades. American Journal of Botany 80(10):1146-1154.

Steward, K.K. and W.H. Ornes. 1975. The autecology of sawgrass in the Florida Everglades. Ecology 56(1):162-171.

Steward, K.K. and W.H. Ornes. 1983. Mineral nutrition of sawgrass (*Cladium jamicense* Crantz) in relation to nutrient supply. Aquatic Botany 16(4):349-359.

Urban, N.H., S.M. Davis, and N.G. Aumen. 1993. Fluctuations in sawgrass and cattail densities in Everglades Water Conservation Area 2A under varying nutrient, hydrologic and fire regimes. Aquatic Botany 46:203-223.

Cladium jamaicense

Variables	Mean all lakes (n=322)	Number of lakes	Mean	10th percentile	Median	90th percentile
pH	6.7	141	6.8	4.9	6.8	8.6
Alkalinity (mg/L as CaCO$_3$)	23.9	141	28.3	1.2	11.5	100.2
Conductance (µS/cm @ 25°C)	149	141	181	42	113	400
Color (Pt-Co units)	52	141	68	5	26	174
Total phosphorus (µg/L)	45	141	32	10	19	73
Total nitrogen (µg/L)	870	141	930	310	680	1810
Chlorophyll a (µg/L)	20	141	17	1	6	39
Secchi (m)	1.8	121	1.7	0.4	1.4	3.6
Calcium (mg/L)	17.6	141	21.9	1.8	10.1	66.9
Magnesium (mg/L)	8.2	141	11.3	1.0	6.3	32.3
Sodium (mg/L)	13.2	133	16.7	3.8	8.9	32.0
Potassium (mg/L)	2.6	141	3.1	0.2	2.0	8.5
Sulfate (mg/L)	15.2	133	16.5	3.7	10.0	46.6
Chloride (mg/L)	23.4	141	30.7	7.9	17.3	43.5
Iron (mg/L)*	0.2	102	0.1	0.0	0.10	0.3
Silicon (mg/L)	1.5	102	1.8	0.1	0.8	5.1

* Denotes a significant difference (p<0.05) from mean of all lakes.

Colocasia esculenta (wild taro)

Kerry Dressler

Kerry Dressler

Description and distribution

Wild taro is an exotic herb with tuberous rhizomes and thick succulent stems usually from 0.5–1.5 m tall. The stiff leaves are large (400–900 mm long by 100–350 mm wide), thick, and ovate with cordate bases. The leaves are always peltate and velvety green. The inflorescence is stalked, fleshy, shorter than the leaf stalk, and enfolded by a green-yellow bract that is constricted below the middle. The flower is small, densely crowded on a finger-like cluster. Female flowers are near the base, and male flowers are above. The fruit is a cluster of berries with viable seeds. Wild taro is native to the Pacific islands and is found throughout the tropical and subtropical regions of the world. It has been naturalized to Florida and other southeastern states because it is often used as an ornamental plant (Godfrey and Wooten 1981). The Florida distribution map shows that wild taro was found infrequently in northwest Florida and primarily in central and south Florida. Lakes are progressively more alkaline and nutrient rich as one moves from northwestern to southern Florida (Canfield and Hoyer 1988). Thus the distribution of wild taro in Florida suggests that it may tend to occur in alkaline, hardwater, nutrient-rich lakes.

Biology

Wild taro flowers from January to June in Florida (Dressler et al. 1987). It reproduces by seed germination and growth of stolons. The plant grows primarily on shore-water interfaces of many aquatic systems but can also be found on floating islands. Optimum growth occurs in hot, humid areas. It is frequently sold as an ornamental or house plant because of its large velvety leaves. Many Pacific Island and Asiatic people cultivate wild taro for the tubers, which are edible only after being thoroughly cooked. The seeds are eaten by many varieties of songbirds, and the tubers are eaten by muskrats and other rodents.

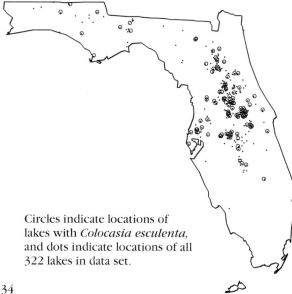

Circles indicate locations of lakes with *Colocasia esculenta*, and dots indicate locations of all 322 lakes in data set.

Florida data

Wild taro was identified in 125 lakes. The 10th and 90th percentiles for pH, alkalinity, total phosphorus, and total nitrogen values in these lakes show that 80% of the lakes with wild taro had levels between 5.8 and 8.8, 1.8 and 100.4 (mg/L as $CaCO_3$), 10 and 127 (µg/L), and 400 and 2200 (µg/L), respectively. These 125 lakes also collectively had significantly higher pH, alkalinity, specific conductance, calcium, magnesium, and potassium levels than all 322 lakes. Thus while wild taro can occur in a range of lake types, it tends to occur in alkaline, hardwater lakes.

Selected references from a total of 227 wild taro citations in the APIRS database:

Aggarwal, A., G. Kaur, and R.S. Mehrotra. 1986. Effect of certain metabolic inhibitors on the growth and respiration of phytophythora *Colocasia racib*. Indian Botanical Reporter 5(2):119-122.

Austin, M.T., M. Constantinides, and S.C. Miyasaka. 1994. Effect of magnesium on early taro growth. Communications in Soil Science and Plant Analysis 25(11-12):2159-2169.

Begley, B.W. 1981. Taro—the flood-irrigated root crop of the Pacific. World Crops (March 1981):28-30.

Fatuesi, S., P. Tauili'ili, F. Taotua, and A. Vargo. 1991. Cultural methods of pest control on taro (*Colocasia esculenta* Schott) in American Samoa. Micronesica 3(Suppl.):123-127.

Figueres, K.C. 1991. *Colocasia esculenta* in the Pacific. Aroideana 4(1):25-30.

Jacobs, B.C. and V. Chand. 1992. Large headsette and improved cultivar enhance growth and development of taro (*Colocasia esculenta* (L.) Schott) during establishment. Journal of Agronomy Crop Science 168:119-127.

Manrique, L.A. 1994. Nitrogen requirements of taro. Journal of Plant Nutrition 17(8):1429-1441.

Nyman, L.P., E.L. Webb, Z. Gu, and J. Arditti. 1986. Structure and *in vitro* growth of zygotic embryos of taro (*Colocasia esculenta* var. *antiquorum*). Annals of Botany 57(5): 623-630.

Yam, T.W., J.L.P. Young, K.P.L. Fan, and J. Arditti. 1990. Induction of callus from axilary buds of taro (*Colocasia esculenta* var. *esculenta*, Araceae) and subsequent plantlet. Plant Cell Reports 9:459-462.

Yamamota, Y. and O. Matsumoto. 1992. Comparison of growth habits of *in vitro* propagated seed corm among taro (*Colocasia esculenta* Schott.) cultivars and their application for semi-forcing culture. Journal of the Japanese Society for Horticultural Science 61(3):581-588.

Zhang, G. and D.X. Zhang. 1990. The relationship between geographic distribution and ploidy level of taro, *Colocasia esculenta*. Euphytica 47(1):25-27.

Colocasia esculenta

Variables	Mean all lakes (n=322)	Number of lakes	Mean	10th percentile	Median	90th percentile
pH*	6.7	125	7.5	5.8	7.7	8.8
Alkalinity (mg/L as $CaCO_3$)*	23.9	125	40.6	1.8	36.0	100.4
Conductance (µS/cm @ 25°C)*	149	125	202	60	178	392
Color (Pt-Co units)	52	125	42	6	24	103
Total phosphorus (µg/L)	45	125	64	10	25	127
Total nitrogen (µg/L)	870	125	1070	400	820	2200
Chlorophyll a (µg/L)	20	125	32	2	15	91
Secchi (m)	1.8	109	1.5	0.4	1.2	3.5
Calcium (mg/L)*	17.6	125	28.6	3.4	19.9	72.4
Magnesium (mg/L)*	8.2	125	12.4	2.0	7.1	33.7
Sodium (mg/L)	13.2	114	17.0	5.0	10.5	33.9
Potassium (mg/L)*	2.6	125	3.7	0.3	2.5	9.2
Sulfate (mg/L)	15.2	114	18.6	4.4	13.2	46.7
Chloride (mg/L)	23.4	125	29.0	9.0	18.7	43.5
Iron (mg/L)	0.2	97	0.1	0.0	0.10	0.3
Silicon (mg/L)	1.5	97	1.9	0.1	0.9	5.3

* Denotes a significant difference (p<0.05) from mean of all lakes.

Crinum americanum (swamp lily)

Kerry Dressler

Kerry Dressler

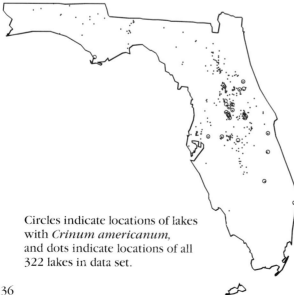

Circles indicate locations of lakes with *Crinum americanum,* and dots indicate locations of all 322 lakes in data set.

Description and distribution

Swamp lily is a perennial herb with an onion-like bulb. Leaf bases arise alternately and sheath each other for some distance, forming a stalk-like portion above the bulb proper; the leaves then ascend, spreading alternately above. The leaf blades gradually become flattened and broadly strap-like from the rounded sheathing base. The upper leaf surface is smooth and the lower smoothed or ribbed. The leaf margins are entire or with small but conspicuous remote and irregularly spaced soft teeth. Swamp lily has two to six flowers at the tip of a stalk that are delicately fragrant and white or white streaked with pink. The floral tube is long, slender, and greenish, extending 100–150 mm beyond the summit of the ovary, 70–140 mm long, at first ascending, then spreading abruptly in a saliform fashion, finally arching reflexed. The fruit is a thin-walled capsule bearing one to several large, fleshy seeds. Swamp lily is a native plant that inhabits the Coastal Plain, from Georgia to Florida and west to Texas (Godfrey and Wooten 1981). The Florida distribution map shows that swamp lily was found infrequently in the state and primarily in south-central Florida.

Biology

Swamp lily flowers year round in Florida (Dressler et al. 1987). It reproduces primarily through seed germination. As the fruit capsule matures the stem is bent over from its own weight, bringing the capsule in contact with the ground. Germination of the seeds commonly begins within the capsule, their enlargement causing irregular rupturing of the wall of the fruit.

Florida data

Swamp lily was identified in only 23 lakes. The 10th and 90th percentiles for pH, alkalinity, total phosphorus, and total nitrogen values in these lakes show that 80% of the lakes with swamp lily had levels between 5.3 and 8.9, 2.0 and 122.5

(mg/L as $CaCO_3$), 11 and 152 (µg/L), and 400 and 3230 (µg/L), respectively. These 23 lakes also collectively averaged significantly higher calcium, magnesium, and chloride levels than all 322 lakes. Thus there is slight evidence that swamp lily may tend to occur in hardwater lakes.

Selected references from a total of 18 swamp lily citations in the APIRS database:

Baden, J., W.T. Batson, and R. Stalter. 1975. Factors affecting the distribution of vegetation of abandoned rice fields, Georgetown County, South Carolina. Castanea 40(3):171-184.

Browder, J.A., P.J. Gleason, and D.R. Swift. 1994. Periphyton in the Everglades: Spatial variation, environmental correlates and ecological implications. Pp. 379-418 in Everglades: The ecosystem and its restoration, S.M. Davis and J.C. Ogden, editors. St. Lucie Press, Delray Beach, Fla.

Chestnut, T.L. and E.H. Barmen Jr. 1974. Aquatic vascular plants of Lake Apopka, Florida. Florida Scientist 37(1):61-64.

Grace, J.B. 1993. The adaptive significance of colonial reproduction in angiosperms: An aquatic perspective. Aquatic Botany 44:159-180.

King, G.M., P. Roslev, and H. Skovgaard. 1990. Distribution and rate of methane oxidation in sediments of the Florida Everglades. Applied and Environmental Microbiology 56(9):2902-2911.

Loftin, J.P. 1994. On the waterfront. Florida Water Magazine 3(2):14-24.

Lowe, E.F. 1986. The relationship between hydrology and vegetational pattern within the floodplain marsh of a subtropical Florida lake. Florida Scientist 49(4):213-233.

Penfound, W.T. and S.S. Hathaway. 1938. Plant communities in the marshlands of southeastern Louisiana. Ecological Monographs 8:1-56 (Abstract).

Thompson, R.L. 1970. Florida sandhill crane nesting on the Loxahatchee National Wildlife Refuge. Auk 87:492-502.

Crinum americanum

Variables	Mean all lakes (n=322)	Number of lakes	Mean	10th percentile	Median	90th percentile
pH	6.7	23	7.5	5.3	7.8	8.9
Alkalinity (mg/L as $CaCO_3$)	23.9	23	52.3	2.0	47.0	122.5
Conductance (µS/cm @ 25°C)	149	23	274	61	214	723
Color (Pt-Co units)	52	23	76	6	45	183
Total phosphorus (µg/L)	45	23	85	11	31	152
Total nitrogen (µg/L)	870	23	1260	400	1030	3230
Chlorophyll a (µg/L)	20	23	31	3	7	118
Secchi (m)	1.8	22	1.1	0.4	0.8	2.9
Calcium (mg/L)*	17.6	23	43.3	5.2	38.5	100.0
Magnesium (mg/L)*	8.2	23	20.0	4.4	13.7	51.8
Sodium (mg/L)	13.2	23	26.3	6.3	14.7	89.9
Potassium (mg/L)	2.6	23	3.5	0.7	3.2	8.4
Sulfate (mg/L)	15.2	23	20.3	3.7	11.6	53.2
Chloride (mg/L)*	23.4	23	48.4	12.3	24.2	168.2
Iron (mg/L)	0.2	21	0.2	0.0	0.1	0.7
Silicon (mg/L)	1.5	21	3.0	0.3	2.5	6.8

* Denotes a significant difference (p<0.05) from mean of all lakes.

Cyperus alternifolius (umbrella flat sedge)

Kerry Dressler

Description and distribution

Umbrella flat sedge is a perennial plant that forms very large clumps. The triangular stems are up to 1.5 m tall and about 20 mm thick basely. The leaves are few, sheathed at the base of the stem, and without blades. The inflorescence is subtended by 10–25 conspicuous foliar bracts, mostly longer than the inflorescence. The inflorescence itself has a central sessile cluster and 15–25 stalked surrounding clusters. Each stalk has a terminal headlike raceme of 18–15 spikelets. The spikelets are linear to oblong, 5–10 mm long, and 1–2 mm wide, with 12-30 flowers. The fruit is a three-angled, brown, elliptic-oblong achene, 0.6–1.0 mm long. Umbrella flat sedge is native to the Old World (Godfrey and Wooten 1981). It is naturalized in Florida because it has been cultivated as an ornamental plant. The Florida distribution map shows that umbrella flat sedge was found primarily in south-central Florida.

Biology

Umbrella flat sedge from January to June in Florida (Dressler et al. 1987). It reproduces primarily by seed germination.

Florida data

Umbrella flat sedge was identified in 27 lakes. The 10th and 90th percentiles for pH, alkalinity, total phosphorus, and total nitrogen values in these lakes show that 80% of the lakes with umbrella flat sedge had levels between 5.1 and 8.8, 1.5 and 105.9 (mg/L as $CaCO_3$), 14 and 91 (µg/L), and 430 and 2180 (µg/L), respectively. These 27 lakes with umbrella flat sedge had water chemistry averages similar to those of all 322 lakes.

Circles indicate locations of lakes with *Cyperus alternifolius*, and dots indicate locations of all 322 lakes in data set.

Selected references from a total of 21 umbrella flat sedge citations in the APIRS database:

Baijnath, H. 1982. A study of *Cyperus alternifolius* L., sens. lat. (Cyperaceae). Bulletin of Miscellaneous Information, Kew Royal Garden 30(3):521–526.

Barclay, A.M. and R.M.M. Crawford. 1982. Plant growth and survival under strict anaerobiosis. Journal of Experimental Biology 33(134):541–549.

Fisher, J.B. 1971. Control of bud inhibition in *Cyperus*. Planta 97:257–268.

Fisher, J.B. 1970. Development of the intercalary meristem of *Cyperus alternifolius*. American Journal of Botany 57:691–703.

Schultz, D.S. 1985. Water gardening at Walt Disney World. Plants and Gardens 41(1):29–35.

Stansch, K. 1992. Aquatic gardening at the turn of the century. Aquatic Gardener 5(1):5–12.

White, D. 1984. New threats investigated in Florida. Aquaphyte 4(2):2.

Cyperus alternifolius

Variables	Mean all lakes (n=322)	Number of lakes	Mean	10th percentile	Median	90th percentile
pH	6.7	27	7.4	5.1	7.8	8.8
Alkalinity (mg/L as CaCO$_3$)	23.9	27	46.1	1.5	48.8	105.9
Conductance (µS/cm @ 25°C)	149	27	227	69	180	475
Color (Pt-Co units)	52	27	68	4	37	197
Total phosphorus (µg/L)	45	27	45	14	35	91
Total nitrogen (µg/L)	870	27	1040	430	820	2180
Chlorophyll a (µg/L)	20	27	28	3	14	83
Secchi (m)	1.8	22	1.5	0.4	1.1	3.4
Calcium (mg/L)*	17.6	27	39.3	3.1	25.0	93.6
Magnesium (mg/L)	8.2	27	14.7	2.2	8.1	44.2
Sodium (mg/L)	13.2	25	19.8	5.8	10.0	65.0
Potassium (mg/L)	2.6	27	3.5	0.7	2.5	8.5
Sulfate (mg/L)	15.2	25	16.7	5.4	13.0	37.4
Chloride (mg/L)	23.4	27	36.6	10.0	23.7	112.0
Iron (mg/L)	0.2	19	0.1	0.0	0.10	0.4
Silicon (mg/L)	1.5	19	1.7	0.2	0.7	5.3

* Denotes a significant difference (p<0.05) from mean of all lakes.

Cyperus articulatus (umbrella sedge)

Description and distribution

Umbrella sedge is a perennial plant with coarse, reddish, scaly rhizomes that occur in large colonies. Flowering stems are 10–20 mm wide at the base, gradually narrowing to the summit, 1–2 m tall, with many cross-walls that are visible as rings around the stem. Umbrella sedge has no bladed leaves and a few sheaths at the base of the stem. The inflorescence usually has unequal primary stalks with terminal spikelet clusters. The spikelets are narrowly linear, 1.5–3.0 mm wide, and 10–40 mm long. The fruit is a three-angled achene, 1.5 mm long, dark brown, and shiny. Umbrella sedge occurs in the Coastal Plain from South Carolina to Florida and west to Texas (Godfrey and Wooten 1981). The Florida distribution map shows that umbrella sedge was found primarily in east-central Florida.

Biology

Umbrella sedge flowers from April to November in Florida (Dressler et al. 1987). It reproduces primarily by seed germination, but vegetative reproduction with rhizomes is common.

Florida data

Umbrella sedge was identified in only 15 lakes. The 10th and 90th percentiles for pH, alkalinity, total phosphorus, and total nitrogen values in these lakes show that 80% of the lakes with umbrella sedge had levels between 6.3 and 8.8, 7.2 and 88.2 (mg/L as $CaCO_3$), 19 and 217 (µg/L), and 740 and 2080 (µg/L), respectively. These 15 lakes also collectively averaged significantly higher pH, specific conductance, color, total phosphorus, chlorophyll *a*, calcium, magnesium, sodium, chloride, and silicon and significantly lower Secchi depth values than all 322 lakes. Thus umbrella sedge tends to occur in alkaline, hardwater, nutrient-rich lakes.

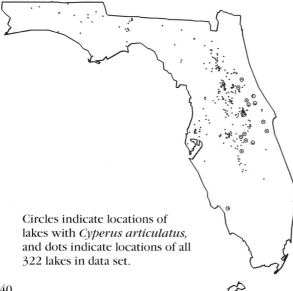

Circles indicate locations of lakes with *Cyperus articulatus,* and dots indicate locations of all 322 lakes in data set.

Selected references from a total of 36 umbrella sedge citations in the APIRS database:

Bennett, B.C. 1992. Hallucinogenic plants of the Shuar and related indigenous groups in Amazonian Ecuador and Peru. Brittonia 44(4):483-493.

Biswas, K. and C.C. Colder. 1936. Handbook of common water and marsh plants of India and Burma. Government Press, Delhi, India. 216 pp.

Denny, P. and D.W. Bowker. 1978. The importance of the littoral epiphyton as food for commercial fish in the recent African man-made lake, Nyumba Ya Mungu Reservoir, Tanzania. Biological Journal of the Linnean Society 10:139-150.

Gopal, B. and M. Kulshreshtha. 1980. Role of aquatic macrophytes as reservoirs of nutrients and in their cycling. International Journal of Ecology and Environmental Science 6:145-152.

Howard-Williams, C. 1972. Limnological studies in an African swamp: Seasonal and spatial changes in the swamps of Lake Chilwa, Malawi. Archives of Hydrobiology 70(3):379-391.

Lubke, R.A., P.E. Reavell, and P.J. Dye. 1984. The effects of dredging on the macrophytic vegetation of the Boro River, Okavango Delta, Botswana. Biological Conservation 30(3):211-236.

Petr, T. 1987. Fish, fisheries, aquatic macrophytes and water quality in inland waters. Water Quality Bulletin 12(3):103-106, 128-129.

Saxena, M.K. 1986. Dry matter production in freshwater and marsh plants around Jaipur. Limnologica (Berlin) 17(1):127-138.

Shiam, R., H.S. Sirohi, R. Rashmi, and P.L. Malik. 1984. Effect of aqueous extract of *Cyperus articulatus* L. tuber on germination and seedlings growth of maize (*Zea mays* L.). Journal of Current Bioscience 1(4):175-178.

Thomas, J.D. 1966. Some preliminary observations on the fauna and flora of a small manmade lake in the west African savanna. Bulletin de l'Institut Francais d'Afrique Noire 28:542-562.

Cyperus articulatus

Variables	Mean all lakes (n=322)	Number of lakes	Mean	10th percentile	Median	90th percentile
pH*	6.7	15	7.8	6.3	7.9	8.8
Alkalinity (mg/L as CaCO₃)	23.9	15	41.7	7.2	44.8	88.2
Conductance (µS/cm @ 25°C)*	149	15	400	69	225	878
Color (Pt-Co units)*	52	15	112	48	102	247
Total phosphorus (µg/L)*	45	15	80	19	52	217
Total nitrogen (µg/L)	870	15	1280	740	1260	2080
Chlorophyll a (µg/L)*	20	15	33	3	19	99
Secchi (m)*	1.8	15	0.6	0.4	0.6	0.9
Calcium (mg/L)*	17.6	15	60.7	12.1	82.2	102.9
Magnesium (mg/L)*	8.2	15	27.4	6.3	12.1	59.6
Sodium (mg/L)*	13.2	15	52.4	6.8	15.8	130.6
Potassium (mg/L)	2.6	15	3.4	0.7	2.5	6.6
Sulfate (mg/L)	15.2	15	30.9	4.2	27.6	74.9
Chloride (mg/L)*	23.4	15	96.9	12.8	27.1	235.7
Iron (mg/L)	0.2	15	0.3	0.1	0.2	0.6
Silicon (mg/L)*	1.5	15	2.9	0.8	3.1	5.0

* Denotes a significant difference (p<0.05) from mean of all lakes.

Cyperus odoratus (flat sedge)

Description and distribution

Flat sedge is a coarse annual plant with solitary or tufted stems, 10–100 mm tall, commonly purplish, and 10–30 mm wide at the base. Flat sedge has loose sheaths at the base, some with leaf blades approximately 10 mm wide and longer than the inflorescence. The inflorescence is subtended by 3–10 leaf-like bracts variable in size and density, the longer ones much longer than the inflorescence. The flowers consist of narrow spikelets with overlapping scales in bottlebrush-like clusters. The spikes are brown when mature. The fruit is a three-angled, oblong or narrowly obovate achene, 1–2.5 mm long. Flat sedge is found throughout the temperate and tropical regions of the world but is most abundant in the Gulf Coast states and the southwest (Godfrey and Wooten 1981). The Florida distribution map shows that flat sedge was found primarily in central Florida.

Biology

Flat sedge flowers year-round in Florida (Dressler et al. 1987) and reproduces primarily by seed germination. It is found commonly in wetlands, ditch banks, and areas susceptible to water level fluctuations. Flat sedge can also survive in upland pasture areas where it is considered a weed. Its seeds are often consumed by birds and rodents and by waterfowl when flooded. The plant is also used as material for nests and nesting habitat by many species of birds.

Florida data

Flat sedge was identified in only 18 lakes. The 10th and 90th percentiles for pH, alkalinity, total phosphorus, and total nitrogen values in these lakes show that 80% of the lakes with flat sedge had levels between 6.3 and 8.3, 2.3 and 48.2 (mg/L as $CaCO_3$), 9 and 47 (µg/L), and 350 and 1200 (µg/L), respectively. These 18 lakes with flat sedge had water chemistry averages and ranges similar to those of all 322 lakes. This suggests that flat sedge can occur in a wide range of aquatic systems.

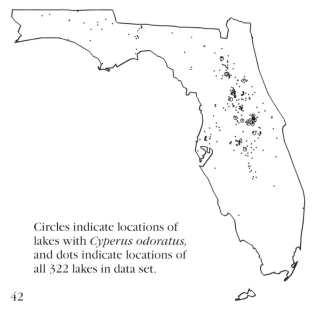

Circles indicate locations of lakes with *Cyperus odoratus,* and dots indicate locations of all 322 lakes in data set.

Selected references from a total of 26 flat sedge citations in the APIRS database:

Baskin, J.M., C.C. Baskin, and D.M. Spooner. 1989. Role of temperature, light, and date: Seeds were exhumed from soil on germination of four wetlands perennials. Aquatic Botany 35:387-394.

Bennett, B.C. 1990. Hallucinogenic plants of the Shuar and related indigenous groups in Amazonian Ecuador and Peru. Brittonia 44(4):483-493.

Bettoli, P.W. and J.A. Gordon. 1990. Aquatic macrophyte studies on Woods Reservoir, Tennessee. Journal of the Tennessee Academy of Science 65(1):4-8.

Dierberg, F.E. 1992. The littoral zone of Lake Okeechobee as a source of phosphate after drawdown. Environmental Management 16(3):371-380.

Landers, L., S. Johnson, P. Morgan, and W. Baldwin. 1976. Duck foods in managed tidal impoundments in South Carolina. Journal of Wildlife Management 40(4):721-728.

Lowe, E.F. 1986. The relationship between hydrology and vegetational pattern within the floodplain marsh of a subtropical Florida lake. Florida Scientist 49(4):213-233.

Meneses Carbonell, R. 1985. Rice water host weevil plants in Cuba. International Rice Research Newsletter 10(1):21-22.

Plasencia Fraga, J.M. and J. Kvet. 1993. Production dynamics of *Typha domingensis* (Pers.) Kunth populations in Cuba. Journal of Aquatic Plant Management 31:240-243.

Watts, W.A., B.C.S. Hansen, and E.C. Grimm. 1992. Camel Lake—a 40,000 year record of vegetational and forest history from northwest Florida. Ecology 73(7):1056-1066.

Welling, C.H. and R.L. Becker. 1993. Reduction of purple loosestrife establishment in Minnesota wetlands. Wildlife Society Bulletin 21(1):56-63.

Cyperus odoratus

Variables	Mean all lakes (n=322)	Number of lakes	Mean	10th percentile	Median	90th percentile
pH	6.7	18	7.2	6.3	7.0	8.3
Alkalinity (mg/L as CaCO$_3$)	23.9	18	19.4	2.3	19.3	48.2
Conductance (µS/cm @ 25°C)	149	18	151	63	137	260
Color (Pt-Co units)	52	18	28	4	16	86
Total phosphorus (µg/L)	45	17	25	9	23	47
Total nitrogen (µg/L)	870	17	770	350	690	1200
Chlorophyll a (µg/L)	20	18	15	3	13	31
Secchi (m)	1.8	15	1.9	0.9	1.6	3.7
Calcium (mg/L)	17.6	18	12.0	3.0	9.6	25.4
Magnesium (mg/L)	8.2	18	4.9	1.5	3.9	11.4
Sodium (mg/L)	13.2	17	11.6	6.1	9.0	20.1
Potassium (mg/L)	2.6	18	4.0	1.1	2.4	11.2
Sulfate (mg/L)	15.2	17	19.9	3.3	12.4	49.2
Chloride (mg/L)	23.4	18	20.3	11.7	16.9	33.4
Iron (mg/L)*	0.2	14	0.10	0.0	0.0	0.2
Silicon (mg/L)	1.5	14	0.6	0.2	0.3	2.3

* Denotes a significant difference (p<0.05) from mean of all lakes.

Decodon verticillatus (swamp loosestrife)

Kerry Dressler

Kerry Dressler

Description and distribution

Swamp loosestrife is a perennial plant with woody lower stems and herbaceous upper stems. The bark is very soft and corky underwater, peeling off in long cinnamon-colored strips above water. The stems are strongly arching with some rooting at the tips. The leaves are alternate or whorled and are short stalked, lanceolate or elliptic-lanceolate, up to 200 mm long and 50 mm wide, and come to a point. The flowers are axillary, about 25 mm across, and occur in short-stalked clusters. The petals are magenta, stalked, lanceolate, and crinkled, with irregular margins and varied length. The fruit is surrounded by the floral tube and contains a seed about 2 mm long, olive-green with a large brown spot on one side. Swamp loosestrife occurs from Nova Scotia to Ontario and Minnesota, south to central Florida and east to Texas (Godfrey and Wooten 1981). The Florida distribution map shows that it occurs from extreme northwestern to central Florida, but not extreme south Florida.

Biology

Swamp loosestrife reproduces by seed germination and vegetatively. It flowers from July to November in Florida (Dressler et al. 1987). Swamp loosestrife can be found on the shores of lakes, but it is more common in swamps, clearings, swampy shores of streams, pools and bogs.

Florida data

Swamp loosestrife was identified in 30 lakes. The 10th and 90th percentiles for pH, alkalinity, total phosphorus, and total nitrogen values in these lakes showed that 80% of the lakes with swamp loosestrife had levels that fell between 4.9 and 8.6, 0.5 and 100.3 (mg/L as $CaCO_3$), 9 and 79 (μg/L), and 320 and 1920 (μg/L), respectively. The range in water chemistry values of the 30 lakes with swamp loosestrife was similar to those of all 322 lakes. This suggests that swamp loosestrife can occur in a wide range of lake types.

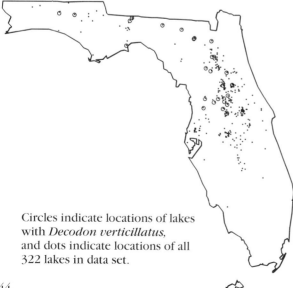

Circles indicate locations of lakes with *Decodon verticillatus,* and dots indicate locations of all 322 lakes in data set.

Selected references from a total of 50 swamp loosestrife citations in the APIRS database:

Cudlip, L.S. and J.A. Perry. 1988. Is in-lake carbon processing phased to correlate with availability? Decomposition of *Decodon verticillatus* (L.) Ell. and *Ceratophyllum demersum* L. in Cedar Bog Lake, Minnesota, USA. Archives of Hydrobiology 111(3):383–396.

Eckert, C.G. and S.C.H. Barrett. 1992. Stochastic loss of style morphs from populations of tristylous *Lythrum salicaria* and *Decodon verticillatus* (Lythraceae). Evolution 46(4):1014–1029.

Eckert, C.G. and S.C.H. Barrett. 1993. Clonal reproduction and patterns of genotypic diversity in *Decodon verticillatus* (Lythraceae). American Journal of Botany 80(10):1175–1182.

Eckert, C.G. and S.C.H. Barrett. 1993. The inheritance of tristyly in *Decodon verticillatus* (Lythraceae). Heredity 71(5):473–480.

Eckert, C.G. and S.C.H. Barrett. 1994. Post-pollination mechanisms and the maintenance of outcrossing in self-compatible, tristylous, *Decodon verticillatus* (Lythraceae). Heredity 72(4):396–411.

Graham, S.A. 1964. The genera of Lythraceae in the southeastern United States. Journal of Arnold Arboretum 45:235–250.

Hunt, K.W. 1943. Floating mats on a southeastern coastal plain reservoir. Bulletin of the Torrey Botanical Club 70(5):481–488.

Tarver, D.P. 1980. Water fluctuation and the aquatic flora of Lake Miccosukee. Journal of Aquatic Plant Management 18:19–23.

Decodon verticillatus

Variables	Mean all lakes (n=322)	Number of lakes	Mean	10th percentile	Median	90th percentile
pH	6.7	30	6.6	4.9	6.5	8.6
Alkalinity (mg/L as $CaCO_3$)	23.9	30	25.8	0.5	6.2	100.3
Conductance (µS/cm @ 25°C)	149	30	101	20	74	260
Color (Pt-Co units)	52	30	39	9	25	90
Total phosphorus (µg/L)	45	30	35	9	17	79
Total nitrogen (µg/L)	870	30	880	320	610	1920
Chlorophyll a (µg/L)	20	30	20	2	8	61
Secchi (m)	1.8	28	1.6	0.5	1.4	3.3
Calcium (mg/L)	17.6	30	16.7	1.6	7.6	51.7
Magnesium (mg/L)	8.2	30	7.4	1.2	3.5	18.1
Sodium (mg/L)	13.2	30	7.8	2.0	7.0	19.5
Potassium (mg/L)	2.6	30	1.3	0.2	0.8	3.5
Sulfate (mg/L)	15.2	30	6.1	3.2	5.6	11.6
Chloride (mg/L)	23.4	30	13.3	3.2	12.0	25.9
Iron (mg/L)	0.2	27	0.2	0.10	0.1	0.3
Silicon (mg/L)	1.5	27	1.1	0.10	0.9	2.9

* Denotes a significant difference ($p<0.05$) from mean of all lakes.

Echinochloa spp. (water grasses)

Jesse Van Dyke

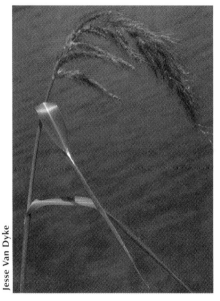

Jesse Van Dyke

Description and distribution

Water grasses are annuals and, as is generally the case with annuals, are highly variable in stature and combinations of diagnostic characteristics. The leaves, however, have compressed sheaths and long flat blades. Ligules are not present. The inflorescence has one principal central axis, bearing spike-like lateral floriferous branches. The spikelets are subsessile or short stalked and solitary on the secondary laterals or congested on short branches of the laterals. Water grasses are common throughout the United States and southeastern Canada (Godfrey and Wooten 1981). The Florida distribution map shows that they were found in lakes throughout the state, but primarily in central and south Florida. Lakes are progressively more alkaline and nutrient rich as one moves from northwestern to southern Florida (Canfield and Hoyer 1988). Thus the distribution of water grasses in Florida suggests that they may tend to occur in alkaline, hardwater, nutrient-rich lakes.

Biology

Water grasses can be found flowering throughout the year in Florida. They reproduce readily by seed germination and can form dense stands as water levels drop. The seeds can also remain viable under water for extended periods of time. The dense stands can impair navigational and recreational uses of some aquatic systems. The seeds of water grasses are used extensively by waterfowl and songbirds. The plants themselves are also used as nesting material and habitat for many species of birds. Water grasses are sometimes cultivated for cattle forage.

Florida data

Water grass was identified in only 36 lakes. The 10th and 90th percentiles for pH, alkalinity, total phosphorus, and total nitrogen values in these lakes show that 80% of the lakes with water grasses had levels between 6.3 and 8.8, 4.9 and 93.4 (mg/L as CaCO$_3$), 16 and 168 (µg/L), and 490 and 2460 (µg/L), respectively. The 36 lakes collectively averaged significantly higher pH, alkalinity, total phosphorus,

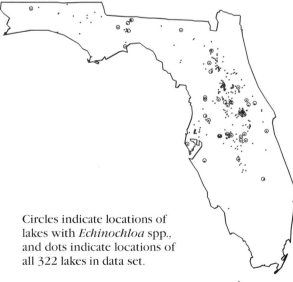

Circles indicate locations of lakes with *Echinochloa* spp., and dots indicate locations of all 322 lakes in data set.

total nitrogen, calcium, and magnesium values than all 322 lakes. Thus while water grasses can occur in a range of lake types, they tend to occur in alkaline, hardwater, nutrient-rich lakes.

Selected references from a total of 656 water grass citations in the APIRS database:

Aslam, Z., M. Salim, R.H. Qureshi, and G.R. Sandhu. 1987. Salt tolerance of *Echinochloa crusgalli*. Biologia Plantarum (Praha) 29(1):66-69.

Bhowmik, P.C. and K.N. Reddy. 1988. Effects of barnyard grass (*Echinochloa crus-galli*) on growth, yield, and nutrient status of transplanted tomato (*Lycopersicon esculentum*). Weed Science 36:775-778.

Cobb, B.G. and R.A. Kennedy. 1987. Distribution of alcohol dehydrogenase in roots and shoots of rice (*Oryza sativa*) and *Echinochloa* seedlings. Plant, Cell and Environments 10(8):633-638.

Everard, J.D., D.R. Lecain, M.E. Rumpho, and R.A. Kennedy. 1991. Mesocotyl root formation in *Echinochloa phyllopogon* (Poaceae) in relation to root zone aeration. American Journal of Botany 78(4):462-469.

Katsuhara, M., K. Sakano, M. Sato, H. Kawakita, and S. Kawabe. 1993. Distribution and production of trans-aconitic acid in barnyard grass (*Echinochloa crus-galli* var. *oryzicola*) as putative antifeedant against brown planthoppers. Plant Cell Physiology 34(2):251-254.

Kelley, P.E. and R.J. Thullen. 1989. Influence of planting date on growth of barnyard grass (*Echinochloa crus-galli*). Weed Science 37:557-561.

Pearce, D.M.E. and M.B. Jackson. 1991. Comparison of growth responses of barnyard grass (*Echinochloa oryzoides*) and rice (*Oryza sativa*) to submergence, ethylene, carbon dioxide and oxygen shortage. Annals of Botany 68:201-209.

Perera, K.K., P.G. Ayres, and H.P.M. Gunasena. 1992. Root growth and the relative importance of root and shoot competition in interactions between rice (*Oryza sativa*) and *Echinochloa crus-galli*. Weed Research 32:67-76.

Rahman, M. and I.A. Ungar. 1990. The effect of salinity on seed germination and seedling growth of *Echinochloa crus-galli*. Ohio Journal of Science 90(1):13-15.

Vanderzee, D. and R.A. Kennedy. 1981. Germination and seedling growth of *Echinochloa crus-galli* var. *oryzicola* under anoxic conditions: Structural aspects. American Journal of Botany 68(9):1269-1277.

Echinochloa spp.

Variables	Mean all lakes (n=322)	Number of lakes	Mean	10th percentile	Median	90th percentile
pH*	6.7	36	7.6	6.3	7.6	8.8
Alkalinity (mg/L as CaCO$_3$)*	23.9	36	41.6	4.9	36.5	93.4
Conductance (µS/cm @ 25°C)	149	36	258	49	171	715
Color (Pt-Co units)	52	36	62	16	51	130
Total phosphorus (µg/L)*	45	36	94	16	57	168
Total nitrogen (µg/L)*	870	36	1250	490	1100	2460
Chlorophyll a (µg/L)	20	36	38	4	21	133
Secchi (m)*	1.8	34	1.0	0.4	0.7	1.6
Calcium (mg/L)*	17.6	36	39.9	7.1	25.1	98.1
Magnesium (mg/L)*	8.2	36	17.6	2.9	9.3	53.3
Sodium (mg/L)	13.2	33	29.0	3.8	10.5	111.2
Potassium (mg/L)	2.6	36	3.1	0.3	2.1	7.1
Sulfate (mg/L)	15.2	33	24.2	3.2	11.7	67.3
Chloride (mg/L)	23.4	36	48.6	7.9	16.2	187.9
Iron (mg/L)	0.2	31	0.2	0.10	0.2	0.6
Silicon (mg/L)	1.5	31	2.7	0.4	2.1	7.0

* Denotes a significant difference (p<0.05) from mean of all lakes.

Egeria densa (Brazilian elodea, common waterweed)

Kerry Dressler

Alison Fox

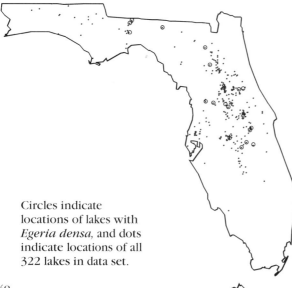

Circles indicate locations of lakes with *Egeria densa*, and dots indicate locations of all 322 lakes in data set.

Description and distribution

Brazilian elodea is a perennial submersed plant that can be rooted or freefloating with stems that are sparsely, dichotomously, branched. The slender stems are usually 200–500 mm long, but can sometimes be much longer. The strap-like leaves are 10–30 mm long and 5 mm wide and have very fine, saw-toothed margins, which require a magnifying lens to be seen. They occur in whorls of three to six around the stem. The whorls grow from nodes, which become more profuse toward the tip of the stem. The white flowers are on short stalks and are about 20 mm in diameter. Brazilian elodea can easily be confused with *Hydrilla verticillata*, another exotic submersed plant in Florida. The easiest way to distinguish between them is by flower size and the underside midrib of the leaves. *Hydrilla* flowers are white and very small. They grow to the surface of the water on long, very thin flower stalks. Brazilian elodea's white flowers, however, are much larger and more conspicuous. The leaves of *Hydrilla* have one or more teeth on the underside midrib, while Brazilian elodea never has teeth on the underside midrib. *Hydrilla* also produces tubers and turions, while Brazilian elodea does not. Brazilian elodea is a South American plant that has been widely naturalized in eastern and Gulf states, sporadically in some other states (Godfrey and Wooten 1981). The Florida distribution map shows that Brazilian elodea was found in lakes scattered around north and central Florida.

Biology

Brazilian elodea flowers from March to June in Florida (Dressler et al. 1987). The plant reproduces only vegetatively in the United States. This reproduction and the high growth potential can lead to levels that impair navigational and recreational uses of some aquatic systems. However, summer and winter water-level fluctuations will usually control the vegetative growth of this plant. Infestations probably occur throughout the world because it is one of the foremost aquarium plants in the world, sold throughout the United States as "anacharis." Brazilian elodea is used as food by coots, gallinules, and some duck species. It also provides refuge and habitat for invertebrates and fish populations.

Florida data

Brazilian elodea was identified in only 19 lakes. The 10th and 90th percentiles for pH, alkalinity, total phosphorus, and total nitrogen values in these lakes showed that 80% of the lakes with swamp loosestrife had levels that fell between 6.0 and 8.7, 2.3 and 108.9 (mg/L as $CaCO_3$), 12 and 126 (µg/L), and 460 and 1710 (µg/L), respectively. The range in water chemistry values of the 19 lakes with Brazilian elodea was similar to the range in water chemistry values in all 322 lakes. This suggests that Brazilian elodea can occur in a wide range of lake types.

Selected references from a total of 382 Brazilian elodea citations in the APIRS database:

Anonymous. 1991. Biologist finds prohibited plants. Resource Management Notes 6(2):5.

Barnett, B.S. and R.W. Schneider. 1974. Fish populations in dense submersed plant communities. Hyacinth Control Journal 12:12–14.

Bartodziej, W. 1991. Epiphytic invertebrate populations of *Hydrilla verticillata* and *Egeria densa* versus native submersed macro-phytes. Pp. 33–40 in Special Publication, Number 1, The Role of Aquatic Plants in Florida's Lakes and Rivers, Proceedings of the Second Annual Meeting of the Florida Lake Management Society. M. Kelly, editor. September 1990, Orlando, Fla.

Blackburn, R.D., L.W. Weldon, R.R. Yeo, and T.M. Taylor. 1969. Identification and distribution of certain similar-appearing submersed aquatic weeds in Florida. Hyacinth Control Journal 8:11–21.

Goldsby, T.L., D. Tarver, R. Theriot, and R. Lazor. 1976. The aquatic plant regulation program in Florida. Journal of Aquatic Plant Management 14:7–9.

Hestand, R.S., J.L. Underwood, and B.Z. Thompson. 1986. Efficacy of triploid grass carp in central Florida lakes. Proceedings of the 26th Annual Meeting of the Aquatic Plant Management Society, July 13–16, 1986, Sarasota, Fla. (Abstract).

Hoyer, M.V. and D.E. Canfield. 1986. Surface area of aquatic macrophytes. Aquatics 8(2):26–27.

Martin, D.F., M.T. Doig, and D.K. Millard. 1971. Potential control of Florida elodea by nutrient-control agents. Hyacinth Control Journal 9(1):36–39.

McLane, W.M. 1969. The aquatic plant business in relation to infestation of exotic aquatic plants in Florida waters. Hyacinth Control Journal 8(1):48–49.

Schmitz, D.C. 1990. The invasion of exotic aquatic plants and wetland plants in Florida: History and efforts to prevent new introductions. Aquatics 12(2):6–13,24.

Egeria densa

Variables	Mean all lakes (n=322)	Number of lakes	Mean	10th percentile	Median	90th percentile
pH	6.7	19	7.4	6.0	7.4	8.7
Alkalinity (mg/L as $CaCO_3$)	23.9	19	38.2	2.3	22.4	108.9
Conductance (µS/cm @ 25°C)	149	19	184	20	111	663
Color (Pt-Co units)	52	19	45	9	41	132
Total phosphorus (µg/L)	45	19	68	12	23	126
Total nitrogen (µg/L)	870	19	100	460	710	1710
Chlorophyll a (µg/L)	20	19	24	3	9	62
Secchi (m)	1.8	13	1.2	0.5	0.8	2.6
Calcium (mg/L)	17.6	19	28.2	2.4	18.3	85.7
Magnesium (mg/L)	8.2	19	9.5	2.1	7.4	17.0
Sodium (mg/L)	13.2	19	16.2	1.9	8.6	82.3
Potassium (mg/L)	2.6	19	1.8	0.1	1.6	4.2
Sulfate (mg/L)	15.2	19	11.6	2.4	8.3	25.7
Chloride (mg/L)	23.4	19	29.4	3.3	15.2	161.3
Iron (mg/L)	0.2	15	0.2	0.0	0.2	0.5
Silicon (mg/L)	1.5	15	2.6	0.1	1.1	8.1

* Denotes a significant difference (p<0.05) from mean of all lakes.

Eichhornia crassipes (water hyacinth)

Alison Fox

Alison Fox

Description and distribution

Water hyacinth is a floating aquatic plant that ranges from a few centimeters to over a meter. The leaf blades are suborbicular to elliptical, leathery, up to 200 mm long, and 50-150 mm wide, attached to petioles that are spongy and inflated. Beneath the plant are numerous dark, fibrous roots that contain many branches. The inflorescence is a loose terminal spike with showy light-blue to violet flowers. Individual flowers have a bright yellow marking on the upper portion of the petal. The fruit is a three-celled capsule with many seeds. Water hyacinth is native to South America and has been naturalized in most of the southern United States and in many of the world's subtropical and tropical climates (Godfrey and Wooten 1981). The Florida distribution map shows that water hyacinth was found in lakes across the whole state, with no apparent geographical pattern.

Biology

Water hyacinth flowers throughout the year in Florida (Dressler et al. 1987). It reproduces primarily by vegetative means, but small seeds do sink into the substrate and remain dormant until drought periods, when they germinate. The reproductive potential of water hyacinth is extremely high, doubling its number in 5-20 days. This means 20 plants can cover a hectare in one growing season. With this reproductive potential, water hyacinth is one of the leading environmental and economic weed problems in the Gulf Coast states. Its fibrous root system is excellent habitat for aquatic invertebrates and small fish; in small quantities, it is valued as fish structure by many anglers. It is also used as food and habitat by several aquatic bird species. Any benefits attributed to water hyacinth, however, are negated by its ability to dominate the aquatic system to the detriment of navigational and recreational uses.

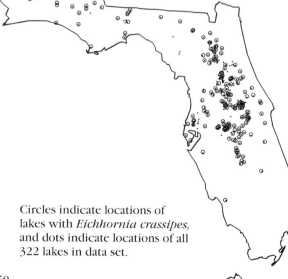

Circles indicate locations of lakes with *Eichhornia crassipes*, and dots indicate locations of all 322 lakes in data set.

Florida data

Water hyacinth was identified in 190 lakes. The 10th and 90th percentiles for pH, alkalinity, total phosphorus, and total nitrogen values in these lakes show that 80% of the lakes with water hyacinth had pH, alkalinity, total phosphorus, and total nitrogen levels between 5.2 and 8.7, 1.5 and 77.6 (mg/L as $CaCO_3$), 10 and 121 (µg/L), and 310 and 1880 (µg/L), respectively. The water chemistry averages of the 190 lakes showed no significant differences from those of all 322 lakes. The range in water chemistry values of the 190 lakes was also similar to the range in water chemistry values in all 322 lakes. This suggests that water hyacinth can occur in a wide range of aquatic systems.

Selected references from a total of 3416 water hyacinth citations in the APIRS database:

Bodle, M. 1988. Water hyacinth biocontrol: A case history. Aquatics 10(3):24,26.

Center, T. D. 1982. The water hyacinth weevils. Aquatics 4(2):8.

Forno, I. W. and A. D. Wright. The biology of Australian weeds. 5. *Eichhornia crassipes* (Mart.) Solms. Journal of the Australian Institute of Agricultural Science 47(1):21-28.

Gopal, B. 1987. Aquatic plant studies. 1. Water hyacinth. Elsevier Science Publications, Amsterdam, The Netherlands. 471 pp.

Gopal, B. and K. P. Sharma. 1981. Water hyacinth (*Eichhornia crassipes*), most troublesome weed of the world. Hindasia Publishers, Delhi, India. 128 pp.

Kumar, T. S., P. Vasudevan, and S. V. Patwardhan. 1983. Azolla as a source of biomass: A comparison with water hyacinth (a survey). International Journal of Environmental Studies 20:275-279.

Langeland, K. A. and J. C. Joyce. 1987. Water hyacinth management on Lake Okeechobee, 1905-1987. Center for Aquatic Plants, IFAS, University of Florida, Gainesville.

Mercado, B. L. 1979. Biology, problems and control of *Eichhornia crassipes* (Mart.) Solm. Biotrop Bulletin 16:52.

Sen, N. S., V. K. Kapoor, and G. Gopalkrishna. 1990. Seasonal growth of *Eichhornia crassipes* (Mart.) and its possible impact on the primary productivity and fishery structure in a tropical reservoir. Acta Hydrochimica et Hydrobiologia 18(3):307–323.

Eichhornia crassipes

Variables	Mean all lakes (n=322)	Number of lakes	Mean	10th percentile	Median	90th percentile
pH	6.7	190	7.0	5.2	7.0	8.7
Alkalinity (mg/L as $CaCO_3$)	23.9	190	28.8	1.5	15.7	77.6
Conductance (µS/cm @ 25°C)	149	190	172	32	113	346
Color (Pt-Co units)	52	190	57	6	32	132
Total phosphorus (µg/L)	45	190	56	10	23	121
Total nitrogen (µg/L)	870	190	940	310	710	1880
Chlorophyll a (µg/L)	20	190	23	2	8	66
Secchi (m)	1.8	172	1.6	0.4	1.3	3.6
Calcium (mg/L)	17.6	190	24.2	2.4	13.2	67.2
Magnesium (mg/L)	8.2	190	11.5	1.2	7.2	31.6
Sodium (mg/L)	13.2	182	16.0	2.7	8.3	25.8
Potassium (mg/L)	2.6	190	2.9	0.2	1.9	8.0
Sulfate (mg/L)	15.2	182	17.3	4.1	10.7	47.0
Chloride (mg/L)	23.4	190	28.5	4.4	15.2	42.1
Iron (mg/L)	0.2	158	0.2	0.0	0.1	0.4
Silicon (mg/L)	1.5	158	1.7	0.1	0.8	3.9

Eleocharis baldwinii (road-grass)

Kerry Dressler

Description and distribution

The perennial road-grass grows well, especially when submersed. The stems are 30–200 mm tall with reddish leaf sheaths. The terminal spike is lanceolate to narrowly ellipsoidal and 4–7 mm long with only a few flowers. The achene is trigonous and smooth and tends to be whitish to gray. Road-grass can be found primarily in the Coastal Plain states (Godfrey and Wooten 1981). The Florida distribution map shows that road-grass occurs from northwest to central Florida but primarily in central Florida.

Biology

Road-grass is a mat-forming aquatic plant that can spread over large areas of a lake by sexual and vegetative reproduction. It can be found growing along shorelines and shallow water regions of lakes, as well as in water as deep as 2–3 m. Road-grass is commonly fed upon by several species of waterfowl and provides good cover for fish and aquatic invertebrates.

Florida data

Road-grass was identified in 136 lakes. The 10th and 90th percentiles for pH, alkalinity, total phosphorus, and total nitrogen values in these lakes showed that 80% of the lakes with road-grass had levels that were between 4.6 and 7.7, 0.1 and 36.2 (mg/L as $CaCO_3$), 7 and 34 (µg/L), and 270 and 1150 (µg/L), respectively. The 136 lakes collectively averaged significantly lower pH, alkalinity, total phosphorus, calcium, and magnesium values than all 322 lakes. Thus road-grass tends to occur in acid, softwater lakes with low nutrient concentrations.

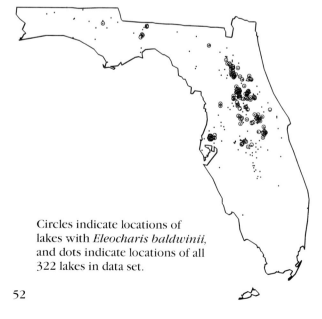

Circles indicate locations of lakes with *Eleocharis baldwinii*, and dots indicate locations of all 322 lakes in data set.

Selected references from a total of 142 *Eleocharis* spp. citations in the APIRS database:

Eyles, D.E. 1940. Three species of *Eleocharis* new to Georgia. Castanea 5:98-99.

Botts, P.S. and B.C. Cowell. 1988. The distribution and abundance of herbaceous angiosperms in west-central Florida marshes. Aquatic Botany 32:225-238.

Browder, J.A., P.J. Gleason, and D.R. Swift. 1994. Periphyton in the Everglades: Spatial variation, environmental correlates, and ecological implications. Pp. 379-418 in Everglades: The ecosystem and its restoration, S.M. Davis and J.C. Ogden, editors. St. Lucie Press, Delray Beach, Fla.

Sutton, D.L. 1990. A method for germination of arrowhead, pickerelweed and spikerush seeds. Aquatics 12(4):8-10.

Svenson, H.K. 1929. Monographic studies in the genus *Eleocharis*. Rhodora 31:120-135, 152-163, 167-191, 199-219, 224-242.

Svenson, H.K. 1937. Monographic studies in the genus *Eleocharis*. IV. Rhodora 39:210-231, 236-273.

Svenson, H.K. 1939. Monographic studies in the genus *Eleocharis*. V. Rhodora 41:2-19, 43-77, 90-110.

Ward, D.B. and E.M.H. Leigh. 1975. Contributions to the flora of Florida—8, *Eleocharis* (Cyperaceae). Castanea 40(1):16-36.

Eleocharis baldwinii

Variables	Mean all lakes (n=322)	Number of lakes	Mean	10th percentile	Median	90th percentile
pH*	6.7	136	6.1	4.6	6.1	7.7
Alkalinity (mg/L as CaCO₃)*	23.9	136	11.6	0.1	2.3	36.2
Conductance (µS/cm @ 25°C)	149	136	110	34	80	211
Color (Pt-Co units)	52	136	43	4	20	125
Total phosphorus (µg/L)*	45	135	20	7	13	34
Total nitrogen (µg/L)	870	135	680	270	590	1150
Chlorophyll a (µg/L)	20	136	8	1	4	20
Secchi (m)	1.8	112	2.1	0.7	1.9	3.8
Calcium (mg/L)*	17.6	135	7.2	0.7	3.5	15.8
Magnesium (mg/L)*	8.2	135	3.7	0.7	2.0	8.4
Sodium (mg/L)	13.2	123	9.5	3.2	7.1	16.2
Potassium (mg/L)	2.6	135	2.2	0.2	1.0	6.2
Sulfate (mg/L)	15.2	123	12.3	2.8	7.5	32.5
Chloride (mg/L)	23.4	135	17.8	6.6	12.5	31.0
Iron (mg/L)	0.2	71	0.1	0.0	0.10	0.3
Silicon (mg/L)	1.5	71	0.7	0.1	0.4	1.8

* Denotes a significant difference (p<0.05) from mean of all lakes.

Eleocharis cellulosa (club-rush)

David Sutton

David Sutton

Description and distribution

Club-rush is a coarse perennial with thick rhizomes that forms dense colonies. It can reach a height of 700 mm and is 3–5 mm thick. The stem is three-sided with a 30–40 mm long spike. The spike is cylindrical and has many flowers. The scales are 5 mm long and light yellow to golden. The smooth achenes are obovate, 2 mm long, and light brown. Club-rush is found from North Carolina south to Florida and west to Texas (Godfrey and Wooten 1981). The Florida distribution map shows that club-rush was found from the northwest to central regions of the state.

Biology

Club-rush reproduces readily by vegetative means and by seed germination. It can be found in both fresh and brackish waters, as dense stands in the shallow regions of lakes. Waterfowl feed on the seeds.

Circles indicate locations of lakes with *Eleocharis cellulosa*, and dots indicate locations of all 322 lakes in data set.

Florida data

Club-rush was identified in 61 lakes. The 10th and 90th percentiles for pH, alkalinity, total phosphorus, and total nitrogen values in these lakes show that 80% of the lakes with club-rush had levels between 5.3 and 8.8, 2.1 and 66.7 (mg/L as $CaCO_3$), 10 and 102 (μg/L), and 310 and 1830 (μg/L), respectively. The 61 lakes collectively averaged significantly higher calcium, and magnesium values than all 322 lakes. Thus club-rush can occur in a range of lake types, but slight evidence suggests it tends to occur in alkaline, hardwater lakes.

Eleocharis cellulosa: see references after *Eleocharis baldwinii*

Eleocharis cellulosa

Variables	Mean all lakes (n=322)	Number of lakes	Mean	10th percentile	Median	90th percentile
pH	6.7	61	7.2	5.8	7.2	8.8
Alkalinity (mg/L as $CaCO_3$)	23.9	61	27.5	2.1	21.7	66.7
Conductance (μS/cm @ 25°C)	149	61	176	59	107	387
Color (Pt-Co units)	52	61	50	5	32	112
Total phosphorus (μg/L)	45	61	40	10	24	102
Total nitrogen (μg/L)	870	61	920	310	750	1830
Chlorophyll a (μg/L)	20	61	21	2	8	64
Secchi (m)	1.8	56	1.5	0.4	1.1	3.3
Calcium (mg/L)*	17.6	61	26.8	3.1	18.3	86.1
Magnesium (mg/L)*	8.2	61	14.1	2.6	10.2	32.3
Sodium (mg/L)	13.2	57	17.2	4.3	8.6	38.4
Potassium (mg/L)	2.6	61	2.7	0.2	2.0	6.6
Sulfate (mg/L)	15.2	57	18.6	5.6	11.8	49.5
Chloride (mg/L)	23.4	61	30.8	8.6	15.8	61.9
Iron (mg/L)	0.2	51	0.2	0.0	0.1	0.4
Silicon (mg/L)	1.5	51	1.6	0.2	1.0	3.8

* Denotes a significant difference (p<0.05) from mean of all lakes.

Eleocharis elongata (water spikerush)

Mark Hoyer

Description and distribution

Water spikerush is a dimorphic member of the genus *Eleocharis*. It has slender rhizomes and stems that are 200–800 mm tall and erect to slightly leaning. The spikes are lanceolate to cylindrical and 10–20 mm long. The achenes are slightly three-angled and 0.8–1.5 mm long. Water spikerush is found in Florida and adjacent areas of Georgia and Alabama (Godfrey and Wooten 1981). The Florida distribution map shows that water spikerush was found in lakes in the north-central regions of the state.

Biology

Water spikerush is dimorphic in that it can be found in a completely aquatic habitat where it is sterile and only spreading vegetatively through rhizomes, or it can be found fruiting only in terrestrial habitats. It is commonly overlooked or misidentified.

Florida data

Water spikerush was identified in 14 lakes. The 10th and 90th percentiles for pH, alkalinity, total phosphorus, and total nitrogen values in these lakes show that 80% of the lakes with water spikerush had levels between 4.5 and 7.4, 0.7 and 33.9 (mg/L as $CaCO_3$), 2 and 21 (μg/L), and 180 and 1200 (μg/L), respectively. The 14 lakes collectively averaged significantly lower calcium and magnesium values than all 322 lakes. Thus water spikerush can occur in a range of lake types, but slight evidence suggests it tends to occur in acidic, softwater lakes.

Circles indicate locations of lakes with *Eleocharis elongata,* and dots indicate locations of all 322 lakes in data set.

Eleocharis elongata: **see references**
after *Eleocharis baldwinii*

Eleocharis elongata

Variables	Mean all lakes (n=322)	Number of lakes	Mean	10th percentile	Median	90th percentile
pH	6.7	14	5.8	4.5	5.7	7.4
Alkalinity (mg/L as CaCO$_3$)	23.9	14	7.2	0.7	2.1	33.9
Conductance (µS/cm @ 25°C)	149	14	79	34	55	169
Color (Pt-Co units)	52	14	19	2	16	50
Total phosphorus (µg/L)	45	14	11	2	10	21
Total nitrogen (µg/L)	870	14	630	180	540	1200
Chlorophyll a (µg/L)	20	14	4	1.0	2	11
Secchi (m)	1.8	12	2.9	1.5	2.5	5.3
Calcium (mg/L)*	17.6	14	4.0	0.4	2.2	12.8
Magnesium (mg/L)*	8.2	14	1.5	0.6	1.0	3.7
Sodium (mg/L)	13.2	10	8.0	3.2	5.6	19.9
Potassium (mg/L)	2.6	14	1.0	0.1	0.3	3.5
Sulfate (mg/L)	15.2	10	7.9	0.5	6.4	23.1
Chloride (mg/L)	23.4	14	14.0	5.8	8.1	35.0
Iron (mg/L)	0.2	4	0.10	0.0	0.10	0.2
Silicon (mg/L)	1.5	4	0.3	0.1	0.2	0.5

* Denotes a significant difference (p<0.05) from mean of all lakes.

Eleocharis interstincta (giant-spikerush)

Jesse Van Dyke

Jesse Van Dyke

Description and distribution

Giant-spikerush is a perennial plant that has stout erect stems 400–1000 mm tall. It has coarse rhizomes and very distinctive cross-partitions in the stem. These cross-partitions are much closer to each other just below the spikelet than farther down the stem. The spike is cylindrical with many flowers and 40 mm long. The light yellow-brown scales are ovate to oblong and 5–6 mm long. The achenes are 1.8–2.2 mm long with fine transverse rectangular pits along the surface forming fine longitudinal rows. Giant-spikerush is found from the panhandle of Florida to the southern end of the state and also in Texas (Godfrey and Wooten 1981). The Florida distribution map shows that giant-spikerush was found in lakes throughout the state with no apparent geographical pattern.

Biology

Giant-spikerush reproduces readily by vegetative means and by seed germination. It tends to be found growing along the shallow water areas of lakes and ponds. The seeds are eaten by waterfowl.

Florida data

Giant-spikerush was identified in 51 lakes. The 10th and 90th percentiles for pH, alkalinity, total phosphorus, and total nitrogen values in these lakes show that 80% of the lakes with giant-spikerush had levels between 5.3 and 8.5, 1.5 and 52.4 (mg/L as CaCO$_3$), 9 and 78 (µg/L), and 250 and 1510 (µg/L), respectively. The water chemistry averages and ranges of the 51 lakes with giant-spikerush are similar to those of all 322 lakes. This suggests that giant-spikerush can occur in a wide range of Florida's aquatic systems.

Circles indicate locations of lakes with *Eleocharis interstincta*, and dots indicate locations of all 322 lakes in data set.

Eleocharis interstincta: see references
after *Eleocharis baldwinii*

Eleocharis interstincta

Variables	Mean all lakes (n=322)	Number of lakes	Mean	10th percentile	Median	90th percentile
pH	6.7	51	6.9	5.3	7.0	8.5
Alkalinity (mg/L as CaCO₃)	23.9	51	20.0	1.5	10.7	52.4
Conductance (µS/cm @ 25°C)	149	51	146	21	101	309
Color (Pt-Co units)	52	51	41	4	29	104
Total phosphorus (µg/L)	45	51	29	9	17	78
Total nitrogen (µg/L)	870	51	750	250	640	1510
Chlorophyll a (µg/L)	20	51	13	2	8	33
Secchi (m)	1.8	49	1.8	0.5	1.6	3.6
Calcium (mg/L)	17.6	51	20.9	1.9	13.2	68.6
Magnesium (mg/L)	8.2	51	11.5	1.6	6.5	31.7
Sodium (mg/L)	13.2	48	14.1	2.1	7.6	18.7
Potassium (mg/L)	2.6	51	2.2	0.2	1.3	6.5
Sulfate (mg/L)	15.2	48	17.5	3.4	11.3	49.3
Chloride (mg/L)	23.4	51	24.9	3.2	14.4	28.7
Iron (mg/L)	0.2	43	0.2	0.0	0.1	0.7
Silicon (mg/L)	1.5	43	1.3	0.2	0.7	3.8

Eriocaulon spp. (hat-pins, pipeworts)

Kerry Dressler

Kerry Dressler

Description and distribution

Eriocaulon are biennial or perennial plants with thick fibrous roots that appear unbranched. The narrow, tapering leaves occur in spiral clusters at the base and are yellowish green. The inflorescence is a spherical head of unisexual flowers terminating a leafless, glabrous, ribbed scape. Some heads contain a mixture of male and female flowers, others only male or female flowers. The fruit of *Eriocaulon* spp. are small capsules with one or two seeds. *Eriocaulon* spp. can be found primarily in coastal plains around the United States (Godfrey and Wooten 1981). The Florida distribution map shows that *Eriocaulon* spp. occur from extreme northwestern to central Florida, but not extreme south Florida. Lakes are progressively more alkaline and nutrient rich as one moves from northwestern to southern Florida (Canfield and Hoyer 1988). Thus the distribution of *Eriocaulon* spp. in Florida suggests that *Eriocaulon* spp. may prefer acid, softwater, nutrient-poor lakes.

Biology

Eriocaulon spp. reproduce primarily by seed germination, but young shoots do arise from rootstocks, suggesting that some reproduction is vegetative. *Eriocaulon* spp. flower throughout the year in Florida (Dressler et al. 1987).

Florida data

Eriocaulon spp. were identified in 57 lakes. The 10th and 90th percentiles for pH, alkalinity, total phosphorus, and total nitrogen values in these lakes showed that 80% of the lakes with *Eriocaulon* spp. had levels that fell between 4.5 and 7.0, 0.2 and 19.2 (mg/L as $CaCO_3$), 5 and 19 (µg/L), and 150 and 1110 (µg/L), respectively. The 57 lakes collectively averaged significantly lower pH, alkalinity, specific conductance, total phosphorus, total nitrogen, chlorophyll *a*, calcium, magnesium, sodium, potassium, chloride, and silicon values than all 322 lakes. Thus while *Eriocaulon* spp. can occur in a range of lake types, it tends to occur in acid, softwater, nutrient-poor lakes.

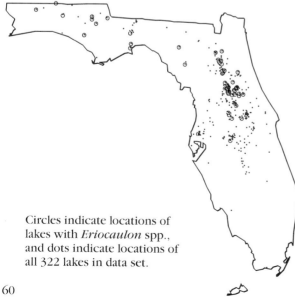

Circles indicate locations of lakes with *Eriocaulon* spp., and dots indicate locations of all 322 lakes in data set.

Selected references from a total of 160 pipewort citations in the APIRS database:

Bridges, E.L. 1994. The taxonomy, distribution and ecology of the Eriocaulaceae in Florida. Palmetto 14(3):14 (Abstract).

Coquery, M. and P.M. Welbourn. 1994. Mercury uptake from contaminated water and sediment by the rooted and submerged aquatic macrophyte *Eriocaulon septangulare*. Archives of Environmental Contamination and Toxicology 26(3):335-341.

Howell, E.T. 1990. Effects of the isoetid macrophytes *Eriocaulon septangulare* and *Lobelia dortmanna* on the periphyton of littoral sediments. Canadian Journal of Botany 68:1903-1910.

Kral, R. 1966. Eriocaulaceae of continental North America north of Mexico. Sida 2(4):285-332.

Kral, R. 1989. The genera of Eriocaulaceae in the southeastern United States. Journal of the Arnold Arboretum 70:131-142.

Moldenke, H.N. 1971. The additional notes on the Eriocaulaceae. XXXVI. Phytologia 21:267-278.

Moldenke, H.N. 1979. Additional notes on the Eriocaulaceae. LXXXII. Phytologia 41(7):451-485.

Ramaswamy, S.N. and G.D. Arekal. 1981. Embryology of *Eriocaulon setaceum* (Eriocaulaceae). Plant Systematics and Evolution 138:175-188.

Thieret, J.W. 1901. *Eriocaulon cinereum* R. Br. in Louisiana. Southwestern Naturalist 15:391.

Eriocaulon spp.

Variables	Mean all lakes (n=322)	Number of lakes	Mean	10th percentile	Median	90th percentile
pH*	6.7	57	5.4	4.5	5.1	7.0
Alkalinity (mg/L as $CaCO_3$)*	23.9	57	4.3	0.2	1.8	19.2
Conductance (µS/cm @ 25°C)*	149	57	67	20	46	145
Color (Pt-Co units)	52	57	39	2	12	161
Total phosphorus (µg/L)*	45	56	11	5	10	19
Total nitrogen (µg/L)*	870	56	510	150	400	1110
Chlorophyll a (µg/L)	20	57	3	1.0	2	6
Secchi (m)*	1.8	55	2.8	1.2	2.5	4.9
Calcium (mg/L)*	17.6	57	3.8	0.6	2.0	12.9
Magnesium (mg/L)*	8.2	57	2.5	0.6	1.1	6.8
Sodium (mg/L)*	13.2	53	5.5	2.3	4.2	10.6
Potassium (mg/L)*	2.6	57	1.2	0.2	0.3	3.9
Sulfate (mg/L)	15.2	53	9.3	3.0	6.1	19.2
Chloride (mg/L)*	23.4	57	10.8	3.1	8.2	21.8
Iron (mg/L)	0.2	30	0.1	0.0	0.10	0.3
Silicon (mg/L)*	1.5	30	0.5	0.10	0.3	1.2

* Denotes a significant difference (p<0.05) from mean of all lakes.

Fontinalis spp. (water-moss)

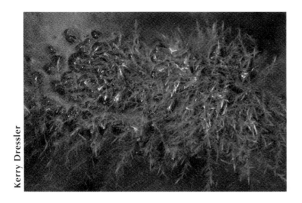

Kerry Dressler

Kerry Dressler

Description and distribution

Fontinalis spp. are submersed mosses that are attached to rocks, logs, and tree bases by false roots at the bases of stems. The branching stems are dark green to brown, up to 150 mm long, with leaves arranged in three rows. The leaves are the same color as the stems and ovate or rhomboidal, 2–10 mm long and 1–5 mm wide, with fine-toothed margins. The leaves also have no midveins. *Fontinalis* spp. are found throughout the United States (Tarver et al. 1986). The Florida distribution map shows that *Fontinalis* spp. were found primarily in north-central Florida.

Biology

Sexual reproduction of *Fontinalis* spp. is accomplished with spores, but the sporangia have not been seen in Florida plants. Thus reproduction is primarily through vegetative means. *Fontinalis* spp. are used to some extent by the aquarium industry. The plants can also be refuge and habitat for invertebrates and small fish populations.

Florida data

Fontinalis spp. were identified in 32 lakes. The 10th and 90th percentiles for pH, alkalinity, total phosphorus, and total nitrogen values in these lakes show that 80% of the lakes with *Fontinalis* spp. had levels between 4.5 and 6.7, 0.0 and 7.8 (mg/L as $CaCO_3$), 5 and 28 (µg/L), and 140 and 690 (µg/L), respectively. These 32 lakes also collectively averaged significantly lower pH, alkalinity, specific conductance, total phosphorus, total nitrogen, calcium, magnesium, and potassium values than all 322 lakes. Thus *Fontinalis* spp. tend to occur in acid, softwater, nutrient-poor lakes.

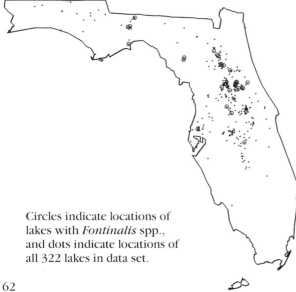

Circles indicate locations of lakes with *Fontinalis* spp., and dots indicate locations of all 322 lakes in data set.

Selected references from a total of 42 water-moss citations in the APIRS database:

Allen, B.H. 1988. Studies on the genus *Fontinalis* (Musci:Fontinalaceae). Brittonia 40(2):180–187.

Glime, J.M. 1982. Response of *Fontinalis hypnoides* to seasonal temperature variations. Journal of the Hattori Botanical Laboratory 53:181–193.

Glime, J.M. 1987. Growth model for *Fontinalis duriaei* based on temperature and flow conditions. Journal of the Hattori Botanical Laboratory 62:101–109.

Glime, J.M. 1987. Phytogeographic implications of a *Fontinalis* (Fontinalaceae) growth model based on temperature and flow conditions for six species. Memoirs of the New York Botanical Gardens 45:154–170.

Glime, J.M. and B.C. Knoop. 1986. Spore germination and protonemal development of *Fontinalis squamosa*. Journal of the Hattori Botanical Laboratory 61:487–497.

Glime, J.M. and F. Rohwer. 1983. The comparative effects of ethylene and 1-amino cyclopropane-1-carboxylic acid on two species of *Fontinalis*. Journal of Bryology 12(4):611–616.

Sayre, G. 1945. The distribution of *Fontinalis* in a series of moraine ponds. Bryologist 48:34–36.

Welch, W. 1948. Vegetative propagation in *Fontinalis*. Bryologist 51:192–193.

Fontinalis spp.

Variables	Mean all lakes (n=322)	Number of lakes	Mean	10th percentile	Median	90th percentile
pH*	6.7	32	5.2	4.5	4.9	6.7
Alkalinity (mg/L as CaCO₃)*	23.9	32	2.2	0.0	1.5	7.8
Conductance (µS/cm @ 25°C)*	149	32	58	31	53	98
Color (Pt-Co units)	52	32	67	3	25	213
Total phosphorus (µg/L)*	45	32	14	5	10	28
Total nitrogen (µg/L)*	870	32	440	140	420	690
Chlorophyll a (µg/L)	20	32	4	1.0	3	9
Secchi (m)	1.8	29	2.5	0.5	2.4	5.2
Calcium (mg/L)*	17.6	32	3.3	0.6	1.6	9.2
Magnesium (mg/L)*	8.2	32	2.3	0.5	1.1	7.4
Sodium (mg/L)	13.2	29	5.7	3.1	4.7	9.5
Potassium (mg/L)*	2.6	32	0.7	0.1	0.4	1.8
Sulfate (mg/L)	15.2	29	7.0	0.6	6.4	11.5
Chloride (mg/L)	23.4	32	10.7	6.0	8.5	18.2
Iron (mg/L)	0.2	18	0.2	0.0	0.10	0.4
Silicon (mg/L)	1.5	18	1.0	0.0	0.3	3.6

* Denotes a significant difference (p<0.05) from mean of all lakes.

Fuirena scirpoidea (rush fuirena)

Kerry Dressler

Kerry Dressler

Description and distribution

Rush fuirena is a perennial with conspicuous long, branching rhizomes from which vertical flowering stems arise at intervals. The jointed stems are about 60 mm tall, with short sheaths at each joint, and end in spikelets. The spikelets are terminal and can be solitary or in clusters of two to several, with subtending bracts shorter than the spikelet. The spikelet has scales that spiral, overlapping, hairy, oblong-ovate, and long pointed. The flower has three paddle-like sepals alternating with barbed bristles. The fruit is a dark brown nutlet. Rush fuirena is found from the coastal plains of Georgia and Florida to southeast Texas (Godfrey and Wooten 1981). The Florida distribution map shows that rush fuirena was found primarily in north-central Florida.

Biology

Rush fuirena flowers throughout the year in Florida (Dressler et al. 1987). It reproduces by seed germination and vegetatively through rhizome growth. It is of little wildlife value and does not grow extensively enough to cause navigational or recreational problems.

Florida data

Rush fuirena was identified in 109 lakes. The 10th and 90th percentiles for pH, alkalinity, total phosphorus, and total nitrogen values in these lakes show that 80% of the lakes with rush fuirena had levels between 4.5 and 7.7, 0.3 and 33.0 (mg/L as $CaCO_3$), 6 and 23 (μg/L), and 190 and 1250 (μg/L), respectively. These 109 lakes also collectively averaged significantly lower pH, alkalinity, color, total phosphorus, total nitrogen, calcium, magnesium, and silicon values than all 322 lakes. Thus rush fuirena tends to occur in acid, softwater, nutrient-poor lakes.

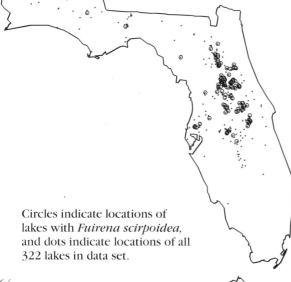

Circles indicate locations of lakes with *Fuirena scirpoidea,* and dots indicate locations of all 322 lakes in data set.

Selected references from a total of 49 rush fuirena citations in the APIRS database:

Austin, D.F. 1976. Vegetation of southeastern Florida. I. Pine jog. Florida Scientist 39(4):230–235.

Chippendale, G.M. 1959. Checklist of central Australian plants. Transactions of the Royal Society of South Australia 82:321–338.

Guillory, V., M.D. Jones, and M. Rebel. 1979. A comparison of fish communities in vegetated and beach habitats. Florida Scientist 42(3):113–122.

Krummrich, J.T. 1992. Northeast region fish management project completion report 1987-1992 study III. Regional Services, Florida Game and Freshwater Fish Commission, Tallahassee. 28 pp.

Napper, D.M. 1965. Cyperaceae of East Africa. III. Journal of East Africa Natural History Society 25(1):1-27.

Watts, W.A. 1980. Late-quaternary vegetation history at White Pond on the inner coastal plain of South Carolina. Quaternary Research 13:187-199.

Fuirena scirpoidea

Variables	Mean all lakes (n=322)	Number of lakes	Mean	10th percentile	Median	90th percentile
pH*	6.7	109	5.9	4.5	5.8	7.7
Alkalinity (mg/L as CaCO₃)*	23.9	109	11.2	0.3	2.0	33.0
Conductance (µS/cm @ 25°C)	149	109	106	34	71	244
Color (Pt-Co units)*	52	109	35	4	13	101
Total phosphorus (µg/L)*	45	108	14	6	10	23
Total nitrogen (µg/L)*	870	108	630	190	490	1250
Chlorophyll a (µg/L)	20	109	6	1.0	3	12
Secchi (m)*	1.8	93	2.5	0.9	2.2	4.4
Calcium (mg/L)*	17.6	109	6.6	0.6	3.4	16.0
Magnesium (mg/L)*	8.2	109	3.6	0.7	2.1	9.7
Sodium (mg/L)	13.2	97	8.6	3.5	7.0	16.1
Potassium (mg/L)	2.6	109	2.1	0.2	0.9	6.7
Sulfate (mg/L)	15.2	97	12.0	3.2	7.5	28.3
Chloride (mg/L)	23.4	109	16.2	6.6	12.3	30.5
Iron (mg/L)	0.2	49	0.1	0.0	0.0	0.3
Silicon (mg/L)*	1.5	49	0.6	0.10	0.3	1.3

* Denotes a significant difference (p<0.05) from mean of all lakes.

Fuirena squarrosa (umbrella-grass)

Kerry Dressler

Kerry Dressler

Description and distribution

Umbrella-grass is a perennial sedge with stems up to 450 mm long and flat leaf blades 150–200 mm long and 3–8 mm wide. The plants have short runners and form clumps as they grow. The terminal inflorescence usually consists of three sessile oblong-cylindrical spikelets, but additional spikelets are common. The spikelets are 10–20 mm long and 5–8 mm wide, many flowered, and subtended by leaf bracts. The fruit is a brown nutlet about 1.8 mm long with three barbed bristles and three perianth scales at its base. Umbrella-grass is common from New Jersey to Florida and east to Texas (Godfrey and Wooten 1981). The Florida distribution map shows that umbrella-grass was found in lakes from central to southern Florida.

Biology

Umbrella-grass flowers from July to October in Florida (Dressler et al. 1987). It reproduces primarily by seed germination. The seeds and stems are not reported as beneficial to wildlife. The growth of umbrella-grass is usually not significant enough to cause impairment of navigational or recreational uses of aquatic systems.

Florida data

Umbrella-grass was identified in 98 lakes. The 10th and 90th percentiles for pH, alkalinity, total phosphorus, and total nitrogen values in these lakes show that 80% of the lakes with umbrella-grass had levels between 5.1 and 8.5, 1.3 and 62.6 (mg/L as $CaCO_3$), 10 and 61 (µg/L), and 270 and 1720 (µg/L), respectively. The water chemistry averages of the 98 lakes with umbrella-grass showed no significant differences from those for all 322 lakes. The 98 lakes also had similar water chemistry ranges to all 322 lakes. This suggests that umbrella-grass can occur in a wide range of aquatic systems in Florida.

Circles indicate locations of lakes with *Fuirena squarrosa,* and dots indicate locations of all 322 lakes in data set.

***Fuirena squarrosa*: see references for**
Fuirena scirpoidea.

Fuirena squarrosa

Variables	Mean all lakes (n=322)	Number of lakes	Mean	10th percentile	Median	90th percentile
pH	6.7	98	6.9	5.1	7.0	8.5
Alkalinity (mg/L as CaCO$_3$)	23.9	98	22.6	1.3	9.5	62.6
Conductance (μS/cm @ 25°C)	149	98	140	49	106	262
Color (Pt-Co units)	52	98	43	4	22	101
Total phosphorus (μg/L)	45	98	29	10	19	61
Total nitrogen (μg/L)	870	98	790	270	650	1720
Chlorophyll a (μg/L)	20	98	14	2	6	37
Secchi (m)	1.8	90	1.9	0.5	1.5	3.8
Calcium (mg/L)	17.6	98	20.2	2.0	12.6	51.5
Magnesium (mg/L)*	8.2	98	11.9	1.5	7.9	31.8
Sodium (mg/L)	13.2	96	11.0	4.1	8.8	16.4
Potassium (mg/L)	2.6	98	2.7	0.2	2.0	6.7
Sulfate (mg/L)	15.2	96	16.7	5.1	11.5	41.3
Chloride (mg/L)	23.4	98	20.0	7.9	16.0	28.3
Iron (mg/L)	0.2	82	0.1	0.0	0.10	0.4
Silicon (mg/L)	1.5	82	1.2	0.1	0.6	3.5

* Denotes a significant difference (p<0.05) from mean of all lakes.

Habenaria repens (water spider orchid)

Kerry Dressler

Kerry Dressler

Description and distribution

Water spider orchids are perennial leafy plants, slender to stout, and 10–90 mm tall. Lower stems often produce few to numerous long runners with plantlets forming at the tips. The leaves are linear-oblong to linear-lanceolate, three-ribbed, succulent, 50–240 mm long, and 3.5–20 mm wide. Water spider orchids have a terminal raceme about 250 mm long with few to many small green flowers. They commonly occur in the Coastal Plain from North Carolina to Florida and west to Texas (Godfrey and Wooten 1981). The Florida distribution map shows that water spider orchids were found in lakes throughout the state, but primarily in central and south Florida.

Biology

Water spider orchids flowers from May through December in Florida (Dressler et al. 1987). They reproduce vegetatively and by seed germination. Water spider orchids are found primarily on the shores of aquatic systems with their runners spreading out toward the open water, forming mats. These mats seldom become large enough to impair navigational or recreational uses of aquatic systems.

Florida data

Water spider orchids were identified in 38 lakes. The 10th and 90th percentiles for pH, alkalinity, total phosphorus, and total nitrogen values in these lakes show that 80% of the lakes with water spider orchids had levels between 5.5 and 8.3, 1.5 and 50.0 (mg/L as $CaCO_3$), 12 and 87 (µg/L), and 300 and 1290 (µg/L), respectively. The water chemistry averages of the 38 lakes with water spider orchids showed only one significant difference (iron) from those for all 322 lakes. The 38 lakes also had water chemistry ranges similar to the water chemistry ranges in all 322 lakes. This suggests that water spider orchids can occur in a wide range of aquatic systems in Florida.

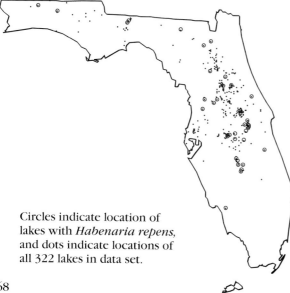

Circles indicate location of lakes with *Habenaria repens*, and dots indicate locations of all 322 lakes in data set.

Selected references from a total of 20 water spider orchid citations in the APIRS database:

Bodle, M.J. 1986. The fringed bog orchids. Aquatics 8:4-6.

Britton, N.L. and P. Wilson. 1924. Botany of Porta Rico and the Virgin Islands. New York. New York Academy of Science Vol. 5, parts 1-4.

Harper, R.M. 1903. The water hyacinth in Georgia. Plant World 6:164-165.

Hunt, K.W. 1943. Floating mats on a southeastern coastal plain reservoir. Bulletin of the Torrey Botanical Club 70(5):481-488.

Manning, J.C. 1989. New combinations and a new species in *Habenaria* (Orchidaceae) from South Africa. South African Journal of Botany 55(2):192-195.

McCartney, C. 1990. The rein orchids of Florida. Palmetto 10(3):3-6.

Renz, J., and S. Vodonaivalu. 1989. Studies in the subtribe Habenariinae (Orchidaceae) IV. *Habenaria, Peristylus,* and *Cynorkis* from the Fiji Islands. Blumea 34:87-98.

Vanhoek, C. 1992. Inventorying McKethan Lake Recreation Area. Palmetto 12(3):10-11.

Habenaria repens

Variables	Mean all lakes (n=322)	Number of lakes	Mean	10th percentile	Median	90th percentile
pH	6.7	38	6.7	5.5	6.4	8.3
Alkalinity (mg/L as $CaCO_3$)	23.9	38	16.5	1.5	5.6	50.0
Conductance (µS/cm @ 25°C)	149	38	101	28	99	184
Color (Pt-Co units)	52	38	58	7	38	154
Total phosphorus (µg/L)	45	38	36	12	22	87
Total nitrogen (µg/L)	870	38	810	300	670	1290
Chlorophyll a (µg/L)	20	38	11	2	7	29
Secchi (m)	1.8	34	1.7	0.6	1.4	3.6
Calcium (mg/L)	17.6	38	17.2	2.4	9.0	45.6
Magnesium (mg/L)	8.2	38	7.2	2.1	7.1	12.1
Sodium (mg/L)	13.2	38	8.6	2.1	7.8	16.2
Potassium (mg/L)	2.6	38	1.7	0.2	1.2	3.9
Sulfate (mg/L)	15.2	38	10.9	3.4	9.3	22.0
Chloride (mg/L)	23.4	38	15.2	3.3	13.5	28.1
Iron (mg/L)*	0.2	33	0.2	0.0	0.2	0.6
Silicon (mg/L)	1.5	33	1.3	0.1	1.0	3.4

* Denotes a significant difference ($p<0.05$) from mean of all lakes.

Hydrilla verticillata (hydrilla)

Alison Fox

Kerry Dressler

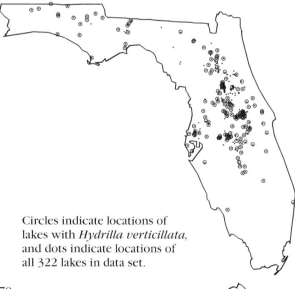

Circles indicate locations of lakes with *Hydrilla verticillata,* and dots indicate locations of all 322 lakes in data set.

Description and distribution

Hydrilla is a submersed perennial plant, with horizontal rhizomes in the substrate forming tubers under certain conditions. It has long branching stems that sometimes fragment and form large floating mats. Stems have been reported up to 8.5 m long. The leaves are strap-like, pointed, distinctly saw-toothed, 8–18 mm long, and 4 mm wide. The leaves have a midrib keeled beneath the leaf, usually bearing one or more teeth, and occur in whorls of three to five. Hydrilla produces reproductive turions, which are dense clusters of apical leaves produced in the leaf axis. It also produces small white flowers in the early fall that arise singularly from long stalks near the growing tip.

Hydrilla can easily be confused with Brazilian elodea (*Egeria densa*), another exotic submersed plant in Florida. The easiest way to distinguish these two plants is by flower size and the underside midrib of the leaves. Hydrilla flowers are very small and grow to the surface of the water on long, very thin stalks. Brazilian elodea's flowers are much larger and more conspicuous. The leaves of hydrilla have one or more teeth on the underside midrib, while Brazilian elodea has none. Hydrilla also produces tubers and turions, while Brazilian elodea does not.

Hydrilla is native to the Old World and has been naturalized in most of the southern United States and in many of the world's subtropical and tropical climates (Godfrey and Wooten 1981). The Florida distribution map shows that hydrilla was found in lakes across the whole state, with no apparent geographical pattern.

Biology

Hydrilla flowers from June to July in Florida (Dressler et al. 1987). It reproduces by tubers, by turions, and vegetatively. Hydrilla requires about 0.5–0.75% sunlight for photosynthesis, while most native plants require at least 1.5% sunlight. This enables hydrilla to out-compete many types of aquatic plants, resulting in large monotypic stands of hydrilla, which can impair navigational and recreational uses of many aquatic systems. Many forms of wildlife use hydrilla as food and habitat.

Ducks and coots consume tubers and vegetative parts of hydrilla, and invertebrates and fish use it for refuge and habitat. These beneficial attributes, however, are outweighed when the infestations are extensive.

Florida data

Hydrilla was identified in 157 lakes. The 10th and 90th percentiles for pH, alkalinity, total phosphorus, and total nitrogen values in these lakes show that 80% of the lakes with hydrilla had levels between 5.4 and 8.6, 1.7 and 77.6 (mg/L as CaCO$_3$), 10 and 106 (μg/L), and 310 and 1820 (μg/L), respectively. The water chemistry averages of the 190 lakes with hydrilla showed no significant differences from those in all 322 lakes. The 157 lakes also had water chemistry ranges similar to all 322 lakes. This suggests that hydrilla can occur in a wide range of aquatic systems.

Selected references from a total of 753 hydrilla citations in the APIRS database:

Center, T.D. and K.K. Steward. 1981. Fighting hydrilla in Florida. Journal of Agricultural Research 29(7-8):8-9.

Deschenes, P. and J. Ludlow. 1993. Maintenance control of hydrilla in the Winter Park chain of lakes, Florida. Aquatics 15(2):13-15.

Dooris, P.M. 1978. *Hydrilla verticillata*, chemical factors in lakes affecting growth. Ph.D. Dissertation, University of South Florida, Tampa.

Dooris, P.M. and D.F. Martin. 1993. Studies of the natural control of hydrilla in Florida. Aquatics 15(1):17-20.

Haller, W.T. 1983. Hydrilla in Florida. Aquatics 5(4):17-18.

Langeland, K.A. 1990. Hydrilla (*Hydrilla verticillata* (L.F.) Royle): A continuing problem in Florida waters. Circular No. 884, Cooperative Extension Service, IFAS, University of Florida, Gainesville.

Langeland, K.A. 1993. Hydrilla response to Mariner applied to lakes. Journal of Aquatic Plant Management 31:175-178.

Lazor, R.L. 1976. The ecology, nomenclature and distribution of hydrilla (*Hydrilla verticillata* sp.) and Brazilian elodea (*Egeria densa* Planch.). Proceedings, Annual Meeting, Southern Weed Science Society 28:269-273.

Norton, B. 1986. The hydrilla menace. Water Spectrum 11(2):36-43.

Sutton, D.L. and V.V. Vandiver. 1986. Grass carp—a fish for biological management of hydrilla and other aquatic weeds in Florida. Florida Agricultural Experiment Station, IFAS, University of Florida, Gainesville, Bulletin 867.

Hydrilla verticillata

Variables	Mean all lakes (n=322)	Number of lakes	Mean	10th percentile	Median	90th percentile
pH	6.7	157	7.1	5.4	7.1	8.6
Alkalinity (mg/L as CaCO$_3$)	23.9	157	29.9	1.7	18.8	77.6
Conductance (μS/cm @ 25°C)	149	157	183	27	128	355
Color (Pt-Co units)	52	157	48	5	26	103
Total phosphorus (μg/L)	45	156	49	10	22	106
Total nitrogen (μg/L)	870	156	900	310	670	1820
Chlorophyll a (μg/L)	20	157	20	2	7	62
Secchi (m)	1.8	143	1.7	0.4	1.4	3.7
Calcium (mg/L)	17.6	157	26.6	2.4	14.9	73.7
Magnesium (mg/L)	8.2	157	12.3	1.5	7.1	33.1
Sodium (mg/L)	13.2	147	17.3	2.5	8.8	33.3
Potassium (mg/L)	2.6	157	2.9	0.2	2.0	7.0
Sulfate (mg/L)	15.2	147	18.3	3.6	11.1	48.5
Chloride (mg/L)	23.4	157	30.7	4.1	15.9	44.7
Iron (mg/L)	0.2	130	0.2	0.0	0.1	0.4
Silicon (mg/L)	1.5	130	1.7	0.1	0.7	4.4

Hydrocotyle umbellata (water pennywort)

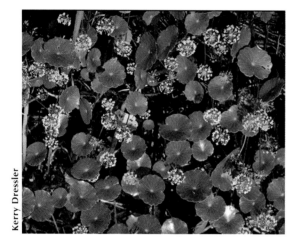

Description and distribution

Water pennywort is a perennial herb with stems that spread horizontally in mud or float on the water surface. The leaves are almost round, attached on the bottom of the leaf in the middle to stalks that can be 300 mm long. The leaf blades are blunt-toothed. Small white flowers appear in an umbrella or head and are borne on stalks that may be as long as the leaf stalk. The fruit is a pair of nutlets, about 3 mm long. Water pennywort is a native plant common throughout the Southeast (Godfrey and Wooten 1981). The Florida distribution map shows that water pennywort was found in lakes across the whole state, with no apparent geographical pattern.

Biology

Water pennywort flowers from March through July in Florida (Dressler et al. 1987). It reproduces by seed germination and vegetatively. The plant begins to grow on shoreline habitats, progressing outward toward open water. Mats can break off and continue to grow as a floating island. These floating mats and those formed on shoreline areas can be extensive, impairing navigational and recreational uses of an aquatic system. Some waterfowl use seeds and foliage of water pennywort for food. It can also be used as habitat and refuge for invertebrates and fish.

Florida data

Water pennywort was identified in 273 lakes. The 10th and 90th percentiles for pH, alkalinity, total phosphorus, and total nitrogen values in these lakes show that 80% of the lakes with water pennywort had levels between 5.0 and 8.7, 1.2 and 72.8 (mg/L as $CaCO_3$), 10 and 92 (µg/L), and 311 and 1790 (µg/L), respectively. The water chemistry averages of the 273 lakes with water pennywort showed no significant differences from those of all 322 lakes. The 273 lakes also had water chemistry ranges similar to all 322 lakes. This suggests that water pennywort can occur in a wide range of aquatic systems.

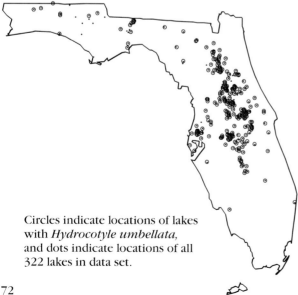

Circles indicate locations of lakes with *Hydrocotyle umbellata,* and dots indicate locations of all 322 lakes in data set.

Selected references from a total of 129 water pennywort citations in the APIRS database:

Agami, M. and K.R. Reddy. 1991. Inter-relationships between *Eichhornia crassipes* (Mart.) Solms and *Hydrocotyle umbellata* L. Aquatic Botany 39:147-157.

Moorhead, K.K. and K.R. Reddy. 1990. Carbon and nitrogen transformations in wastewater during treatment with *Hydrocotyle umbellata* L. Aquatic Botany 37:153-161.

Newman, S. 1988. Medicinal uses of aquatic plants common to Florida. Aquatics 10(3):4-8.

Ogwada, R.A. 1983. Growth, nutrient uptake, and nutrient regeneration by selected aquatic macrophytes. Master's Thesis, University of Florida, Gainesville.

Reddy, K.R. 1984. Nutrient removal potential of aquatic plants. Aquatics 6(1):15-16.

Reddy, K.R. and W.F. DeBusk. 1983. Growth characteristics of aquatic macrophytes cultured in nutrient enriched water. I. Water hyacinth, water lettuce, and pennywort. Economic Botany 38(2):229-239.

Reddy, K.R. and J.C. Tucker. 1985. Growth and nutrient uptake of pennywort (*Hydrocotyle umbellata* L.), as influenced by the nitrogen concentration of the water. Journal of Aquatic Plant Management 23:35-40.

Hydrocotyle umbellata

Variables	Mean all lakes (n=322)	Number of lakes	Mean	10th percentile	Median	90th percentile
pH	6.7	273	6.9	5.0	7.0	8.7
Alkalinity (mg/L as $CaCO_3$)	23.9	273	26.6	1.2	11.8	72.8
Conductance (µS/cm @ 25°C)	149	273	164	39	117	312
Color (Pt-Co units)	52	273	47	5	24	111
Total phosphorus (µg/L)	45	272	45	10	20	92
Total nitrogen (µg/L)	870	272	880	310	680	1790
Chlorophyll a (µg/L)	20	273	20	2	8	58
Secchi (m)	1.8	234	1.7	0.5	1.4	3.6
Calcium (mg/L)	17.6	272	19.9	1.6	10.1	51.5
Magnesium (mg/L)	8.2	272	9.3	1.0	4.8	22.9
Sodium (mg/L)	13.2	251	14.6	3.5	8.6	21.6
Potassium (mg/L)	2.6	272	2.9	0.2	2.0	7.8
Sulfate (mg/L)	15.2	251	16.6	4.2	10.9	39.7
Chloride (mg/L)	23.4	272	25.9	6.9	15.9	39.5
Iron (mg/L)	0.2	195	0.1	0.0	0.10	0.4
Silicon (mg/L)	1.5	195	1.6	0.2	0.6	3.8

Hypericum spp. (St. John's-wort)

Description and distribution

Godfrey and Wooten (1981) describe 27 species in the genus *Hypericum* that commonly occur in the Southeast. They can be annual or perennial and herbaceous but most often shrubby. Leaves are sessile, with or without an articulation at the base. The flowers are yellow to orange-yellow with four or five petals and rarely three to six petals. The petals can fall quickly or persist as withered remains. The Florida distribution map shows that *Hypericum* spp. occurred from extreme northwestern to south-central Florida.

Biology

One of the several species of *Hypericum* spp. can be found flowering throughout the year in Florida (Dressler et al. 1987). The plant grows in many habitats but is mostly a shoreline or moist-soil plant. *Hypericum* spp. are beneficial as a food source and habitat for many birds and mammals.

Florida data

Hypericum spp. were identified in 95 lakes. The 10th and 90th percentiles for pH, alkalinity, total phosphorus, and total nitrogen values in these lakes showed that 80% of the lakes with *Hypericum* spp. had levels that fell between 4.6 and 7.0, 0.3 and 17.4 (mg/L as $CaCO_3$), 5 and 27 (µg/L), and 156 and 1110 (µg/L), respectively. The 95 lakes collectively averaged significantly lower pH, alkalinity, specific conductance, total phosphorus, total nitrogen, calcium, magnesium, sodium, potassium, and chloride values than all 322 lakes. Thus while *Hypericum* spp. can occur in a range of lake types, they tend to occur in acid, softwater lakes with low nutrient concentrations.

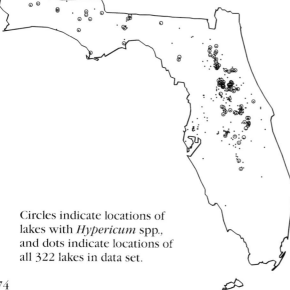

Circles indicate locations of lakes with *Hypericum* spp., and dots indicate locations of all 322 lakes in data set.

Selected references from a total of 106 *Hypericum* spp. citations in the APIRS database:

Botts, P. S. 1988. The distribution and abundance of herbaceous angiosperms in west-central Florida marshes. Aquatic Botany 32:225-238.

Buhrman, J. 1993. Round the year on Kissimmee Prairie Sanctuary. Palmetto 13(2):14-15.

Kushlan, J.A. 1990. Freshwater marshes. Pp. 324-363 in Ecosystems of Florida, R.L. Myers and J.J. Ewel, editors. University of Central Florida Press, Orlando.

Shipley, B. and P.A. Keddy. 1988. The relationship between relative growth rate and sensitivity to nutrient stress in twenty-eight species of emergent macrophytes. Journal of Ecology 76:1101-1110.

Vickery, A.R. 1981. Traditional uses and folklore of *Hypericum* in the British Isles. Economic Botany 35(3):289-295.

Hypericum spp.

Variables	Mean all lakes (n=322)	Number of lakes	Mean	10th percentile	Median	90th percentile
pH*	6.7	95	5.7	4.6	5.6	7.0
Alkalinity (mg/L as $CaCO_3$)*	23.9	95	5.3	0.3	2.0	17.4
Conductance (µS/cm @ 25°C)*	149	95	80	20	55	146
Color (Pt-Co units)	52	95	40	2	13	136
Total phosphorus (µg/L)*	45	94	14	5	11	27
Total nitrogen (µg/L)*	870	94	520	160	440	1110
Chlorophyll a (µg/L)	20	95	4	1.0	3	10
Secchi (m)*	1.8	86	2.7	0.8	2.5	5.0
Calcium (mg/L)*	17.6	94	6.3	0.7	2.5	15.4
Magnesium (mg/L)*	8.2	94	4.6	0.6	1.8	10.9
Sodium (mg/L)*	13.2	86	8.1	2.2	5.1	12.8
Potassium (mg/L)*	2.6	94	1.4	0.2	0.4	3.6
Sulfate (mg/L)	15.2	86	11.5	3.5	7.1	24.2
Chloride (mg/L)*	23.4	95	14.4	3.1	8.7	25.1
Iron (mg/L)	0.2	54	0.2	0.0	0.10	0.7
Silicon (mg/L)	1.5	54	0.8	0.10	0.3	2.4

* Denotes a significant difference (p<0.05) from mean of all lakes.

Juncus effusus (soft rush)

Kerry Dressler

Description and distribution

Soft rush is a large, grass-like perennial herb with cylindrical stems, 1500 mm tall and 2–4 mm in diameter, that originates from scaly rhizomes. The leaf blades are absent, but soft rush does have a 50–150 mm chestnut-colored basal leaf sheath. The inflorescence is stalked and consists of a multiply branched compact cluster of 30 to 100 flowers. The fruit is an obovoid capsule 2–2.5 mm long that contains irregularly shaped, minute amber-colored seeds. It is a cosmopolitan plant, common throughout the eastern United States (Godfrey and Wooten 1981). The Florida distribution map shows that soft rush was found in lakes across the state, with no apparent geographical pattern.

Biology

Soft rush flowers throughout the year in Florida (Dressler et al. 1987). It reproduces by seed germination and vegetatively. Soft rush tends to form large tussocks or clumps along the edges of freshwater marshes, lakes, and ponds. It can also be found along ditch banks and wet depressions. Waterfowl tend to feed upon the seeds, while the foliage is a food source for deer during fall and winter. Its tussocks may harbor nests for several species of rodent.

Florida data

Soft rush was identified in 87 lakes. The 10th and 90th percentiles for pH, alkalinity, total phosphorus, and total nitrogen values in these lakes show that 80% of the lakes with soft rush had levels between 5.6 and 8.8, 2.1 and 61.1 (mg/L as $CaCO_3$), 10 and 86 (µg/L), and 330 and 1870 (µg/L), respectively. The water chemistry values for the 87 lakes with soft rush showed similar averages and ranges to all 322 lakes. This suggests that soft rush can occur in a wide range of aquatic systems in Florida.

Circles indicate locations of lakes with *Juncus effusus,* and dots indicate locations of all 322 lakes in data set.

Selected references from a total of 259 soft rush citations in the APIRS database:

Adamson, R.S. 1925. On the leaf structure of *Juncus*. Annals of Botany 39:599-612.

Boyd, C.E. 1971. The dynamics of dry matter and chemical substances in a *Juncus effusus* population. American Midland Naturalist 86:28-45.

Fernald, M.L. and K.M. Wiegand. 1910. The North American variations of *Juncus effusus*. Rhodora 12(137):81-93.

Hamet-Ahti, L. 1980. The *Juncus effusus* aggregate in eastern North America. Annales Botanici Fennici 17:183-191.

Loftin, J.P. 1994. On the waterfront. Florida Water Magazine 3(2):14-24.

Stott, R.F. and S.J.L. Wright. 1991. Sewage treatment with plants. Letters in Applied Microbiology 12:99-105.

Tweed, R.D. 1947. The taxonomy of *Juncus effusus* L. and *Juncus conglomeratus* L. Northwestern Naturalist 22:216-222.

Vilovsek, D. and J. Bulc. 1994. Development of constructed wetlands in Slovenia. Aquaphyte 14(2):1, 14-15.

Juncus effusus

Variables	Mean all lakes (n=322)	Number of lakes	Mean	10th percentile	Median	90th percentile
pH	6.7	87	7.2	5.6	7.1	8.8
Alkalinity (mg/L as $CaCO_3$)	23.9	87	27.1	2.1	18.8	61.1
Conductance (µS/cm @ 25°C)	149	87	145	32	113	280
Color (Pt-Co units)	52	87	45	6	24	93
Total phosphorus (µg/L)	45	87	43	10	26	86
Total nitrogen (µg/L)	870	87	950	330	780	1870
Chlorophyll a (µg/L)	20	87	23	2	11	63
Secchi (m)	1.8	75	1.5	0.4	1.3	3.5
Calcium (mg/L)	17.6	86	19.5	2.8	13.3	47.8
Magnesium (mg/L)*	8.2	86	10.5	1.9	7.1	23.2
Sodium (mg/L)	13.2	80	11.2	2.4	8.7	16.9
Potassium (mg/L)	2.6	86	3.1	0.3	2.1	8.1
Sulfate (mg/L)	15.2	80	14.3	3.2	11.5	30.5
Chloride (mg/L)	23.4	86	20.1	4.5	16.0	31.1
Iron (mg/L)	0.2	69	0.2	0.0	0.1	0.6
Silicon (mg/L)	1.5	69	1.2	0.1	0.7	3.5

* Denotes a significant difference ($p < 0.05$) from mean of all lakes.

Lachnanthes caroliana (redroot)

Kerry Dressler

Kerry Dressler

Description and distribution

Redroot is a perennial herb that has distinctive red to red-orange roots. The blade-like alternate leaves enfold each other at the base and taper gradually towards the tip. Stems are hairy towards the inflorescence and smooth below. The inflorescence is a solitary, terminal cyme that has flowers with three outer petals and three yellow inner petals. The fruit is a smooth capsule with blackish brown seeds. Redroot is found throughout the Coastal Plain of the United States (Godfrey and Wooten 1981). The Florida distribution map shows that redroot was found primarily in central Florida.

Biology

Redroot reproduces by seed germination and vegetatively. This member of the Haemodoraceae family flowers from May through October in Florida (Dressler et al. 1987). It tends to colonize along lake and pond shorelines and can be found in wet ditches, swamps, and low pine flatwoods.

Florida data

Redroot was identified in 63 lakes. The 10th and 90th percentiles for pH, alkalinity, total phosphorus, and total nitrogen values in these lakes show that 80% of the lakes with redroot had levels between 4.5 and 7.4, 0.0 and 25.1 (mg/L as $CaCO_3$), 6 and 45 (μg/L), and 180 and 1170 (μg/L), respectively. These 63 lakes also collectively averaged significantly lower pH, alkalinity, total phosphorus, and calcium values than all 322 lakes. Thus redroot tends to occur in acid, softwater, nutrient-poor lakes.

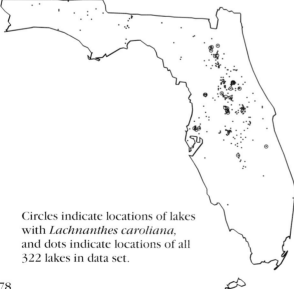

Circles indicate locations of lakes with *Lachnanthes caroliana*, and dots indicate locations of all 322 lakes in data set.

Selected references from a total of 14 redroot citations in the APIRS database:

Bodle, M. 1984. Redroot *Lachnanthes caroliniana* (Lam.) and Dandy. Aquatics 6(1):21–23.

Bosserman, R.W. 1981. Elemental composition of aquatic plants from Okefenokee Swamp. Journal of Freshwater Ecology 1(3):307–320.

Francis, G. 1994. A biosphere reserve for Atlantic coastal plain flora, south-western Nova Scotia. Biological Conservation 68:275–279.

Landers, L., S. Johnson, P. Morgan, and W. Baldwin. 1976. Duck ponds in managed tidal impoundments in South Carolina. Journal of Wildlife Management 40(4):721–728.

Lowe, E.F. 1986. The relationship between hydrology and vegetational pattern within the floodplain marsh of a subtropical Florida lake. Florida Scientist 49(4):213–233.

Mitsch, W.J. and J.G. Gosselink. 1993. Southern deepwater swamps. Pp. 412–449 in Wetlands, 2nd ed. Van Nostrand Reinhold, New York.

Morris, C.D., J.L. Callahan, and R.H. Lewis. 1990. Distribution and abundance of larval *Coquillettidia perturbans* in a Florida freshwater marsh. Journal of American Mosquito Control Association 6(3):452–460.

Wisheu, I.C., C.J. Keddy, P.A Keddy, and N.M Hill. 1994. Disjunct Atlantic Coastal Plain species in Nova Scotia: Distribution, habitat and conservation priorities. Biological Conservation 68:217–224.

Lachnanthes caroliana

Variables	Mean all lakes (n=322)	Number of lakes	Mean	10th percentile	Median	90th percentile
pH*	6.7	63	5.9	4.5	5.8	7.4
Alkalinity (mg/L as CaCO$_3$)*	23.9	63	8.1	0.0	2.1	25.1
Conductance (µS/cm @ 25°C)	149	63	98	40	73	179
Color (Pt-Co units)	52	63	50	4	24	166
Total phosphorus (µg/L)*	45	62	21	6	12	45
Total nitrogen (µg/L)	870	62	660	180	550	1170
Chlorophyll a (µg/L)	20	63	6	1	4	11
Secchi (m)	1.8	51	2.2	0.8	2.0	4.2
Calcium (mg/L)*	17.6	63	7.8	0.7	4.6	16.1
Magnesium (mg/L)	8.2	63	4.3	0.8	2.7	11.0
Sodium (mg/L)	13.2	63	9.1	3.5	7.1	16.9
Potassium (mg/L)	2.6	63	1.6	0.2	0.9	3.7
Sulfate (mg/L)	15.2	63	11.4	2.9	7.8	25.8
Chloride (mg/L)	23.4	63	16.7	7.1	12.5	31.9
Iron (mg/L)	0.2	38	0.1	0.0	0.10	0.4
Silicon (mg/L)	1.5	38	1.0	0.10	0.5	3.5

* Denotes a significant difference ($p<0.05$) from mean of all lakes.

Leersia hexandra (southern cutgrass)

Kerry Dressler

Kerry Dressler

Description and distribution

Southern cutgrass is a perennial herb that has slender stems and rhizomes. Roots tend to form at the nodes, which have a band of short hairs around them. The narrow leaves are 150–180 mm long and 3–6 mm wide. The leaf margins are very sharp and have an abrasive, sandpaper feel. The seedheads are 20–90 mm long with several thin alternate branches extending from the primary branch. The flattened flowers have short, stiff hairs and are clustered towards the ends of the branches. The elliptical seeds are 4–5 mm long and reddish. Southern cutgrass is primarily found along the Coastal Plain of the United States from Virginia south to Florida and west towards southeastern Texas and Tennessee (Godfrey and Wooten 1981). The Florida distribution map shows that southern cutgrass occurs from the Florida panhandle to central Florida. Lakes are progressively more alkaline and nutrient rich as one moves from northwestern to southern Florida (Canfield and Hoyer 1988). Thus the distribution of southern cutgrass in Florida suggests that it tends to prefer acid, softwater, nutrient-poor lakes.

Biology

Southern cutgrass reproduces by seed germination and vegetatively by rhizomes and leafy stolons. It flowers throughout the year in Florida (Dressler et al. 1987) and can be found along lake and pond shorelines. It frequently grows as dense floating mats offshore in water 1–2 m deep. These floating islands provide good cover for small fish and aquatic insects and can be used by wading birds as feeding and resting sites.

Florida data

Southern cutgrass was identified in 104 lakes. The 10th and 90th percentiles for pH, alkalinity, total phosphorus, and total nitrogen values in these lakes showed that 80% of the lakes with southern cutgrass had levels that fell between 4.5 and 7.8,

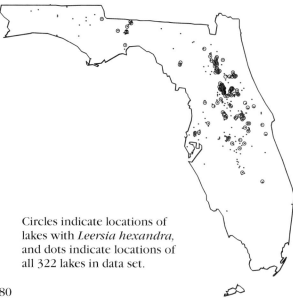

Circles indicate locations of lakes with *Leersia hexandra*, and dots indicate locations of all 322 lakes in data set.

0.0 and 45.1 (mg/L as CaCO$_3$), 7 and 42 (µg/L), and 160 and 1160 (µg/L), respectively. The 104 lakes collectively averaged significantly lower pH, alkalinity, total phosphorus, total nitrogen, calcium, and potassium values than all 322 lakes. This suggests that southern cutgrass tends to occur in acid, softwater, nutrient-poor lakes.

Selected references from a total of 112 southern cutgrass citations in the APIRS database:

Datta, S.C. and A.K. Banerjee. 1978. Useful weeds of the west Bengal rice fields. Economic Botany 32:297-310.

Holm, L.G., D.L. Plucknett, J.V. Pancho, and J.P. Herberger. 1977. The world's worst weeds: Distribution and biology. University Press of Hawaii, Honolulu.

Kirkman, L.K. and R.R. Sharitz. 1993. Growth in controlled water regimes of three grasses common in freshwater wetlands of the southeastern USA. Aquatic Botany 44:345-359.

Naiman, R.J. and H. Decamps. 1990. The ecology and management of aquatic-terrestrial ecotones. Man and the Biosphere series, Vol. 4. UNESCO, Parthenon Publishing Group, Park Ridge, N.J.

Oka, H.I. 1991. Ecology of wild rice planted in Taiwan. I. Sequential distribution of species and their interactions in weed communities. Botanical Bulletin of Academia Sinica 32:281-293.

Roth, H.H. and E. Waitkuwait. 1986. Distribution and status of large mammals in the Ivory Coast. III. Lamantins. Mammalia 50(2):227-242.

Schalles, J.F. and D.J. Shure. 1989. Hydrology, community structure, and productivity patterns of a dystrophic Carolina bay wetland. Ecological Monographs 59(4):365-385.

Terry, W.S. and G.W. Tanner. 1986. Nitrogen and phosphorus concentrations within freshwater marsh plant species. Journal of Freshwater Ecology 3(3):347-358.

Leersia hexandra

Variables	Mean all lakes (n=322)	Number of lakes	Mean	10th percentile	Median	90th percentile
pH*	6.7	104	5.9	4.5	5.5	7.8
Alkalinity (mg/L as CaCO$_3$)*	23.9	104	12.3	0.0	2.0	45.1
Conductance (µS/cm @ 25°C)	149	104	127	31	60	290
Color (Pt-Co units)	52	104	46	4	20	129
Total phosphorus (µg/L)*	45	104	22	7	12	42
Total nitrogen (µg/L)*	870	104	590	160	470	1160
Chlorophyll a (µg/L)	20	104	8	1.0	3	17
Secchi (m)	1.8	96	2.3	0.6	2.1	4.3
Calcium (mg/L)*	17.6	104	13.6	0.6	2.8	40.1
Magnesium (mg/L)	8.2	104	7.7	0.6	1.9	29.4
Sodium (mg/L)	13.2	95	13.9	2.8	5.5	21.3
Potassium (mg/L)*	2.6	104	1.7	0.1	0.5	4.9
Sulfate (mg/L)	15.2	95	14.1	2.8	7.0	48.1
Chloride (mg/L)	23.4	104	24.7	5.8	10.0	33.2
Iron (mg/L)	0.2	57	0.2	0.0	0.1	0.4
Silicon (mg/L)	1.5	57	1.4	0.1	0.5	4.0

* Denotes a significant difference (p<0.05) from mean of all lakes.

Lemna minor (common duckweed)

Alison Fox

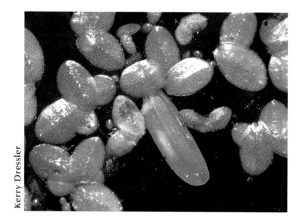

Kerry Dressler

Description and distribution

Common duckweed is a small floating plant that has one or two obovate to elliptical fronds (leaves) that are 2–4 mm long. These fronds are green to yellow-green on the upper surface and sometimes reddish on the underside. Each frond has a single root extending from the underside of the leaf. Common duckweed has subtle flowers that are rarely seen. The fruit and solitary seed are ovoid to ellipsoid. It is a widespread aquatic plant that is found almost worldwide (Godfrey and Wooten 1981). The Florida distribution map shows that common duckweed was found in lakes throughout the state, with no apparent geographical pattern.

Biology

Common duckweed reproduces by budding or through seed germination. It flowers throughout the year in Florida (Dressler et al. 1987). Common duckweed tends to be found in lakes, ponds, swamps, canals, and ditches, commonly in association with other floating aquatic plants. Although it is native to Florida, it can become a problem by colonizing a whole lake surface and hindering light from reaching submersed aquatic plants. It is a valuable food source for many species of waterfowl.

Florida data

Common duckweed was identified in 124 lakes. The 10th and 90th percentiles for pH, alkalinity, total phosphorus, and total nitrogen values in these lakes show that 80% of the lakes with common duckweed had levels between 5.6 and 8.8, 2.1 and 100.0 (mg/L as $CaCO_3$), 12 and 129 (µg/L), and 410 and 1980 (µg/L), respectively. These 124 lakes also collectively averaged significantly higher pH, alkalinity, specific conductance, total phosphorus, total nitrogen, calcium, magnesium, sodium, potassium, and chloride than all 322 lakes. The average Secchi depth value for the 124 lakes was significantly lower than for all 322 lakes. Thus while common duckweed can occur in a range of lake types, it tends to occur in alkaline, hardwater, eutrophic lakes.

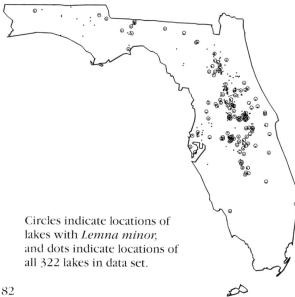

Circles indicate locations of lakes with *Lemna minor*, and dots indicate locations of all 322 lakes in data set.

Selected references from a total of 1093 common duckweed citations in the APIRS database:

Ashby, E. and T.A. Oxley. 1935. The interaction of factors in the growth of *Lemna*. VI. An analysis of the influence of light intensity and temperature on the assimilation rate and the rate of frond multiplication. Annals of Botany 49:309–336.

Bowker, D.W. and P. Denny. 1980. The seasonal succession and distribution of epiphytic algae in the phyllosphere of *Lemna minor* L. Archiv fur Hydrobiologie 90(1):39–55.

Ericsson, T., C.M. Larsson, and E. Tillberg. 1981. Growth responses of *Lemna* to different levels of nitrogen limitation. Zeitschrift fuer Pflanzenphysiologie 105(4):331–340.

Humphrey, T.J., S. Sarawek, and D.D. Davies. 1977. The effect of nitrogen deficiency on the growth and metabolism of *Lemna minor*. Planta 137:259–264.

Keddy, P.A. 1976. Lakes as islands: The distributional ecology of two aquatic plants, *Lemna minor* and *Lemna trisulca* L. Ecology 57:353–359.

Kobuszewska, D.M. 1973. Experimentally increased fish stock in the pond type Lake Warniak. XIII. Distribution and biomass of the Lemnaceae and the fauna associated with them. Ekologia Polska 21(39):611–629.

Lockhart, W.L., B.N. Billeck, and C.L. Baron. 1989. Bioassays with a floating plant (*Lemna minor*) for effects of sprayed and dissolved glyphosate. Hydrobiologia 188/189:353–359.

Scotland, M.B. 1940. Review and summary of studies of insects associated with *Lemna minor*. Journal of the New York Entomological Society 48:319–333.

Underwood, G.J.C. and J.H. Baker. 1991. The effects of various aquatic bacteria on the growth and senescence of duckweed (*Lemna minor*). Journal of Applied Bacteriology 70:192–196.

Vasseur, L. and L.W. Aarssen. 1992. Interpretation of adaptive plasticity in *Lemna minor*. Oikos 65(2):233–241.

Lemna minor

Variables	Mean all lakes (n=322)	Number of lakes	Mean	10th percentile	Median	90th percentile
pH*	6.7	124	7.4	5.6	7.5	8.8
Alkalinity (mg/L as CaCO₃)*	23.9	124	36.3	2.1	24.1	100.0
Conductance (µS/cm @ 25°C)*	149	124	213	59	140	436
Color (Pt-Co units)	52	124	62	7	39	135
Total phosphorus (µg/L)*	45	123	69	12	30	129
Total nitrogen (µg/L)*	870	123	1100	410	990	1980
Chlorophyll a (µg/L)	20	124	27	3	13	75
Secchi (m)*	1.8	108	1.3	0.4	0.9	2.9
Calcium (mg/L)*	17.6	124	30.9	4.0	18.9	87.2
Magnesium (mg/L)*	8.2	124	14.4	2.3	8.6	39.2
Sodium (mg/L)*	13.2	118	20.9	5.0	10.3	49.9
Potassium (mg/L)*	2.6	124	3.5	0.3	2.3	8.8
Sulfate (mg/L)	15.2	118	19.7	4.3	12.5	48.5
Chloride (mg/L)*	23.4	123	36.9	8.6	17.4	86.4
Iron (mg/L)	0.2	104	0.2	0.0	0.1	0.4
Silicon (mg/L)	1.5	104	2.1	0.2	1.3	5.2

* Denotes a significant difference (p<0.05) from mean of all lakes.

Limnobium spongia (frog's-bit)

Kerry Dressler

Kerry Dressler

Description and distribution

Frog's-bit is an aquatic herb with horizontal runners from which vertical stems grow. The plants can be rooted in the mud or floating on the water. The heart-shaped leaves are often confused with those of water hyacinth. Frog's-bit has two types of leaves. The out-of-water leaves are leathery, robust, and on tall stems. The partially submersed leaves are thickened below with spongy tissue. Both leaf types are 20–50 mm wide and faintly five-veined with interconnecting veins. Frog's-bit has small, unisexual, white flowers on stalks approximately one third the height of the leaves. The fruit is a many seeded berry on a short stalk. Frog's-bit is a common plant in the eastern United States (Godfrey and Wooten 1981). The Florida distribution map shows that it was found primarily in lakes from north-central to south Florida. Lakes are progressively more alkaline and nutrient rich as one moves from northwestern to southern Florida (Canfield and Hoyer 1988). Thus the distribution of frog's-bit in Florida suggests that it may tend to occur in alkaline, hardwater, nutrient-rich lakes.

Biology

Frog's-bit flowers from May through October (Dressler et al. 1987). It reproduces readily by seed germination and vegetatively from runners. Frog's-bit can grow well floating or rooted in a substrate. Under the right conditions it can form extensive mats that have the potential to impair navigational and recreational activities in some aquatic systems. The seeds are eaten by many forms of wildlife. Floating mats of frog's-bit are also good refuge and habitat for invertebrate and fish populations.

Florida data

Frog's-bit was identified in 52 lakes. The 10th and 90th percentiles for pH, alkalinity, total phosphorus, and total nitrogen values in these lakes show that 80% of the lakes with frog's-bit had levels

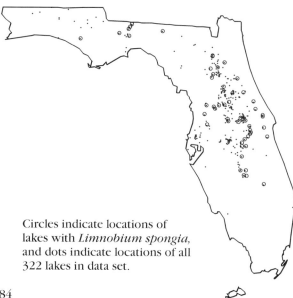

Circles indicate locations of lakes with *Limnobium spongia,* and dots indicate locations of all 322 lakes in data set.

between 5.6 and 8.6, 2.1 and 90.3 (mg/L as CaCO$_3$), 13 and 190 (µg/L), and 450 and 1810 (µg/L), respectively. The 36 lakes collectively averaged significantly higher pH, color, total phosphorus, chlorophyll *a*, calcium, and magnesium values than all 322 lakes. Thus while frog's-bit can occur in a range of lake types, it tends to occur in alkaline, hardwater, nutrient-rich lakes.

Selected references from a total of 65 frog's-bit citations in the APIRS database:

Bodle, M.J. 1986. American frog's-bit. Aquatics 8(3):4,6.

Conway, K.E. 1978. A new species of *Cercospora* from *Limnobium spongia*. Transactions of the British Mycological Society 71(3):521–523.

Elakovich, S.D. and J.W. Wooten. 1989. Allelopathic potential of sixteen aquatic and wetland plants. Journal of Aquatic Plant Management 27:78–84.

Hoyer, M.V. and D.E. Canfield. 1986. Surface area of aquatic macrophytes. Aquatics 8(2):26–27.

Knight, E.D. 1985. Control of frog's-bit. Aquatics 7(1):24.

Knight, R.L., B.H. Winchester, and J.C. Higman. 1985. Ecology, hydrology, and advanced wastewater treatment potential of an artificial wetland in north-central Florida. Wetlands 5:167–180.

Sutton, D.L. 1991. The Hydrocharitaceae or frog's-bit family. Aquatics 13(1):4–12.

Sutton, D.L. 1993. Characteristics of flowering aquatic plants. Aquatic Gardener 6(6):177–181.

Wilder, G.J. 1974. Symmetry and development of *Limnobium spongia* (Hydrocharitaceae). American Journal of Botany 61(6):624–642.

Limnobium spongia

Variables	Mean all lakes (n=322)	Number of lakes	Mean	10th percentile	Median	90th percentile
pH*	6.7	52	7.1	5.6	7.1	8.6
Alkalinity (mg/L as CaCO$_3$)	23.9	52	29.9	2.1	17.7	90.3
Conductance (µS/cm @ 25°C)	149	52	205	44	109	693
Color (Pt-Co units)*	52	52	84	13	56	190
Total phosphorus (µg/L)*	45	51	56	13	30	107
Total nitrogen (µg/L)	870	51	990	450	860	1810
Chlorophyll a (µg/L)*	20	52	18	3	8	42
Secchi (m)	1.8	45	1.2	0.5	0.8	2.8
Calcium (mg/L)*	17.6	52	29.7	3.9	18.0	87.9
Magnesium (mg/L)*	8.2	52	13.9	2.2	9.6	34.2
Sodium (mg/L)	13.2	50	22.6	4.1	8.8	85.6
Potassium (mg/L)	2.6	52	2.2	0.2	1.8	5.1
Sulfate (mg/L)	15.2	50	18.8	3.2	11.1	56.1
Chloride (mg/L)	23.4	52	39.1	5.3	14.9	155.8
Iron (mg/L)	0.2	45	0.3	0.0	0.2	0.7
Silicon (mg/L)	1.5	45	2.3	0.10	1.3	7.0

* Denotes a significant difference (p<0.05) from mean of all lakes.

Ludwigia arcuata (long-stalked ludwigia)

Kerry Dressler

Kerry Dressler

Description and distribution

Ludwigia arcuata is a perennial plant with creeping branches that root at the lower nodes. The stems are pubescent with short, hooked hairs that sometimes are shed on older portions of the stems. The leaves are opposite, sessile, and oblanceolate or narrowly or widely elliptic; the three shapes often are on the same plant. The leaves are mostly 8–20 mm long, sometimes glabrous, sometimes minutely scabrid on and near the margins, with hooked hairs on the midrib beneath. The flowers are solitary in leaf axils, usually only one in the axil of one leaf pair at a given node and relatively few nodes bearing flowers. The bright yellow flowers have four petals and rest on long slender stalks that are longer than the subtending leaves. The seed capsule is obconical in outline, obscurely quadrangular, usually curved, and 6–8 mm long. The seed is ellipsoidal, about 0.5 mm long. *Ludwigia arcuata* occurs in the Coastal Plain from South Carolina to south Florida and west to southern Alabama (Godfrey and Wooten 1981). The Florida distribution map shows that the few lakes with *Ludwigia arcuata* were found across the whole state, with no apparent geographical pattern.

Biology

Ludwigia arcuata usually flowers in the summer and early fall in Florida. It usually grows in soils along shoreline habitats or in moist soil systems. Occasionally, the plant can mat from the substrate to the surface of a shallow lake.

Florida data

Ludwigia arcuata was identified in 19 lakes. The 10th and 90th percentiles for pH, alkalinity, total phosphorus, and total nitrogen values in these lakes show that 80% of the lakes with *Ludwigia arcuata* had levels between 5.8 and 7.1, 1.6 and 19.8 (mg/L as $CaCO_3$), 10 and 63 (µg/L), and 220 and 1110 (µg/L), respectively. The water chemistry averages of the 19 lakes with *Ludwigia arcuata* showed no significant differences from those in all 322 lakes.

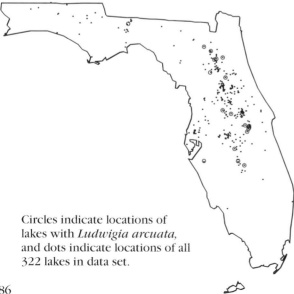

Circles indicate locations of lakes with *Ludwigia arcuata,* and dots indicate locations of all 322 lakes in data set.

Selected references from a total of 442 *Ludwigia arcuata* citations in the APIRS database:

Butler, R.S., E.J. Moyer, M.W. Hulon, and V.P. Williams. 1992. Littoral zone invertebrate communities as affected by a habitat restoration project on Lake Tohopekaliga, Florida. Journal of Freshwater Ecology 7(3):317–328.

Hulon, M.W., E.J. Moyer, R.S. Butler, and V.P. Williams. 1992. Aquatic plant response to the 1987 drawdown/muck removal project on Lake Tohopekaliga, Florida. Aquatics 14(3):18–21.

Kim, S.C. and K. Moody. 1990. Growth dynamics of rice and several weed species under density and fertilizer stresses. Weedwatcher 13/14:6 (Abstract).

Sutton, D.L. 1982. Growth of native aquatic species by integrated control (chemicals and fish) of weeds and re-establishment of natural aquatic plants. Annual Report, USDA/SEA/ARS, University of Florida, Gainesville.

Terry, W.S. and G.W. Tanner. 1986. Nitrogen and phosphorus concentrations within freshwater marsh plant species. Journal of Freshwater Ecology 3(3):347–358.

Ludwigia arcuata

Variables	Mean all lakes (n=322)	Number of lakes	Mean	10th percentile	Median	90th percentile
pH	6.7	19	6.3	5.8	6.2	7.1
Alkalinity (mg/L as CaCO₃)	23.9	19	6.3	1.6	2.8	19.8
Conductance (µS/cm @ 25°C)	149	19	93	42	96	134
Color (Pt-Co units)	52	19	52	6	32	101
Total phosphorus (µg/L)	45	19	29	10	16	63
Total nitrogen (µg/L)	870	19	660	220	530	1110
Chlorophyll a (µg/L)	20	19	8	2	5	31
Secchi (m)	1.8	18	1.9	0.8	1.6	3.7
Calcium (mg/L)	17.6	19	9.2	3.0	7.3	22.4
Magnesium (mg/L)	8.2	19	7.0	2.6	6.8	11.8
Sodium (mg/L)	13.2	19	8.4	4.9	7.7	11.8
Potassium (mg/L)	2.6	19	2.1	0.2	1.9	3.0
Sulfate (mg/L)	15.2	19	13.0	3.3	10.6	31.8
Chloride (mg/L)	23.4	19	16.1	7.0	13.6	27.7
Iron (mg/L)	0.2	18	0.2	0.0	0.1	0.4
Silicon (mg/L)	1.5	18	1.0	0.1	0.5	3.5

Ludwigia octovalvis (water primrose)

Mark Hoyer

Mark Hoyer

Description and distribution

Water primrose is a medium to large shrub reaching almost 3 m, with numerous branching stems that appear woody near the base. The leaf blades are ovate to narrowly lanceolate, 50–150 mm long and 5–15 mm wide, with 12 to 22 veins on each side of the midrib. Minute soft hairs cover both sides of the leaf. Solitary flowers on short stalks consist of four light green sepals 8–13 mm long and four yellow heart-shaped petals 15–30 mm long. Numerous light brown seeds are enclosed in a four-angled, cylindrical capsule, 25–45 mm long and 8–13 mm wide. Water primrose is native to South America and is now common in the Coastal Plain from North Carolina to Florida and west to Texas (Godfrey and Wooten 1981). The Florida distribution map shows that water primrose was found in lakes across the whole state, with no apparent geographical pattern.

Biology

Water primrose flowers in the summer and fall in Florida. It reproduces by seed germination and vegetatively from rhizomes. It is an aggressive invader of disturbed wet habitats. Water primrose is found primarily on shoreline habitats and can grow extensively, impairing navigational and recreational uses of some aquatic systems. It is used as refuge and nesting habitat for several species of songbird. Some waterfowl use the seeds as food. Extensive tangles of water primrose are a favorite resting area for migrating black-crowned night-herons (*Nycticorax nycticorax*) in the spring and fall.

Florida data

Water primrose was identified in 225 lakes. The 10th and 90th percentiles for pH, alkalinity, total phosphorus, and total nitrogen values in these lakes show that 80% of the lakes with water primrose had levels between 5.6 and 8.8, 1.6 and 75.9 (mg/L as $CaCO_3$), 10 and 113 (µg/L), and 370 and 1960 (µg/L), respectively. These

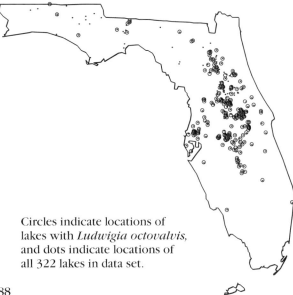

Circles indicate locations of lakes with *Ludwigia octovalvis,* and dots indicate locations of all 322 lakes in data set.

225 lakes also collectively averaged significantly higher pH, alkalinity, specific conductance, total phosphorus, calcium, magnesium, potassium, and chloride values than all 322 lakes. Thus while water primrose can occur in a range of lake types, it tends to occur in alkaline, hardwater, eutrophic lakes.

***Ludwigia octovalvis*: see references for *Ludwigia arcuata*.**

Ludwigia octovalvis

Variables	Mean all lakes (n=322)	Number of lakes	Mean	10th percentile	Median	90th percentile
pH*	6.7	225	7.2	5.6	7.3	8.8
Alkalinity (mg/L as CaCO$_3$)*	23.9	225	31.2	1.6	20.5	75.9
Conductance (µS/cm @ 25°C)*	149	225	187	57	147	343
Color (Pt-Co units)	52	225	46	6	26	107
Total phosphorus (µg/L)*	45	224	56	10	23	113
Total nitrogen (µg/L)	870	224	980	370	770	1960
Chlorophyll a (µg/L)	20	225	26	2	11	69
Secchi (m)	1.8	187	1.5	0.4	1.3	3.0
Calcium (mg/L)*	17.6	225	23.1	2.7	13.7	59.6
Magnesium (mg/L)*	8.2	225	10.9	1.8	6.9	28.1
Sodium (mg/L)	13.2	210	16.5	5.0	9.9	25.7
Potassium (mg/L)*	2.6	225	3.4	0.3	2.3	8.4
Sulfate (mg/L)	15.2	210	18.5	4.7	12.3	43.8
Chloride (mg/L)*	23.4	224	29.4	8.9	17.9	41.6
Iron (mg/L)	0.2	170	0.2	0.0	0.10	0.4
Silicon (mg/L)	1.5	170	1.7	0.2	0.8	3.9

* Denotes a significant difference (p<0.05) from mean of all lakes.

Ludwigia repens (red ludwigia)

Description and distribution

Red ludwigia is a perennial plant that is prostrate or creeping when growing terrestrially; it is completely submersed or has only the tip floating, rooted in the substrate with flaccid ascending stems, when growing in the water. The stems may be glabrous throughout or more commonly have sparse hooked hairs on parts and usually have considerable purple pigment, especially in submersed plants. The leaves are opposite, with elliptical to subround distal portions, which abruptly or gradually narrow to petiolar bases. The leaves of terrestrial plants are mostly 10–30 mm long and 5–10 mm wide at the widest portion of the leaf, while submersed leaves are generally flaccid and vary in size up to 50 mm long, with their distal portions 20–30 mm wide. Flowers are mostly sessile, rarely with stalks less than 3 mm long and solitary in the leaf axils of one or two leaves per node. The flowers have four yellow petals, which fall quickly and are rarely seen. Red ludwigia occurs in the Coastal Plain from South Carolina to south Florida and west to Texas (Godfrey and Wooten 1981). The Florida distribution map shows that red ludwigia was found across the whole state, with no apparent geographical pattern.

Biology

Red ludwigia usually flowers in the summer and early fall in Florida. The plant usually grows in soils along shoreline habitats or in moist soil systems. Occasionally, the plant can mat from the substrate to the surface of a shallow lake.

Florida data

Red ludwigia was identified in 114 lakes. The 10th and 90th percentiles for pH, alkalinity, total phosphorus, and total nitrogen values in these lakes show that 80% of the lakes with red ludwigia had levels between 4.7 and 8.3, 0.9 and 50.9 (mg/L as $CaCO_3$), 9 and 63 (µg/L), and 290 and 1460 (µg/L), respectively. The water chemistry averages and ranges of the 114 lakes with red ludwigia are similar to those in all 322 lakes. This suggests that red ludwigia can occur in a wide range of aquatic systems in Florida.

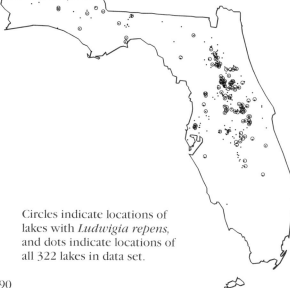

Circles indicate locations of lakes with *Ludwigia repens,* and dots indicate locations of all 322 lakes in data set.

Ludwigia repens: see references for
Ludwigia arcuata.

Ludwigia repens

Variables	Mean all lakes (n=322)	Number of lakes	Mean	10th percentile	Median	90th percentile
pH	6.7	114	6.3	4.7	6.2	8.3
Alkalinity (mg/L as $CaCO_3$)	23.9	114	17.2	0.9	3.0	50.9
Conductance (µS/cm @ 25°C)	149	114	130	34	86	246
Color (Pt-Co units)	52	114	45	5	22	121
Total phosphorus (µg/L)	45	113	31	9	14	63
Total nitrogen (µg/L)	870	113	750	290	600	1460
Chlorophyll a (µg/L)	20	114	11	1.0	4	30
Secchi (m)	1.8	100	2.1	0.6	1.8	4.1
Calcium (mg/L)	17.6	114	15.3	0.8	5.4	43.7
Magnesium (mg/L)	8.2	114	7.9	0.8	2.9	22.3
Sodium (mg/L)	13.2	107	12.5	3.2	7.5	18.7
Potassium (mg/L)	2.6	114	1.9	0.2	1.0	5.2
Sulfate (mg/L)	15.2	107	13.8	3.3	7.9	32.6
Chloride (mg/L)	23.4	113	22.6	6.5	14.0	34.6
Iron (mg/L)	0.2	72	0.2	0.0	0.1	0.5
Silicon (mg/L)	1.5	72	1.4	0.1	0.5	3.8

Luziola fluitans (southern water-grass)

Jesse Van Dyke

Jeff Schardt

Description and distribution

Southern water-grass is a rooted semisubmersed slender perennial. Southern water-grass has rhizomes and stolons with stems that can grow up to one meter long. The leaves are flat and short, only 20–30 mm long, and 2–4 mm wide. Both male and female flowers are inconspicuous and found on the same plant. The seed is 1.5 mm long and rarely seen. Southern water-grass is native to the Coastal Plain states from North Carolina to Texas (Godfrey and Wooten 1981). The Florida distribution map shows that southern water-grass was found in lakes across the whole state with no apparent geographical pattern.

Biology

Southern water-grass flowers throughout the year in Florida (Dressler et al. 1987). Reproduction is primarily by seed and fragmentation. It grows primarily in standing and slow-flowing water and forms thick carpet-like mats. The plant can be found along the edges of lakes and ponds as well as occasionally in deeper water. It can sometimes impede recreational use of water bodies due to its tendency to form dense mats along lake shorelines. Southern water-grass is good cover for small fish and aquatic insects. Waterfowl feed on its leaves and seeds.

Florida data

Southern water-grass was identified in 87 lakes. The 10th and 90th percentiles for pH, alkalinity, total phosphorus, and total nitrogen values in these lakes show that 80% of the lakes with southern water-grass had levels between 5.3 and 8.4, 1.3 and 51.7 (mg/L as $CaCO_3$), 11 and 90 (µg/L), and 310 and 1380 (µg/L), respectively. The water chemistry averages of the 87 lakes were significantly higher than the averages of all 322 lakes only for color and magnesium values. This suggests that southern water-grass can occur in many of Florida's diverse aquatic habitats.

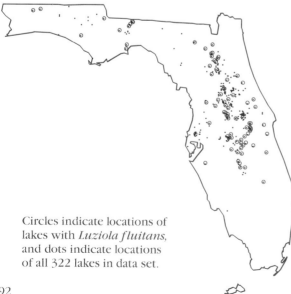

Circles indicate locations of lakes with *Luziola fluitans,* and dots indicate locations of all 322 lakes in data set.

Selected references from a total of 48 southern water-grass citations in the APIRS database:

Ager, L.A. 1970. Vegetational changes associated with water level stabilization in Lake Okeechobee, Florida. Proceedings of the Annual Conference of the Southeast Association of Game and Fish Commissioners.

Felley, J.D. 1992. Medium-low gradient streams of the Gulf Coastal Plain. Pp. 233–269 in Biodiversity of the southeastern United States—Aquatic communities, C.T. Hackney, editor. John Wiley & Sons, Inc., New York.

Finlayson, C.M., I.D. Cowie, and B.J. Bailey. 1990. Sediment seedbanks in grassland on the Magela Creek floodplain, Northern Australia. Aquatic Botany 38:163–176.

Hulon, M.W., E.J. Moyer, R.S. Butler, and V.P. Williams. 1992. Aquatic plant response to the 1987 drawdown/muck removal project on Lake Tohopekaliga, Florida. Aquatics 14(3):18–21.

Sutton, D.L. 1982. Growth of native aquatic species by integrated control (chemicals and fish) of weeds and re-establishment of natural aquatic plants. Annual Report, USDA/SEA/ARS, University of Florida, Gainesville.

Weldon, L.W., R.D. Blackburn, and D.S. Harrison. 1969. Common aquatic weeds. U.S. Department of Agriculture, Agricultural Handbook No. 352.

Luziola fluitans

Variables	Mean all lakes (n=322)	Number of lakes	Mean	10th percentile	Median	90th percentile
pH	6.7	87	6.7	5.3	6.6	8.4
Alkalinity (mg/L as CaCO$_3$)	23.9	87	18.9	1.3	6.0	51.7
Conductance (µS/cm @ 25°C)	149	87	145	28	100	288
Color (Pt-Co units)*	52	87	67	8	49	154
Total phosphorus (µg/L)	45	87	38	11	20	90
Total nitrogen (µg/L)	870	87	820	310	690	1380
Chlorophyll a (µg/L)	20	87	13	3	8	32
Secchi (m)	1.8	81	1.6	0.5	1.2	3.6
Calcium (mg/L)	17.6	87	20.2	2.8	9.6	52.9
Magnesium (mg/L)*	8.2	87	11.2	2.1	7.1	31.8
Sodium (mg/L)	13.2	86	14.9	2.7	8.4	20.2
Potassium (mg/L)	2.6	87	2.0	0.2	1.4	5.2
Sulfate (mg/L)	15.2	86	14.8	3.4	8.3	44.9
Chloride (mg/L)	23.4	87	27.1	4.3	15.5	36.0
Iron (mg/L)	0.2	80	0.3	0.0	0.2	0.7
Silicon (mg/L)	1.5	80	1.7	0.1	1.1	3.8

* Denotes a significant difference (p<0.05) from mean of all lakes.

Mayaca fluviatilis (bog moss)

Kerry Dressler

Kerry Dressler

Description and distribution

Bog moss is a perennial herb that grows in dense tufted mats along the shore or completely submersed. Lanceolate to linear leaves are 3–14 mm long and 0.5–1 mm wide and spirally arranged along the stem. In shallow water, the leaves are densely crowed together, but in deep water they are farther apart and tend to be thinner. The pink to whitish flowers, located in the leaf axils, are 4 mm long. The flowers consist of three sepals and three petals. The fruit is an oval capsule filled with 4 to 25 brown seeds.

Bog moss can be found primarily in the Coastal Plain states of the United States (Godfrey and Wooten 1981). The Florida distribution map shows that bog moss occurs from extreme northwestern to south-central Florida, but does not tend to be in extreme southern Florida. Lakes are progressively more alkaline and nutrient rich as one moves from northwestern to southern Florida (Canfield and Hoyer 1988). Thus the distribution of bog moss in Florida suggests that it may prefer acid, softwater, nutrient-poor lakes.

Biology

Bog moss reproduces primarily by seed germination, as well as by fragmentation. It grows in lakes, ponds, spring runs, marshes, and canals. Bog moss can form mats in shallow water near lake shore areas. It also can grow in water as deep as 2 m, flowering and fruiting under water.

Florida data

Bog moss was identified in 83 lakes. The 10th and 90th percentiles for pH, alkalinity, total phosphorus, and total nitrogen values in these lakes showed that 80% of the lakes with bog moss had pH, alkalinity, total phosphorus, and total nitrogen levels that were between 4.6 and 7.2, 0.2 and 26.2 (mg/L as $CaCO_3$), 6 and 27 (µg/L), and 160 and 1090 (µg/L), respectively. The 83 lakes collectively averaged significantly lower pH, alkalinity, specific conductance, total phosphorus,

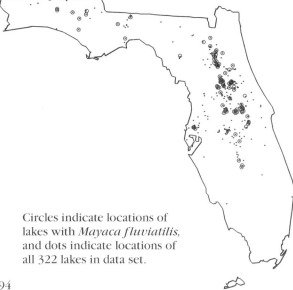

Circles indicate locations of lakes with *Mayaca fluviatilis*, and dots indicate locations of all 322 lakes in data set.

total nitrogen, and calcium values than all 322 lakes. The average Secchi disc depth value for bog moss was significantly higher than for all 322 lakes. Thus bog moss tends to occur in acid, softwater lakes with low nutrient concentrations.

Selected references from a total of 23 bog moss citations in the APIRS database:

Armora, J.P.R.G. 1991. Flora acuatica vascular (Monocotiledoneas) del Estrado de Chiapas. Master's Thesis, Universidad Nacional Autonoma de Mexico, Coyoacan.

Felley, J.D. 1992. Medium-low gradient streams of the Gulf coastal plain. Pp. 233–269 in Biodiversity of the southeastern United States—Aquatic communities, C.T. Hackney, editor, John Wiley & Sons, Inc., New York.

Fernald, M.L. 1902. Some little known plants from Florida and Georgia. Botanical Gazette 33:154–157.

Piresobrien, M.J. 1990. Report on a remote swampy rock savanna, at the mid Jari River Basin. Botanical Journal of the Linnean Society 108(1):21–34.

Thieret, J.W. 1975. The Mayacaceae in the southeastern United States. Journal of the Arnold Arboretum 56:248–255.

Mayaca fluviatilis

Variables	Mean all lakes (n=322)	Number of lakes	Mean	10th percentile	Median	90th percentile
pH*	6.7	83	5.9	4.6	5.8	7.2
Alkalinity (mg/L as $CaCO_3$)*	23.9	83	7.5	0.2	2.1	26.2
Conductance (μS/cm @ 25°C)*	149	83	102	23	70	189
Color (Pt-Co units)	52	83	38	3	14	103
Total phosphorus (μg/L)*	45	82	17	6	11	27
Total nitrogen (μg/L)*	870	82	550	160	410	1090
Chlorophyll a (μg/L)	20	83	7	1.0	3	11
Secchi (m)*	1.8	75	2.4	0.8	2.1	4.6
Calcium (mg/L)*	17.6	82	8.8	0.9	3.7	18.3
Magnesium (mg/L)	8.2	82	6.2	0.8	2.4	12.4
Sodium (mg/L)	13.2	79	10.4	2.6	7.0	16.7
Potassium (mg/L)	2.6	82	1.8	0.2	0.9	5.3
Sulfate (mg/L)	15.2	79	13.3	4.0	7.8	27.7
Chloride (mg/L)	23.4	83	18.6	4.2	12.1	27.5
Iron (mg/L)	0.2	60	0.1	0.0	0.10	0.4
Silicon (mg/L)	1.5	60	0.9	0.10	0.3	3.4

* Denotes a significant difference (p<0.05) from mean of all lakes.

Melaleuca quinquenervia (melaleuca)

David Sutton

Description and distribution

Melaleuca is an exotic tree that can reach heights of 20–25 m. It is a distinctive tree that has whitish to tan spongy, papery bark, which peels off in many layers. The evergreen leaves are 60–70 mm long and narrowly elliptical. The leaves are arranged spirally in five rows along the stem and are aromatic when crushed. The white bottlebrush-like spikes of the flowers are crowded at the tips of the branches. The fruit is a cylindrical to squarish woody capsule that holds many reddish brown wedge-shaped seeds. Melaleuca is a native of Australia and has become a nuisance invader species to south Florida (Godfrey and Wooten 1981). The Florida distribution map shows that melaleuca was found primarily from south-central to south Florida.

Biology

Melaleuca flowers from May to December in Florida (Dressler et al. 1987). It reproduces vegetatively through sprouting from the roots and base of the tree. Melaleuca can colonize a large variety of wet habitats. This tree has become a major problem in south Florida because it out competes native vegetation. The State of Florida is spending large amounts of money to manage melaleuca in the Everglades and throughout the state.

Florida data

Melaleuca was identified in 27 lakes. The 10th and 90th percentiles for pH, alkalinity, total phosphorus, and total nitrogen values in these lakes show that 80% of the lakes with melaleuca had levels between 5.3 and 8.4, 1.0 and 53.9 (mg/L as $CaCO_3$), 10 and 106 (μg/L), and 320 and 1810 (μg/L), respectively. These 27 lakes collectively averaged water chemistry values similar to all 322 lakes with one exception: Average magnesium values for lakes with melaleuca were significantly higher. Thus melaleuca can occur in lakes with a wide variety of water chemistry conditions.

David Sutton

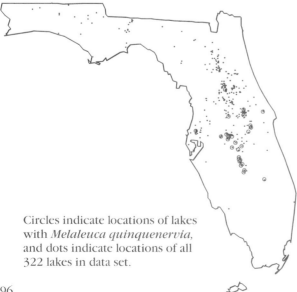

Circles indicate locations of lakes with *Melaleuca quinquenervia*, and dots indicate locations of all 322 lakes in data set.

Selected references from a total of 212 melaleuca citations in the APIRS database:

Anonymous. 1990. *Melaleuca* control in federal, state and local laws. Aquatics 12(3):22.

Balciunas, J.K. and D.W. Burrows. 1993. The rapid suppression of the growth of *Melaleuca quinquenervia* saplings in Australia by insects. Journal of Aquatic Plant Management 31:265-270.

Bodle, M. 1994. Biocontrol and *Melaleuca*. Resource Management 6(1):13-15.

Bodle, M.J., A.P. Ferriter, and D.D. Thayer. 1994. The biology, distribution, and ecological consequences of *Melaleuca quinquenervia* in the Everglades. Pp. 341-355 in Everglades: The ecosystem and its restoration, S.M. Davis and J.C. Ogden, editors. St. Lucie Press, Delray Beach, Fla.

DeStefano, J.F. and R.F. Fisher. 1983. Invasion potential of *Melaleuca quinquenervia* in southern Florida, USA. Forest Ecology and Management 7:133-141.

Holiday, I. 1990. *Melaleuca*. Australian Plants 16(125):27-37.

Ladiges, P.Y., P.C. Foord, and R.J. Willis. 1981. Salinity and waterlogging tolerance of some populations of *Melaleuca ericifolia* Smith.

Australian Journal of Ecology 6(2):203-215.

Langeland, K. 1990. Controlling *Melaleuca*, trees from hell. Aquatics 12(3):10,12,14.

Laroche, F.B. and A.P. Ferriter. 1992. The rate of expansion of *Melaleuca* in south Florida. Journal of Aquatic Plant Management 30:62-65.

Myers, R.L. 1983. Site susceptibility to invasion by the exotic tree *Melaleuca quinquenervia* in southern Florida. Journal of Applied Ecology 20(2):645-658.

Small, B.E.J. 1981. Effects of plant spacing and season on growth of *Melaleuca alternifolia* and yield of tea tree oil. Australian Journal of Experimental Agriculture and Animal Husbandry 21(111):439-442.

Thayer, D.D. and M. Bodle. 1990. *Melaleuca quinquenervia* (cav.) S.T. Blake: The paperbark tree in Florida or an Aussie out of control. Aquatics 12(3):4-6,8-9.

Thayer, D., M. Bodle, K. Rutchey, et al. 1990. *Melaleuca* management plan for South Florida. Recommendations, *Melaleuca* Task Force, South Florida Water Management District, West Palm Beach. 50 pp.

Woodall, S.L. 1983. Establishment of *Melaleuca quinquenervia* seedlings in the pine-cypress ecotone of southwest Florida. Florida Scientist 46(2):65-72.

Melaleuca quinquenervia

Variables	Mean all lakes (n=322)	Number of lakes	Mean	10th percentile	Median	90th percentile
pH	6.7	27	6.8	5.3	6.7	8.4
Alkalinity (mg/L as CaCO$_3$)	23.9	27	19.1	1.0	4.6	53.9
Conductance (µS/cm @ 25°C)	149	27	174	59	117	304
Color (Pt-Co units)	52	27	50	4	23	145
Total phosphorus (µg/L)	45	27	35	10	22	106
Total nitrogen (µg/L)	870	27	800	320	680	1810
Chlorophyll a (µg/L)	20	27	13	2	6	37
Secchi (m)	1.8	23	1.7	0.4	1.1	4.3
Calcium (mg/L)	17.6	27	17.4	3.9	9.2	36.1
Magnesium (mg/L)*	8.2	27	13.0	2.6	9.3	29.4
Sodium (mg/L)	13.2	26	16.6	5.4	9.8	31.9
Potassium (mg/L)	2.6	27	3.4	1.0	2.6	7.0
Sulfate (mg/L)	15.2	26	21.9	9.0	19.4	43.3
Chloride (mg/L)	23.4	27	29.3	9.8	17.1	49.4
Iron (mg/L)	0.2	20	0.2	0.0	0.10	0.5
Silicon (mg/L)	1.5	20	1.7	0.3	1.1	3.9

* Denotes a significant difference ($p<0.05$) from mean of all lakes.

Micranthemum glomeratum (hemianthus)

Mark Hoyer

Description and distribution

Hemianthus is a small, mat-forming herb with opposite leaves, which are oblanceolate and variable in size. Many times, hemianthus produces thread-like yellow roots from the nodes that are up to 50 mm long. The minute flowers are white to pink, and the yellow-brown seeds are cylindrical. Hemianthus is endemic to the peninsula of Florida (Godfrey and Wooten 1981). The Florida distribution map shows that hemianthus was found infrequently in the state and primarily in central Florida.

Biology

Hemianthus reproduces through seed germination and vegetatively. This aquatic plant is found in and along the shores of lakes, ponds, swamps, and streams.

Florida data

Hemianthus was identified in 32 lakes. The 10th and 90th percentiles for pH, alkalinity, total phosphorus, and total nitrogen values in these lakes show that 80% of the lakes with hemianthus had levels between 6.3 and 8.6, 2.8 and 55.2 (mg/L as $CaCO_3$), 10 and 152 (µg/L), and 410 and 1810 (µg/L), respectively. These 32 lakes also collectively had significantly higher specific conductance, calcium, magnesium, potassium and sulfate levels than the average values for all 322 lakes. Thus there is slight evidence that hemianthus tends to occur in hardwater lakes.

Circles indicate locations of lakes with *Micranthemum glomeratum*, and dots indicate locations of all 322 lakes in data set.

Selected references from a total of 17 hemianthus citations in the APIRS database:

Butler, R.S., E.J. Moyer, M.W. Hulon, and V.P. Williams. 1992. Littoral zone invertebrate communities as affected by a habitat restoration project on Lake Tohopekaliga. Journal of Freshwater Ecology 7(3):317-328.

Davis, A.F. 1993. Rare wetland plants and their habitats in Pennsylvania. Pp. 254-262 in Wetland plants: Diversity, function, and importance—a symposium, Vol. 144, Proceedings of the Academy of Natural Sciences of Philadelphia.

Ferren, W.R. Jr. and A.E. Schuyler. 1980. Intertidal vascular plants of river systems near Philadelphia. Proceedings of the Academy of Natural Sciences of Philadelphia 132:86-120.

Hoyer, M.V. and D.E. Canfield. 1986. Surface area of aquatic macrophytes. Aquatics 8(2):26-27.

Hulon, M.W., E.J. Moyer, R.S. Butler, and V.P. Williams. 1992. Aquatic plant response to the 1987 drawdown/muck removal project on Lake Tohopekaliga, Florida. Aquatics 14(3):18-21.

Schuyler, A.E., S.B. Andersen, and V.J. Kolaga. 1993. Plant zonation changes in the tidal portion of the Delaware River. Pp. 263-266 in Wetland plants: Diversity, function, and importance—a symposium, Vol. 144, Proceedings of the Academy of Natural Sciences of Philadelphia.

Walstad, D. 1994. Soil substrate experiment. Aquatic Gardener 7(5):171-183.

Micranthemum glomeratum

Variables	Mean all lakes (n=322)	Number of lakes	Mean	10th percentile	Median	90th percentile
pH	6.7	32	7.4	6.3	7.4	8.6
Alkalinity (mg/L as $CaCO_3$)	23.9	32	29.5	2.8	26.5	55.2
Conductance (µS/cm @ 25°C)*	149	32	249	75	179	762
Color (Pt-Co units)	52	32	60	4	53	132
Total phosphorus (µg/L)	45	32	80	10	39	152
Total nitrogen (µg/L)	866	32	923	406	693	1813
Chlorophyll a (µg/L)	20	32	21	2	12	58
Secchi (m)	1.8	30	1.6	0.4	0.8	4.9
Calcium (mg/L)*	17.6	32	34.0	8.2	22.8	96.2
Magnesium (mg/L)*	8.2	32	19.2	3.7	10.8	54.0
Sodium (mg/L)	13.2	31	26.9	6.2	9.6	116.6
Potassium (mg/L)*	2.6	32	4.0	1.0	3.1	8.0
Sulfate (mg/L)*	15.2	31	28.4	6.6	27.0	64.5
Chloride (mg/L)	23.4	32	47.5	11.8	16.1	207.9
Iron (mg/L)	0.2	28	0.2	0.0	0.2	0.5
Silicon (mg/L)	1.5	28	2.0	0.1	1.6	4.0

* Denotes a significant difference ($p<0.05$) from mean of all lakes.

Micranthemum umbrosum (baby-tears)

Description and distribution

Baby-tears is a low, extensively branched, and usually matted herb, commonly forming dense circular heads a few meters in diameter. Leaves are opposite, orbicular, 4–9 mm broad, up to 15 mm long, rarely appearing in whorls of three. The flowers are minute (scarcely perceptible to the unaided eye) and short stalked; the stalks do not have bracts. Hair-like roots are produced at the nodes of submersed plants. The capsule is about 1 mm long. The brownish yellow seeds are cylindrical and ribbed longitudinally, with fine transverse lines between the ribs. Baby-tears commonly occurs in the Coastal Plain from Virginia to Florida and west to Texas (Godfrey and Wooten 1981). The Florida distribution map shows that the few lakes with baby-tears were found throughout the state, but primarily in central and south Florida.

Biology

Baby-tears are sometimes confused with hydrilla because of the head-like growth form. Baby-tears, however, is not prone to matting in large areas, so it rarely impairs navigational or recreational activities in aquatic systems. The matted heads are good refuge and habitat for invertebrates and fish populations.

Florida data

Baby-tears was identified in 38 lakes. The 10th and 90th percentiles for pH, alkalinity, total phosphorus, and total nitrogen values in these lakes show that 80% of the lakes with baby-tears had levels between 5.4 and 8.2, 1.9 and 58.6 (mg/L as $CaCO_3$), 10 and 112 (µg/L), and 320 and 1100 (µg/L), respectively. The water chemistry averages of the 38 lakes with baby-tears showed no significant differences from those for all 322 lakes. The 38 lakes also had water chemistry ranges similar to those of all 322 lakes. This suggests that baby tears can occur in a wide range of aquatic systems.

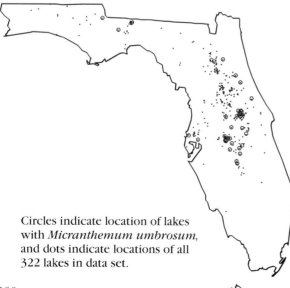

Circles indicate location of lakes with *Micranthemum umbrosum*, and dots indicate locations of all 322 lakes in data set.

Micranthemum umbrosum: **See references for** *Micranthemum glomeratum.*

Micranthemum umbrosum

Variables	Mean all lakes (n=322)	Number of lakes	Mean	10th percentile	Median	90th percentile
pH	6.7	38	7.0	5.4	7.0	8.2
Alkalinity (mg/L as $CaCO_3$)	23.9	38	22.3	1.9	14.0	58.6
Conductance (µS/cm @ 25°C)	149	38	157	54	122	285
Color (Pt-Co units)	52	38	48	6	25	135
Total phosphorus (µg/L)	45	38	53	10	21	112
Total nitrogen (µg/L)	870	38	690	320	630	1100
Chlorophyll a (µg/L)	20	38	13	3	9	21
Secchi (m)	1.8	31	1.6	0.5	1.1	3.2
Calcium (mg/L)	17.6	37	16.3	3.0	10.3	39.5
Magnesium (mg/L)	8.2	37	8.8	1.4	6.3	24.0
Sodium (mg/L)	13.2	33	13.6	5.0	8.8	24.5
Potassium (mg/L)	2.6	37	3.5	0.6	2.5	9.2
Sulfate (mg/L)	15.2	33	20.4	4.3	16.3	47.0
Chloride (mg/L)	23.4	38	22.6	8.7	15.4	36.8
Iron (mg/L)	0.2	26	0.2	0.0	0.1	0.7
Silicon (mg/L)	1.5	26	1.5	0.10	0.8	3.3

Mikania scandens (climbing hempvine)

Kerry Dressler

Kerry Dressler

Description and distribution

Climbing hempvine is a sprawling, herbaceous vine, commonly forming mats over herbs, shrubs, or small trees. The triangular to heart-shaped leaves are opposite, stalked, and palmately veined with the bases of the blades notched. The leaves are 25–100 mm long and about as wide as they are long. The inflorescence is a head on a stalk that is longer than the leaves. The white, pink, or bluish flowers occur in dense clusters and are elongated-bell shaped. The fruit is a nutlet surrounded by cottony hairs, which is showier than the flowers. Climbing hempvine is common from Maine to southern Ontario, Michigan, Illinois, Missouri, and southward to Florida, southeast Oklahoma, and southeastern Texas (Godfrey and Wooten 1981). The Florida distribution map shows that climbing hempvine was found in lakes scattered throughout the state, but primarily in central and south Florida. Lakes are progressively more alkaline and nutrient rich as one moves from northwestern to southern Florida (Canfield and Hoyer 1988). Thus the distribution of climbing hempvine in Florida suggests that it may tend to occur in alkaline, hardwater, nutrient-rich lakes.

Biology

Climbing hempvine flowers throughout the year in Florida (Dressler et al. 1987). It reproduces readily vegetatively and by seed germination. It usually is found in marshy or shrubby shoreline thickets, wetlands, and borders of swamps and lakes, often growing from the shoreline toward the open water. Climbing hempvine seldom grows extensively enough to impair navigational or recreational uses of aquatic systems. The seeds are used to some extent by bird populations. The plants themselves are also used as nesting material and habitat for several species of birds.

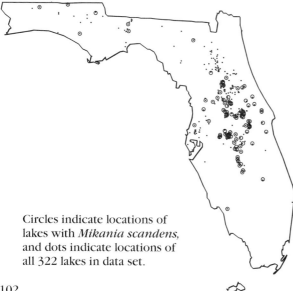

Circles indicate locations of lakes with *Mikania scandens,* and dots indicate locations of all 322 lakes in data set.

Florida data

Climbing hempvine was identified in 98 lakes. The 10th and 90th percentiles for pH, alkalinity, total phosphorus, and total nitrogen values in these lakes show that 80% of the lakes with climbing hempvine had levels between 5.8 and 8.7, 2.4 and 100.3 (mg/L as $CaCO_3$), 11 and 114 (µg/L), and 330 and 1980 (µg/L), respectively. The 98 lakes collectively averaged significantly higher pH, alkalinity, specific conductance, calcium, and magnesium values than all 322 lakes. Thus while climbing hempvine can occur in a range of lake types, it tends to occur in alkaline, hardwater lakes.

Selected references from a total of 45 climbing hempvine citations in the APIRS database:

Anderson, R.R., R.G. Brown, and R.D. Rappleye. 1968. Water quality and plant distribution along the upper Patuxent River, Maryland. Chesapeake Science 9(3):145-156.

Banerjee, A. and S. Matai. 1990. Composition of Indian aquatic plants in relation to utilization as animal forage. Journal of Aquatic Plant Management 28:69-73.

Hestand, R.S. and C.C. Carter. 1974. The effects of winter drawdown on aquatic vegetation in a shallow water reservoir. Hyacinth Control Journal 12:9-12.

Latham, P.J., L.G. Pearlstine, and W.M. Kitchens. 1994. Species association changes across a gradient of freshwater, oligohaline, and mesohaline tidal marshes along the lower Savannah River. Wetlands 14(3):174-183.

Moon, M., M.R. Rattray, F.E. Putz, and G. Bowes. 1993. Acclimatization to flooding of the herbaceous vine *Mikania scandens*. Functional Ecology 7:610-615.

Robinson, B.L. 1934. *Mikania scandens* and its near relatives. Contributions to the Grey Herbarium 104:55-71.

White, D.A. 1993. Vascular plant community development on mudflats in the Mississippi River Delta, Louisiana, USA. Aquatic Botany 45:171-194.

Mikania scandens

Variables	Mean all lakes (n=322)	Number of lakes	Mean	10th percentile	Median	90th percentile
pH*	6.7	98	7.3	5.8	7.4	8.7
Alkalinity (mg/L as $CaCO_3$)*	23.9	98	36.2	2.4	24.9	100.3
Conductance (µS/cm @ 25°C)*	149	98	204	58	131	430
Color (Pt-Co units)	52	98	60	6	35	152
Total phosphorus (µg/L)	45	98	55	11	25	114
Total nitrogen (µg/L)	870	98	1050	330	840	1980
Chlorophyll a (µg/L)	20	98	25	2	10	73
Secchi (m)	1.8	87	1.5	0.4	1.0	3.4
Calcium (mg/L)*	17.6	98	30.0	4.6	19.1	86.0
Magnesium (mg/L)*	8.2	98	14.2	2.9	9.6	35.6
Sodium (mg/L)	13.2	94	19.0	4.4	9.4	45.7
Potassium (mg/L)	2.6	98	3.3	0.3	2.4	8.8
Sulfate (mg/L)	15.2	94	18.1	5.1	12.3	42.3
Chloride (mg/L)	23.4	98	33.8	8.3	17.4	73.4
Iron (mg/L)	0.2	81	0.2	0.0	0.10	0.4
Silicon (mg/L)	1.5	81	2.0	0.1	1.1	4.4

* Denotes a significant difference (p<0.05) from mean of all lakes.

Myrica cerifera (wax myrtle)

Mark Hoyer

Mark Hoyer

Description and distribution

Wax myrtle is an evergreen shrub or small tree that commonly has several trunks originating from the base. The yellowish green leaves are alternate, 50–100 mm long, 10–25 mm wide, oblanceolate, tapering at the base, aromatic, and more or less twisted and contain irregularly serrated margins. The leaves also have dark glandular spots on the surface and are orange on the bottom. The flowers are in the form of dense catkins. Wax myrtle has hard fleshy fruit, about 3 mm in diameter and with a center stone, that are densely crowded on the branches, greenish in the summer, and heavily coated with a bluish-white wax in the fall. Wax myrtle is common in the Coastal Plain from New Jersey to south Florida, west to Texas, southeast Oklahoma, Arkansas, and Wisconsin (Godfrey and Wooten 1981). The Florida distribution map shows that wax myrtle was found primarily in central Florida.

Biology

Wax myrtle flowers from January to August in Florida (Dressler et al. 1987). It reproduces primarily by seed germination. Wax myrtle grows in several terrestrial and moist soil habitats. On lakes it is restricted to shoreline habitats, rarely interfering with navigational or recreational uses. Several species of birds use the berries as food and the plant for nesting habitat. The yellow-bellied sapsucker frequently drills small holes in the tree, then returns to feed on the sap. Boaters should be wary of wax myrtle growing on the shores of lakes because it is the favorite habitat for wasp and bee nests (speaking from personal experience).

Florida data

Wax myrtle was identified in 47 lakes. The 10th and 90th percentiles for pH, alkalinity, total phosphorus, and total nitrogen values in these lakes show that 80% of the lakes with wax myrtle had levels

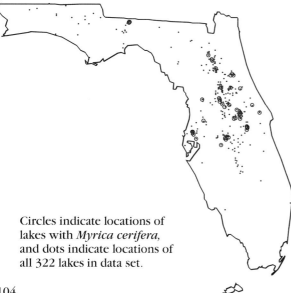

Circles indicate locations of lakes with *Myrica cerifera,* and dots indicate locations of all 322 lakes in data set.

between 5.4 and 9.1, 0.2 and 72.4 (mg/L as CaCO₃), 9 and 178 (µg/L), and 400 and 2220 (µg/L), respectively. These 47 lakes with wax myrtle had averages and ranges in water chemistry values similar to those for all 322 lakes. Thus wax myrtle can inhabit many different aquatic systems in Florida.

Selected references from a total of 44 wax myrtle citations in the APIRS database:

Brown, S. 1981. A comparison of the structure, primary productivity, and transpiration of cypress ecosystems in Florida. Ecological Monographs 51(4):403-427.

Buhrman, J. 1993. Round the year on Kissimmee Prairie Sanctuary. Palmetto 13(3):10-11.

Clewell, A.F. 1993. Do nurse crops facilitate bottomland forest establishment? Wetland Journal 5(2):19,20.

Johnson, F.A. and F. Montalbano. 1989. Southern reservoirs and lakes. Pp. 93-116 in Habitat management for migrating and wintering waterfowl in North America, L.M. Smith, R.L. Pederson, and R.M. Kaminski, editors. Texas Technology University Press, Lubbock.

Kalmbacher, R.S., J.E. Eger, and A.J. Rowland-Bamford. 1993. Response of southern wax myrtle *Myrica cerifera* to herbicides in Florida. Weed Technology 7(1):84-91.

Loftin, J.P. 1994. On the waterfront. Florida Water Magazine 3(2):14-24.

Reid, G.K. 1952. Some considerations and problems in the ecology of floating islands. Journal of Florida Academy of Science 15(1):63-66.

Titus, J.H. 1990. Microtopography and woody plant regeneration in a hardwood flood plain swamp in Florida. Bulletin of the Torrey Botanical Club 117(4):429-437.

Myrica cerifera

Variables	Mean all lakes (n=322)	Number of lakes	Mean	10th percentile	Median	90th percentile
pH	6.7	47	7.3	5.4	7.4	9.1
Alkalinity (mg/L as CaCO₃)	23.9	47	30.2	0.2	21.7	72.4
Conductance (µS/cm @ 25°C)	149	47	202	58	154	342
Color (Pt-Co units)	52	47	39	7	20	116
Total phosphorus (µg/L)	45	46	64	9	23	178
Total nitrogen (µg/L)	870	46	1010	400	750	2220
Chlorophyll a (µg/L)	20	47	30	2	12	80
Secchi (m)	1.8	18	1.5	0.5	1.2	3.7
Calcium (mg/L)	17.6	46	14.8	2.5	7.7	36.4
Magnesium (mg/L)	8.2	46	6.8	1.7	4.2	13.9
Sodium (mg/L)	13.2	44	18.2	6.5	10.9	21.3
Potassium (mg/L)	2.6	46	3.4	0.5	2.5	7.4
Sulfate (mg/L)	15.2	44	17.1	2.8	13.0	35.3
Chloride (mg/L)	23.4	46	33.8	12.0	20.4	37.0
Iron (mg/L)	0.2	15	0.10	0.0	0.10	0.3
Silicon (mg/L)	1.5	15	1.1	0.1	0.4	3.5

Myriophyllum aquaticum (parrot feather)

Alison Fox

Kerry Dressler

Description and distribution

Parrot feather is a perennial herb with moderately long stems. The stems are relatively stout, partially submersed but with considerable portions of leafy branches emersed. The grayish green leaves are whorled, stiffish, usually with 20 or more linear filiform divisions, appearing markedly feather-like. The flowers are borne in the leaf axils but are rarely seen. Parrot feather is native to South America and has been naturalized in the southeastern United States by the aquarium industry (Godfrey and Wooten 1981). The Florida distribution map shows that parrot feather was found primarily in central and south Florida. Lakes are progressively more alkaline and nutrient rich as one moves from northwestern to southern Florida (Canfield and Hoyer 1988). Thus the distribution of parrot feather in Florida suggests that it may tend to occur in alkaline, hardwater, nutrient-rich lakes.

Biology

Though rarely seen, parrot feather flowers from March through October in Florida (Dressler et al. 1987). It occurs in many aquatic habitats and commonly in dense, sometimes floating, mats. These mats are often thick enough to impair navigational and recreational activities. Parrot feather is also good refuge and habitat for some invertebrate and fish populations.

Florida data

Parrot feather was identified in 28 lakes. The 10th and 90th percentiles for pH, alkalinity, total phosphorus, and total nitrogen values in these lakes show that 80% of the lakes with parrot feather had levels between 6.8 and 8.8, 8.2 and 70.8 (mg/L as $CaCO_3$), 14 and 138 (μg/L), and 450 and 1580 (μg/L), respectively. The 28 lakes collectively averaged significantly higher pH, alkalinity, total phosphorus, calcium, and magnesium values than all 322 lakes. Thus while parrot feather can occur in a range of lake types, it tends to occur in alkaline, hardwater, nutrient-rich lakes.

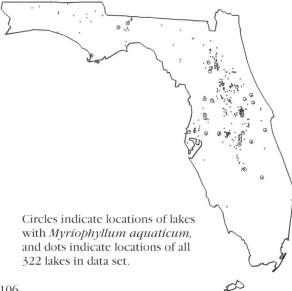

Circles indicate locations of lakes with *Myriophyllum aquaticum,* and dots indicate locations of all 322 lakes in data set.

Selected references from a total of 262 *Myriophyllum* spp. citations in the APIRS database:

Boon, J.J., W. Winding, R.G. Wetzel, and G.L. Godshalk. 1983. The analytical pyrolysis of particulate residues of decomposing *Myriophyllum heterophyllum*. Aquatic Botany 15(3):307–320.

England, W.H. and R.J. Tolbert. 1964. A seasonal study of the vegetative shoot apex of *Myriophyllum heterophyllum*. American Journal of Botany 51(4):349–353.

Kane, M.E. and L.S. Albert. 1989. Abscisic acid induction of aerial leaf development in *Myriophyllum* and *Proserpinaca* species cultured *in vitro*. Journal of Aquatic Plant Management 27:102–111.

Kane, M.E. and L.S. Albert. 1989. Comparative shoot and root regeneration from juvenile and adult aerial leaf explants of variable-leaf milfoil. Journal of Aquatic Plant Management 27:1–10.

Kane, M.E. and E.F. Gilman. 1991. *In vitro* propagation and bioassay systems for evaluating growth regulator effects on *Myriophyllum* species. Journal of Aquatic Plant Management 29:29–32.

Kimball, K.D. and A.L. Baker. 1983. Temporal and morphological factors related to mineral composition in *Myriophyllum heterophyllum* Michx. Aquatic Botany 16(2):189–205.

Magdych, W.P. 1979. The micro distribution of mayflies Ephemeroptera in *Myriophyllum* beds in Pennington Creek, Johnson County, Oklahoma, USA. Hydrobiologia 66(2):161–176.

Morin, J.O. 1986. Initial colonization of periphyton on natural and artificial apices of *Myriophyllum heterophyllum* Michx. Freshwater Biology 16(5):685–694.

Nelson, E.N. and R.W. Couch. 1985. History of the introduction and distribution of *Myriophyllum aquaticum* in North America. Pp. 19–26 in First International Symposium of the Watermilfoil and Related Haloragaceae Species, July 1985, Vancouver, B.C., Canada, L.W.J. Anderson, editor. Aquatic Plant Management Society, Vickburg, Miss.

Rehman, H., M. Mushtaque, G.M. Baloch, and M.A. Ghani. 1969. Preliminary observations on the biological control of water-milfoils (*Myriophyllum* spp. Haloragaceae). Technical Bulletin, Commonwealth Institute of Biological Control 11:165–171.

Sutton, D.L. 1985. Parrot-feather. Aquatics 7(4):6–7.

Sytsma, M.D. and L.W.J. Anderson. 1993. Nutrient limitation in *Myriophyllum aquaticum*. Journal of Freshwater Ecology 8(2):165–176.

Myriophyllum aquaticum

Variables	Mean all lakes (n=322)	Number of lakes	Mean	10th percentile	Median	90th percentile
pH*	6.7	28	7.5	6.8	7.5	8.8
Alkalinity (mg/L as CaCO$_3$)*	23.9	28	33.6	8.2	24.1	70.8
Conductance (µS/cm @ 25°C)	149	28	233	66	126	677
Color (Pt-Co units)	52	28	66	9	56	131
Total phosphorus (µg/L)*	45	28	82	14	36	138
Total nitrogen (µg/L)	870	28	900	450	840	1580
Chlorophyll a (µg/L)	20	28	19	3	10	62
Secchi (m)	1.8	26	1.2	0.5	0.8	3.1
Calcium (mg/L)*	17.6	28	40.2	8.3	25.3	98.0
Magnesium (mg/L)*	8.2	28	17.9	3.3	10.6	52.9
Sodium (mg/L)	13.2	27	26.9	5.5	8.8	100.3
Potassium (mg/L)	2.6	28	2.3	0.2	1.8	5.3
Sulfate (mg/L)	15.2	27	22.1	3.1	12.7	56.4
Chloride (mg/L)	23.4	28	47.2	8.9	15.5	177.8
Iron (mg/L)	0.2	26	0.3	0.0	0.2	0.7
Silicon (mg/L)	1.5	26	2.6	0.2	2.1	7.0

* Denotes a significant difference ($p<0.05$) from mean of all lakes.

Myriophyllum heterophyllum (variable-leaf milfoil)

Jesse Van Dyke

Jesse Van Dyke

Jesse Van Dyke

Description and distribution

Variable-leaf milfoil is a rooted plant, with elongated reddish stems that are occasionally much branched. It has two leaf forms, both in whorls of four to six leaves. The submersed leaves are flaccid, feather-like in appearance, 20–60 mm long, and 20–40 mm wide and have 8–18 paired linear capillary segments. The emersed leaves ascend upwards on a stem 100–150 mm above the water surface. These leaves are bright green, stiff, reflexed, entire or serrated, 10–30 mm long, and 2–6 mm wide. Sessile flowers 1–3 mm long consist of four reddish ovate petals and are in whorls of four to six. Variable-leaf milfoil is a native plant commonly found in southwestern Quebec and Ontario to North Dakota and generally southward to Florida (Godfrey and Wooten 1981). The Florida distribution map shows that variable-leaf milfoil was found in lakes throughout the state, but primarily in central and north Florida. Lakes are progressively more alkaline and nutrient rich as one moves from northwestern to southern Florida (Canfield and Hoyer 1988). Thus the distribution of variable-leaf milfoil in Florida suggests that it may tend to occur in acid, softwater, nutrient-poor lakes.

Biology

Plants in the genus *Myriophyllum* flower from March through October in Florida (Dressler et al. 1987). They reproduce readily by fragmentation and seed germination. They have a tremendous growth potential and given the correct conditions can completely dominate an aquatic system and drastically impair navigational and recreational uses. Variable-leaf milfoil is also sold as an aquarium plant. It is good refuge and habitat for invertebrate and fish populations. These benefits, however, can be quickly eliminated when it reaches excessive levels.

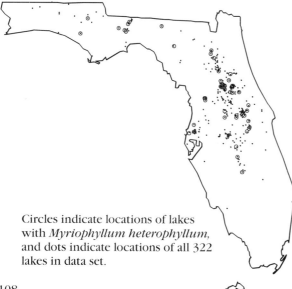

Circles indicate locations of lakes with *Myriophyllum heterophyllum,* and dots indicate locations of all 322 lakes in data set.

Florida data

Variable-leaf milfoil was identified in 51 lakes. The 10th and 90th percentiles for pH, alkalinity, total phosphorus, and total nitrogen values in these lakes show that 80% of the lakes with variable-leaf milfoil had levels between 4.7 and 7.5, 1.0 and 41.4 (mg/L as $CaCO_3$), 7 and 21 (µg/L), and 240 and 1320 (µg/L), respectively. The 51 lakes collectively averaged significantly lower pH, alkalinity, total phosphorus, and potassium values than all 322 lakes. Thus while variable-leaf milfoil can occur in a range of lake types, it tends to occur in acidic, softwater, nutrient-poor lakes.

Myriophyllum heterophyllum: See references for *Myriophyllum aquaticum*

Myriophyllum heterophyllum

Variables	Mean all lakes (n=322)	Number of lakes	Mean	10th percentile	Median	90th percentile
pH*	6.7	51	6.0	4.7	5.9	7.5
Alkalinity (mg/L as $CaCO_3$)*	23.9	51	9.7	1.0	2.3	41.4
Conductance (µS/cm @ 25°C)	149	51	112	27	57	204
Color (Pt-Co units)	52	51	45	6	23	150
Total phosphorus (µg/L)*	45	51	22	7	13	21
Total nitrogen (µg/L)	870	51	670	240	530	1320
Chlorophyll a (µg/L)	20	51	7	1.0	3	10
Secchi (m)	1.8	46	2.4	0.8	2.1	4.2
Calcium (mg/L)	17.6	51	11.0	0.7	4.5	22.4
Magnesium (mg/L)	8.2	51	7.1	0.7	2.1	23.1
Sodium (mg/L)	13.2	48	12.2	2.5	5.2	14.4
Potassium (mg/L)*	2.6	51	1.5	0.1	0.3	5.8
Sulfate (mg/L)	15.2	48	12.0	3.1	6.8	29.4
Chloride (mg/L)	23.4	51	22.3	4.1	9.3	28.1
Iron (mg/L)	0.2	31	0.2	0.0	0.1	0.7
Silicon (mg/L)	1.5	31	1.0	0.10	0.4	3.5

* Denotes a significant difference (p<0.05) from mean of all lakes.

Najas guadalupensis (southern naiad)

Alison Fox

Kerry Dressler

Description and distribution

Southern naiad is a submersed aquatic herb, with slender stems that are much branched. The deep green to greenish-purple leaves are 10–25 mm long, 0–1 mm wide, ribbon-like, narrow, and slightly broadened at the base. They usually occur opposite or arranged in a whorl of three. Minute spines occur around the margins. The fruit is a single seed surrounded by a membranous coat embraced by the leaf sheath. Southern naiad occurs in the Atlantic and Gulf Coast states west to California, Oregon, Mexico, Central America, and Wisconsin (Godfrey and Wooten 1981). The Florida distribution map shows that southern naiad was found in lakes throughout the state with no apparent geographical pattern.

Biology

Southern naiad flowers throughout the year in Florida (Dressler et al. 1987). It reproduces readily by fragmentation and seed germination. Its growth potential is great and before the introduction of hydrilla, which has replaced it in many aquatic systems, it was a major problem plant in Florida. The Florida distribution map shows that southern naiad occurs in many freshwater systems throughout Florida. Southern naiad is a major food for waterfowl in Florida, with all plant parts being consumed. It is also good refuge and habitat for invertebrates and fish populations.

Florida data

Southern naiad was identified in 112 lakes. The 10th and 90th percentiles for pH, alkalinity, total phosphorus, and total nitrogen values in these lakes show that 80% of the lakes with southern naiad had levels between 5.9 and 8.6, 2.3 and 94.0 (mg/L as $CaCO_3$), 10 and 85 (µg/L), and 370 and 1800 (µg/L), respectively. The 112 lakes collectively averaged significantly higher pH, alkalinity, calcium, and magnesium values than all 322 lakes. Thus while southern naiad can occur in a range of lake types, it tends to occur in alkaline, hardwater lakes.

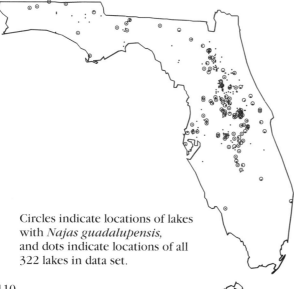

Circles indicate locations of lakes with *Najas guadalupensis,* and dots indicate locations of all 322 lakes in data set.

Selected references from a total of 409 southern naiad citations in the APIRS database:

Blackburn, R.D. and L.W. Weldon. 1964. Control of southern naiad in Florida drainage and irrigation channels. Weeds 12(4):295-298.

De La Vega, E.L., J.R. Cassani, and H. Allaire. 1993. Seasonal relationship between southern naiad and associated periphyton. Journal of Aquatic Plant Management 31:84-88.

Fernald, M.L. 1923. Notes on the distribution of *Najas* in northeastern America. Rhodora 25:105-109.

Haller, W.T. 1974. Photosynthetic characteristics of the submersed aquatic plants *Hydrilla*, southern naiad and *Vallisneria*. Ph.D. dissertation, University of Florida, Gainesville.

Lawson, P. 1991. Southern naiad—a neglected native. Aquatics 13(4):4,6.

Lowden, R.M. 1986. Taxonomy of the genus *Najas* L. (Najadaceae) in the neotropics. Aquatic Botany 24(2):147-184.

Wentz, W.A. and R.L. Stuckey. 1971. The changing distribution of the genus *Najas* (Najadaceae) in Ohio. Ohio Journal of Science 71(5):292-303.

Najas guadalupensis

Variables	Mean all lakes (n=322)	Number of lakes	Mean	10th percentile	Median	90th percentile
pH*	6.7	112	7.2	5.9	7.2	8.6
Alkalinity (mg/L as $CaCO_3$)*	23.9	112	31.4	2.3	20.9	94.0
Conductance (µS/cm @ 25°C)	149	112	191	50	117	421
Color (Pt-Co units)	52	112	49	7	30	110
Total phosphorus (µg/L)	45	111	44	10	23	85
Total nitrogen (µg/L)	870	111	920	370	710	1800
Chlorophyll a (µg/L)	20	112	18	2	8	41
Secchi (m)	1.8	98	1.6	0.5	1.2	3.5
Calcium (mg/L)*	17.6	112	28.0	4.1	16.0	80.1
Magnesium (mg/L)*	8.2	112	12.8	2.2	8.2	32.5
Sodium (mg/L)	13.2	109	18.2	3.9	8.9	45.1
Potassium (mg/L)	2.6	112	2.7	0.3	1.9	6.6
Sulfate (mg/L)	15.2	109	17.7	3.3	11.5	48.5
Chloride (mg/L)	23.4	111	32.9	7.3	16.0	69.9
Iron (mg/L)	0.2	94	0.2	0.0	0.1	0.5
Silicon (mg/L)	1.5	94	1.9	0.2	0.9	5.0

* Denotes a significant difference ($p < 0.05$) from mean of all lakes.

Nelumbo lutea (American lotus)

Kerry Dressler

Kerry Dressler

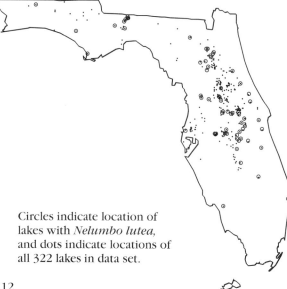

Kerry Dressler

Description and distribution

American lotus is a perennial, floating, leafed aquatic herb. Leaves and flowers arise from a long, cylindrical rhizome 10 mm in diameter. The bluish-green leaves are circular and 300–600 mm in diameter. Some of the leaves float on the water surface, while others extend above as much as 1 m. The floating leaves are flat, while the center of the emergent leaves become funnel shaped. The large, showy, pale yellow flowers are 250 mm across and have more than 20 petals. The cone- or shower-head-shaped fruit has multiple circular openings in which rest individual nutlike hard seeds, 10–12 mm in diameter. American lotus is found from New York and south Ontario to Minnesota and Iowa and with increasing frequency southward to south Florida and west to east Oklahoma and Texas (Godfrey and Wooten 1981). The Florida distribution map shows that American lotus is found throughout the state with no apparent geographical pattern.

Biology

American lotus flowers from May through August in Florida (Dressler et al. 1987). It is commonly found along lake and pond margins, marshes, and slow-flowing streams. American lotus provides good cover and habitat for many species of fish and aquatic invertebrates. The seeds are a food source for many species of wildlife. The dried seedheads are commonly used in flower arrangements and can be found in many craft and flower shops.

Florida data

American lotus was identified in 62 lakes. The 10th and 90th percentiles for pH, alkalinity, total phosphorus, and total nitrogen values in these lakes show that 80% of the lakes with American lotus had levels between 5.8 and 8.7, 2.0 and 88.7 (mg/L as CaCO$_3$), 10 and 111 (µg/L), and 330 and 1910 (µg/L), respectively. Most of the water chemistry averages of the 62

Circles indicate location of lakes with *Nelumbo lutea*, and dots indicate locations of all 322 lakes in data set.

lakes with American lotus showed no significant differences from those for all 322 lakes. Average magnesium and calcium values were significantly higher than those for all 322 lakes. This suggests that American lotus can occur in a wide range of aquatic systems in Florida.

Selected references from a total of 449 American lotus citations in the APIRS database:

Esau, K. and H. Kosaki. 1975. Laticifers in *Nelumbo nucifera* Gaertn.: Distribution and structure. Annals of Botany 39(162):713-719.

Francko, D.A., L. Delay, and S. Al-Hamdani. 1993. Effect of hexavalent chromium on photosynthetic rates and petiole growth in *Nelumbo lutea* seedlings. Journal of Aquatic Plant Management 31:29-33.

Gilbert, J. 1979. Minnesota's lotus lily. Minnesota Horticulture 107(7):217.

Grubaugh, J.W., R.V. Anderson, D.M. Day, K.S. Lubinski, and R.E. Sparks. 1986. Production and fate of organic material from *Sagittaria latifolia* and *Nelumbo lutea* on pool 19, Mississippi River. Journal of Freshwater Ecology 3(4):477-484.

Hall, T.F. and W.T. Penfound. 1944. The biology of the American lotus, *Nelumbo lutea* (Willd.) Pers. American Midland Naturalist 31:744-758.

Johnston, D.L., D.L. Sutton, V.V. Vandiver, and K.A. Langeland. 1983. Replacement of hydrilla by other aquatic plants in a pond with emphasis on growth of American lotus. Journal of Aquatic Plant Management 21:41-43 (notes).

Meyer, W.C. 1930. Dormancy and growth studies of the American lotus, *Nelumbo lutea*. Plant Physiology 5:225-237.

Nohara, S. and T. Tsuchiya. 1990. Effects of water level fluctuation on the growth of the *Nelumbo nucifera* Gaertn. in Lake Kasumigaura, Japan. Ecological Research 5:237-252.

Rodgers, J.A. 1981. The American lotus– *Nelumbo lutea* (Willd.) Pers. Aquatics 3(3):4,8.

Taylor, H.J. 1927. The history and distribution of yellow *Nelumbo*, water chinquapin, or American lotus. Proceedings of the Iowa Academy of Science 34:119-124.

Nelumbo lutea

Variables	Mean all lakes (n=322)	Number of lakes	Mean	10th percentile	Median	90th percentile
pH	6.7	62	7.2	5.8	7.1	8.7
Alkalinity (mg/L as $CaCO_3$)	23.9	62	27.9	2.0	17.7	88.7
Conductance (µS/cm @ 25°C)	149	62	168	33	112	321
Color (Pt-Co units)	52	62	55	10	50	113
Total phosphorus (µg/L)	45	62	61	10	33	111
Total nitrogen (µg/L)	866	62	969	327	765	1914
Chlorophyll a (µg/L)	20	62	25	2	9	73
Secchi (m)	1.8	57	1.5	0.5	0.8	3.9
Calcium (mg/L)*	17.6	62	26.5	2.9	18.9	76.0
Magnesium (mg/L)*	8.2	62	12.3	2.0	7.8	34.2
Sodium (mg/L)	13.2	58	16.0	2.7	8.8	33.7
Potassium (mg/L)	2.6	62	2.6	0.2	1.6	7.7
Sulfate (mg/L)	15.2	58	19.2	3.0	10.7	56.8
Chloride (mg/L)	23.4	61	28.2	4.4	15.2	46.7
Iron (mg/L)	0.2	53	0.3	0.0	0.2	0.6
Silicon (mg/L)	1.5	53	2.1	0.1	1.6	5.2

* Denotes a significant difference (p<0.05) from mean of all lakes.

Nitella spp. (stonewort)

Alison Fox

Kerry Dressler

Description and distribution

Stonewort is a multicellular green algae commonly confused with another large algae, muskgrass. The main stem is 20–1500 mm long depending on the species. Stonewort has a whorl at the node of six to eight branches, which are again branched and can be forked at the end. The antheridias (male sex organs) are found in the axils of the branches, and the oogonias (female sex organs) are located in a cluster on the sides of the branches below the antheridias. Stonewort is found throughout the United States (Tarver et al. 1986). The Florida distribution map shows that it was found in lakes across the whole state, with no apparent geographical pattern.

Biology

Stonewort reproduces primarily by sexual reproduction or fragmentation. It grows in a thick carpet along the bottom of many lakes or in head-like clumps. Some species grow in water as deep as 6 or 7 m. It provides good cover for fish and other aquatic life.

Florida data

Stonewort was identified in 64 lakes. The 10th and 90th percentiles for pH, alkalinity, total phosphorus, and total nitrogen values in these lakes show that 80% of the lakes with stonewort had levels between 5.9 and 8.2, 2.0 and 60.8 (mg/L as $CaCO_3$), 9 and 42 (μg/L), and 270 and 1280 (μg/L), respectively. The water chemistry averages of the 64 lakes with stonewort showed no significant differences from those for all 322 lakes. The 64 lakes also had water chemistry ranges similar to those for all 322 lakes. This suggests that stonewort can occur in a wide range of aquatic systems in Florida.

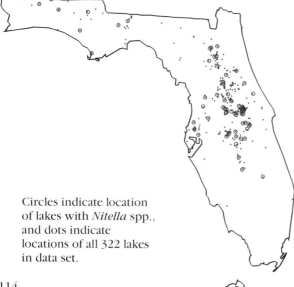

Circles indicate location of lakes with *Nitella* spp., and dots indicate locations of all 322 lakes in data set.

Selected references from a total of 291 stonewort citations in the APIRS database:

Bhatnagar, R. and S.K. Bhatnagar. 1978. Cytotaxonomic studies on *Nitella furcata* subsp. flagellifera f patula Gr. ex Allen and comparison with other taxa of *N. furcata* complex. Caryologia 31(4):457–462.

Buliot, E.W.J. 1927. Effects on mosquito larvae of a Queensland *Nitella*. Proceedings of the Royal Society of Queensland 38:59–61.

Burkhart, C.A. and R.G. Stross. 1990. An aquatic bioassay of herbicide bleaching in the charophyte sporeling, *Nitella furcata*. Journal of Aquatic Plant Management 28:50–51.

Jervis, C.K., B.C. Parker, and F.K. Daily. 1988. *Nitella megacarpa* T. F. A. (Characeae), the dominant macrophyte in Mountain Lake, Virginia. Castanea 53(4):290–294.

Kairesalo, T., G. St. Jonsson, C. Lindegaard, and P.M. Jonasson. 1992. Metabolism and community dynamics within *Nitella opaca* (Charophyceae) beds in Thingvallavatn. Oikos 64(1-2):241–256.

Kairesalo, T., G. St. Jonsson, K. Gunnarsson, and P.M. Jonasson. 1989. Macro- and microalgal production within a *Nitella opaca* bed in Lake Thingvallavatn, Iceland. Journal of Ecology 77(2):332–342.

Kashimura, T. 1956. Distribution of stoneworts in Lake Towada in its relation to the light factor. Ecological Review 14(2):149–153.

Starling, M.B., V.J. Chapman, and J.M.A. Brown. 1974. A contribution to the biology of *Nitella hookeri* A. Br. in the Rotorua Lakes, New Zealand. I. Inorganic nutritional requirements. Hydrobiologia 45(1):91–113.

Stross, R.G. 1979. Density and boundary regulations of the *Nitella* meadow in Lake George, New York. Aquatic Botany 6:285–300.

Stross, R.G., J. Huvane, and R.C. Sokol. 1988. Internal structure of deep-dwelling *Nitella* meadows. Aquatic Botany 29:329–345.

Nitella spp.

Variables	Mean all lakes (n=322)	Number of lakes	Mean	10th percentile	Median	90th percentile
pH	6.7	64	7.0	5.9	7.0	8.2
Alkalinity (mg/L as CaCO₃)	23.9	64	23.0	2.0	13.7	60.8
Conductance (µS/cm @ 25°C)	149	64	134	44	112	257
Color (Pt-Co units)	52	64	36	4	17	93
Total phosphorus (µg/L)	45	64	24	9	16	42
Total nitrogen (µg/L)	870	64	680	270	570	1280
Chlorophyll a (µg/L)	20	64	9	2	5	22
Secchi (m)	1.8	59	2.3	0.7	2.0	4.3
Calcium (mg/L)	17.6	64	21.1	4.0	14.5	53.5
Magnesium (mg/L)	8.2	64	10.6	2.1	7.0	28.1
Sodium (mg/L)	13.2	62	9.8	4.0	8.8	16.3
Potassium (mg/L)	2.6	64	2.8	0.3	1.9	7.4
Sulfate (mg/L)	15.2	62	16.9	3.9	11.5	45.9
Chloride (mg/L)	23.4	64	17.1	5.8	15.5	28.1
Iron (mg/L)	0.2	57	0.2	0.0	0.10	0.5
Silicon (mg/L)	1.5	57	1.1	0.1	0.5	3.6

Nuphar luteum (spatterdock)

Kerry Dressler

Kerry Dressler

Description and distribution

Spatterdock is a rooted, floating, leaved aquatic plant that has a large spongy rhizome. The leaves are 200–400 mm long and 250 mm wide and are ovate to heart shaped. They can be either floating, emergent, or submersed. The submersed leaves tend to be very thin, light green, and almost transparent. The sphere-shaped flowers are at the surface or above and have six to nine green sepals and yellow petals. The fruit is ovoid with a flat top and yellow to greenish. There are 30 or more seeds in the seed head. Spatterdock is native to the southeastern United States (Godfrey and Wooten 1981). The Florida distribution map shows that spatterdock was found in lakes across the state, with no apparent geographical pattern.

Biology

Spatterdock reproduces through seed germination or vegetatively through long-spreading rhizomes. It is commonly found along lake margins, but also in deeper open water. This species has nine subspecies, five of which occur in the southeastern United States (Godfrey and Wooten 1981). Spatterdock is an important plant because it is the host to the common bonnet worm, which is a preferred food of bluegill and redear sunfish. The large leaves provide good cover, and the thick large roots provide good spawning substrate for many species of fish.

Florida data

Spatterdock was identified in 262 lakes. The 10th and 90th percentiles for pH, alkalinity, total phosphorus, and total nitrogen values in these lakes show that 80% of the lakes with spatterdock had levels between 6.6 and 8.5, 1.0 and 61.8 (mg/L as $CaCO_3$), 10 and 80 (μg/L), and 300 and 1560 (μg/L), respectively. The water chemistry averages of the 262 lakes with spatterdock showed no significant differences from those for all 322 lakes. The 262 lakes also had water chemistry ranges similar to those for all 322 lakes. This suggests that spatterdock can occur in a wide range of aquatic systems.

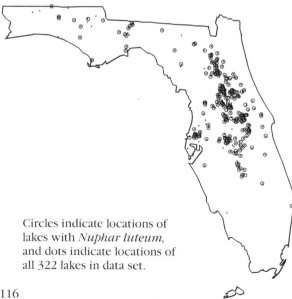

Circles indicate locations of lakes with *Nuphar luteum*, and dots indicate locations of all 322 lakes in data set.

Selected references from a total of 1030 spatterdock citations in the APIRS database:

Brock, T.C.M., M.J.H. De Lyon, E.M.J.M. van Laar, and E.M.M. van Loon. 1985. Field studies on the breakdown of *Nuphar lutea* (L.) Sm. (Nymphaeaceae), and comparison of three mathematical models for organic weight loss. Aquatic Botany 21:1-22.

Dacey, J.W.H. and M.J. Klug. 1982. Ventilation by floating leaves in *Nuphar*. American Journal of Botany 69(6):999-1003.

Delbecque, E.J.P. and R.E.M. Suykerbuyk. 1988. A comparison of the periphyton of *Nuphar lutea* and *Nymphaea alba*. Spatial and temporal changes in the occurrence of sessile microfauna. Archiv fuer Hydrobiologie 112(4):541-566.

Elakovich, S.D. and J.W. Wooten. 1991. Allelopathic potential of *Nuphar lutea* (L.) Sibth. & Sm. (Nymphaeaceae). Journal of Chemical Ecology 17(4):707-714.

Giesen, T.G. and G. van der Velde. 1983. Ultraviolet reflectance and absorption patterns in flowers of *Nymphaea alba* L., *Nymphaea candida* Presl. and *Nuphar lutea* (L.) Sm. (Nymphaeacea). Aquatic Botany 16(4):369-376.

Hanlon, C. and B. Haller. 1990. The impact of 2,4-D used in water hyacinth control programs on the growth of non-target spatterdock. Aquatics 12(1):14-16.

Mackey, A.P. 1977. Quantitative studies on the Chironomidae (Diptera) of the Rivers Thames and Kennet. III. The *Nuphar* zone. Archiv fuer Hydrobiologie 79(1):62-102.

Pilarski, J. 1974. Photosynthetic production of *Nuphar luteum*. Bulletin de l'Academie Polonaise des Sciences, Serie des Sciences Biologiques 21(9):609-615.

Smits, A.J.M., M.J.H. De Lyon, G. van der Velde, P.L.M. Steentjes, and J.G.M. Roelofs. 1988. Distribution of three Nymphaeid macrophytes (*Nymphaea alba* L., *Nuphar lutea* (L.) Sm. and *Nymphoides peltata* (Gmel.) O. Kuntze) in relation to alkalinity and uptake of inorganic carbon. Aquatic Botany 32:45-62.

Smits, A.J.M., P.H. van Avesaath, and G. van der Velde. 1990. Germination requirements and seed banks of some Nymphaeid macrophytes: *Nymphaea alba* L., *Nuphar lutea* (L.) Sm. and *Nymphoides peltata* (Gmel.) O. Kuntze. Freshwater Biology 24:315-326.

Twilley, R.R., M.M. Brinson, and G.J. Davis. 1977. Phosphorus absorption, translocation, and secretion in *Nuphar luteum*. Limnology and Oceanography 22:1022-1032.

Nuphar luteum

Variables	Mean all lakes (n=322)	Number of lakes	Mean	10th percentile	Median	90th percentile
pH	6.7	262	6.6	4.8	6.7	8.5
Alkalinity (mg/L as $CaCO_3$)	23.9	262	21.7	1.0	7.7	61.8
Conductance (µS/cm @ 25°C)	149	262	146	34	100	295
Color (Pt-Co units)	52	262	57	5	25	133
Total phosphorus (µg/L)	45	261	38	10	18	80
Total nitrogen (µg/L)	870	261	830	300	643	1560
Chlorophyll a (µg/L)	20	262	16	1	6	37
Secchi (m)	1.8	233	1.8	0.5	1.5	3.7
Calcium (mg/L)	17.6	262	16.9	1.1	8.5	47.2
Magnesium (mg/L)	8.2	262	8.5	0.8	4.0	21.5
Sodium (mg/L)	13.2	243	13.5	3.3	7.7	20.3
Potassium (mg/L)	2.6	262	2.6	0.2	1.4	6.7
Sulfate (mg/L)	15.2	243	15.1	3.5	9.7	37.3
Chloride (mg/L)	23.4	262	23.8	6.6	14.3	36.9
Iron (mg/L)	0.2	178	0.2	0.0	0.10	0.4
Silicon (mg/L)	1.5	178	1.4	0.1	0.5	3.7

Nymphaea mexicana (yellow water lily)

Alison Fox

Description and distribution

Yellow water lily is a rooted, floating, leaved aquatic plant. It has a short rhizome with many fibrous roots. The leaves are approximately circular in outline with a split to the petiole and are green on top and red underneath. The large showy yellow flowers are 60–100 mm across. The ovoid fruit is 30 mm long with gray to brown, oblong to oval seeds. The seeds are 5–6 mm long and 3 mm wide. Yellow water lily can be found from Florida west to Texas and Arizona and has been introduced into eastern North Carolina (Godfrey and Wooten 1981). The Florida distribution map shows that yellow water lily was primarily found in lakes from north-central to south-central Florida.

Biology

Yellow water lily flowers from April through December in Florida (Dressler et al. 1987). It reproduces readily vegetatively and by seed germination. It grows along the margins of lakes. The rhizomes are eaten by several species of rodents, and the foliage is occasionally food for deer.

Florida data

Yellow water lily was identified in 30 lakes. The 10th and 90th percentiles for pH, alkalinity, total phosphorus, and total nitrogen values in these lakes show that 80% of the lakes with yellow water lily had levels between 6.0 and 8.7, 2.3 and 100.3 (mg/L as $CaCO_3$), 12 and 126 (μg/L), and 390 and 1880 (μg/L), respectively. The 30 lakes collectively averaged significantly higher pH, alkalinity, calcium, and magnesium values than all 322 lakes. Thus yellow water lily tends to occur in alkaline, hardwater lakes.

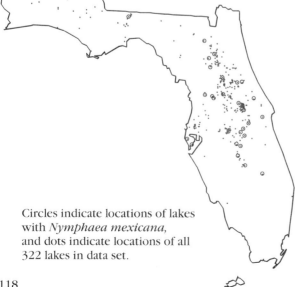

Circles indicate locations of lakes with *Nymphaea mexicana*, and dots indicate locations of all 322 lakes in data set.

Selected references from a total of 36 yellow water lily citations in the APIRS database:

Amaral, M.C.E., A.J.R. Silva, and A. Salatino. 1990. Alkanes of surface waxes from eight species of aquatic angiosperms. Aquatic Botany 36:281-286.

Austin, D.F. 1978. Exotic plants and their effects in southeastern Florida. Environmental Conservation 5(1):25-34.

Capperino, M.E. and E.L. Schneider. 1985. Floral biology of *Nymphaea mexicana* Zucc. (Nymphaeaceae). Aquatic Botany 23(1):83-93.

Conard, H.S. 1905. The waterlilies. A monograph of the genus *Nymphaea*. Carnegie Institution, Washington, D.C. 279 pp.

Conard, H.S. 1937. The banana floating heart (*Nymphoides aquaticum*). Proceedings of the Iowa Academy of Science 44:61-64.

Garcia-Murillo, P. 1993. *Nymphaea mexicana* Zuccarini in the Iberian Peninsula. Aquatic Botany 44:407-409.

Hu, S. 1968. The genus *Barclaya* (Nymphaeaceae). Dansk Botanical Archives 23:533-540.

Johnstone, I.M. 1982. Yellow waterlily (*Nymphaea mexicana*) in Lake Ohakuri, North Island, New Zealand. New Zealand Journal of Botany 20:387-389.

Mauve, A.A. 1968. The yellow water-lily of the Vaal River. Fauna and Flora 19.24.

Morton, J.F. 1976. Pestiferous spread of many ornamental and fruit species in south Florida. Proceedings of the Florida State Horticulture Society 89:348-353.

Nieuwland, J.A. 1916. Habits of waterlily seedlings. American Midland Naturalist 4(7):291-297.

Sutton, D.L. 1984. The yellow water-lily. Aquatics 6(4):4,9.

Weidlich, W.H. 1976. The organization of the vascular system in the stems of the Nymphaeaceae. I. *Nymphaea* subgenera *Castalia* and *Hydrocallis*. American Journal of Botany 63(5):499-509.

Nymphaea mexicana

Variables	Mean all lakes (n=322)	Number of lakes	Mean	10th percentile	Median	90th percentile
pH*	6.7	30	7.6	6.0	7.9	8.7
Alkalinity (mg/L as CaCO$_3$)*	23.9	30	43.1	2.3	37.1	100.3
Conductance (µS/cm @ 25°C)	149	30	288	50	174	841
Color (Pt-Co units)	52	30	49	5	37	112
Total phosphorus (µg/L)	45	30	51	12	36	126
Total nitrogen (µg/L)	870	30	980	390	890	1880
Chlorophyll a (µg/L)	20	30	22	3	11	66
Secchi (m)	1.8	26	1.3	0.4	0.8	2.8
Calcium (mg/L)*	17.6	30	48.9	4.2	35.3	97.5
Magnesium (mg/L)*	8.2	30	20.3	2.7	12.0	55.3
Sodium (mg/L)	13.2	30	31.3	5.2	9.6	120.9
Potassium (mg/L)	2.6	30	2.8	0.2	2.3	6.1
Sulfate (mg/L)	15.2	30	27.2	3.2	16.0	72.6
Chloride (mg/L)	23.4	30	57.6	8.4	15.7	219.3
Iron (mg/L)	0.2	26	0.2	0.0	0.2	0.3
Silicon (mg/L)	1.5	26	2.7	0.2	1.3	7.8

* Denotes a significant difference (p<0.05) from mean of all lakes.

Nymphaea odorata (fragrant water lily)

Kerry Dressler

Kerry Dressler

Description and distribution

Fragrant water lily is a rooted, emersed plant with creeping, often branched rhizomes that are 25–30 mm in diameter. The floating leaves are circular and split to the centrally attached stem. Usually lying flat on the water, the leaves are 150–300 mm in diameter, green on top and purplish on the bottom with numerous veins beneath. Arising from a long stalk is a sweet-scented, showy white flower. The flower consists of 25 or more petals that are ovate-lanceolate and from 70–100 mm long. A depressed globe-shaped fruit, 25–30 mm in diameter, ripens under water. The seed is oblong-oval, grayish olive to orange, 1.5–2.0 mm long and 1.0 mm wide. Fragrant water lily is common in the eastern half of the United States (Godfrey and Wooten 1981). The Florida distribution map shows that fragrant water lily was found in lakes across the whole state, with no apparent geographical pattern.

Biology

Fragrant water lily flowers from April to December in Florida (Dressler et al. 1987). It reproduces by seed germination and vegetative branching of the rhizomes. It grows to about 2.5 meters and in shallow lakes can cover the entire surface. When excessive levels are reached, it can impair navigational and recreational uses of aquatic systems. In shallow situations white-tailed deer and some rodent species use the leaves and stems for food; some waterfowl species also use it as a food source. The underside of the leaves provide habitat for some invertebrate species. Largemouth bass sometimes use the rhizome mats for a nest site, when other hard habitat is not available.

Florida data

Fragrant water lily was identified in 194 lakes. The 10th and 90th percentiles for pH, alkalinity, total phosphorus, and total nitrogen values in these lakes show that 80% of the lakes with fragrant water lily had levels between 4.8 and 8.5, 1.2 and

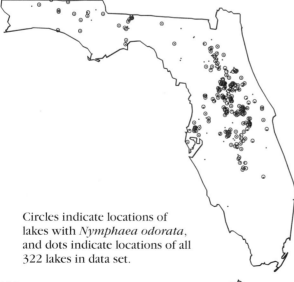

Circles indicate locations of lakes with *Nymphaea odorata*, and dots indicate locations of all 322 lakes in data set.

61.6 (mg/L as CaCO$_3$), 9 and 58 (µg/L), and 310 and 1520 (µg/L), respectively. The water chemistry averages of the 190 lakes with fragrant water lily showed no significant differences from those for all 322 lakes. The 194 lakes also had water chemistry ranges similar to those of all 322 lakes. This suggests that fragrant water lily can occur in a wide range of aquatic systems.

Selected references from a total of 286 fragrant water lily citations in the APIRS database:

Bowerman, L. and R.D. Goos. 1991. Physiological studies of two fungi isolated from *Nymphaea odorata*. Mycologia 83(5):624-632.

Conrad, H.S. 1902. Note on the embryo of *Nymphaea*. Science 15(373):316.

Durden, W. and R.D. Blackburn. 1972. Control of fragrant water-lily (*Nymphaea odorata*). Hyacinth Control Journal 10:30-32.

Else, M.J. and D.N. Riemer. 1984. Factors affecting germination of seeds of fragrant water-lily (*Nymphaea odorata*). Journal of Aquatic Plant Management 22:22-25.

Gaudet, J.J. 1960. Ontogeny of the foliar sclereids in *Nymphaea odorata*. American Journal of Botany 47:525-532.

Hanlon, C. 1990. Some characteristics of fragrant water-lily. Aquatics 12(2):4-5.

James, D.L. 1881. *Nymphaea odorata*. Botanical Gazette 6:266-267.

Riemer, D.N. and W.V. Walker. 1974. Control of fragrant water-lily and spatterdock with glyphosate. Hyacinth Control Journal 12:40-41.

Schneider, E.L. and T. Chaney. 1981. The floral biology of *Nymphaea odorata* (Nymphaeaceae). The Southwestern Naturalist 26(2):159-165.

Williams, G.R. 1970. Investigations in the white water-lilies (*Nymphaea*) of Michigan. Michigan Botanist 9:72-80.

Nymphaea odorata

Variables	Mean all lakes (n=322)	Number of lakes	Mean	10th percentile	Median	90th percentile
pH	6.7	194	6.7	4.8	6.7	8.5
Alkalinity (mg/L as CaCO$_3$)	23.9	194	21.8	1.2	9.1	61.6
Conductance (µS/cm @ 25°C)	149	194	157	28	106	310
Color (Pt-Co units)	52	194	46	5	24	112
Total phosphorus (µg/L)	45	193	29	9	15	58
Total nitrogen (µg/L)	870	193	800	310	630	1520
Chlorophyll a (µg/L)	20	194	14	1	5	32
Secchi (m)	1.8	166	2.0	0.6	1.6	3.9
Calcium (mg/L)	17.6	194	18.0	1.2	9.0	50.8
Magnesium (mg/L)	8.2	194	9.3	0.8	4.8	27.8
Sodium (mg/L)	13.2	186	14.8	2.7	8.3	21.2
Potassium (mg/L)	2.6	194	2.6	0.2	1.7	6.8
Sulfate (mg/L)	15.2	186	15.9	3.2	10.2	41.3
Chloride (mg/L)	23.4	193	27.0	4.4	15.8	38.3
Iron (mg/L)	0.2	137	0.2	0.0	0.10	0.4
Silicon (mg/L)	1.5	137	1.4	0.1	0.5	3.7

Nymphoides aquatica (banana lily)

Description and distribution

Banana lily is a perennial aquatic herb with thick rhizomes in the mud that, when examined closely, resemble bananas. Long slender stems arise from the rhizomes, each with one to several leaves. The floating leaves are green on the upper surface and purple beneath, kidney to heart shaped, and 20-150 mm in diameter. Flower clusters originate 10-80 mm below the water in association with modified rhizomes. The white flowers are small and about 15 mm in diameter and consist of five sepals and five petals. The fruit is a capsule containing many small seeds. Banana lily is common in the Coastal Plain from New Jersey to Florida and west to Texas (Godfrey and Wooten 1981). The Florida distribution map shows that banana lily occurs from extreme northwestern to south-central Florida.

Biology

Banana lily reproduces by seed formation and vegetatively from sprouting of rhizomes. It flowers from March through November in Florida (Dressler et al. 1987). It is not considered significant for wildlife use, but is a popular aquarium and aquascaping plant.

Florida data

Banana lily was identified in 144 lakes. The 10th and 90th percentiles for pH, alkalinity, total phosphorus, and total nitrogen values in these lakes show that 80% of the lakes with banana lily had levels between 4.6 and 7.6, 1.0 and 26.5 (mg/L as $CaCO_3$), 8 and 37 (µg/L), and 250 and 1240 (µg/L), respectively. The 144 lakes collectively averaged significantly lower pH, alkalinity, specific conductance, total phosphorus, calcium, and magnesium values than all 322 lakes. The average Secchi disc depth value for banana lily was significantly higher than for all 322 lakes. Thus banana lily tends to occur in acid, softwater lakes with low nutrient concentrations.

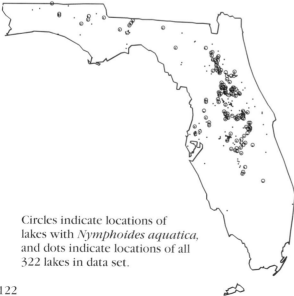

Circles indicate locations of lakes with *Nymphoides aquatica*, and dots indicate locations of all 322 lakes in data set.

Selected references from a total of 42 banana lily citations in the APIRS database:

Canfield, D.E., M.J. Maceina, L.M. Hodgson, and K.A. Langeland. 1983. Limnological features of some northwestern Florida lakes. Journal of Freshwater Ecology 2(1):67-79.

Conard, H.S. 1937. The banana floating heart (*Nymphoides aquaticum*). Proceedings of the Iowa Academy of Sciences 44:61-64.

Dress, W.J. 1954. The identity of the aquatic banana plant. Baileya 2:19-21.

Sutton, D.L. 1992. Characteristics of flowering aquatic plants. Aquatics 14(3):10-14.

Sutton, D.L. 1993. Characteristics of flowering aquatic plants. Aquatic Gardener 6(6):177-181.

Terry, W.S. and G.W. Tanner. 1984. Mineral concentration within freshwater marsh plant communities. Journal of Freshwater Ecology 2(5):509-518.

Terry, W.S. and G.W. Tanner. 1986. Nitrogen and phosphorus concentrations within freshwater marsh plant species. Journal of Freshwater Ecology 3(3):347-358.

Thompson, R.L. 1970. Florida sandhill crane nesting on the Loxahatchee National Wildlife Refuge. Auk 87:492-502.

Watts, W.A., B.C.S. Hansen, and E.C. Grimm. 1992. Camel Lake—a 40,000 year record of vegetational and forest history from northwest Florida. Ecology 73(3):1056-1066.

West, E. 1938. Banana water lilies. Proceedings of the Florida Academy of Science 11:86.

Nymphoides aquatica

Variables	Mean all lakes (n=322)	Number of lakes	Mean	10th percentile	Median	90th percentile
pH*	6.7	144	6.1	4.6	6.1	7.6
Alkalinity (mg/L as $CaCO_3$)*	23.9	144	9.5	1.0	2.5	26.5
Conductance (µS/cm @ 25°C)*	149	144	89	28	71	183
Color (Pt-Co units)	52	144	41	4	19	105
Total phosphorus (µg/L)*	45	143	19	8	13	37
Total nitrogen (µg/L)	870	143	660	250	530	1240
Chlorophyll a (µg/L)	20	144	7	1.0	4	17
Secchi (m)*	1.8	134	2.2	0.7	2.0	4.1
Calcium (mg/L)*	17.6	144	9.0	0.7	4.0	23.7
Magnesium (mg/L)	8.2	144	5.6	0.7	2.5	12.4
Sodium (mg/L)	13.2	137	7.7	2.6	7.0	13.8
Potassium (mg/L)	2.6	144	1.7	0.2	0.9	3.8
Sulfate (mg/L)	15.2	137	11.0	3.0	7.2	24.2
Chloride (mg/L)	23.4	144	14.4	4.3	12.5	25.8
Iron (mg/L)	0.2	94	0.2	0.0	0.10	0.4
Silicon (mg/L)	1.5	94	0.9	0.1	0.4	2.6

* Denotes a significant difference ($p<0.05$) from mean of all lakes.

Panicum hemitomon (maidencane)

Description and distribution

Maidencane is a perennial grass with extensive rhizomes that form large, almost pure stands. The grass has narrow stems that are usually 500–1000 mm tall. The leaf blades are 100–250 mm long and 7–15 mm wide, rough on the surface and smooth on the bottom; the leaf sheaths are smooth to hairy. The inflorescence is a narrow panicle 150–300 mm long consisting of ascending branches 20–100 mm in length. Spikelets 2.5 mm long, with a first glume about 1.2 mm long, are irregularly clustered along the branches. Maidencane is a common grass found in the Coastal Plain from New Jersey to Florida west to Texas (Godfrey and Wooten 1981). The Florida distribution map shows that maidencane was found in lakes across the state, with no apparent geographical pattern.

Biology

Maidencane flowers from March to November in Florida (Dressler et al. 1987). It reproduces by seed germination and vegetative branching of the rhizomes. It grows best in moist soil but can grow on dry soil in cultivated fields. Once maidencane is established on a shoreline habitat, it moves out toward open water and is capable of forming floating islands. The extensive stands and floating islands can impair navigational and recreational uses of some aquatic systems. In Florida maidencane is an extremely valuable plant for fish populations, as well as excellent refuge for invertebrates. Several aquatic and songbird species also use maidencane seeds as food.

Florida data

Maidencane was identified in 300 lakes. The 10th and 90th percentiles for pH, alkalinity, total phosphorus, and total nitrogen values in these lakes show that 80% of the lakes with maidencane had levels between 4.7 and 8.6, 0.8 and 67.0 (mg/L as $CaCO_3$), 9 and 82 (µg/L), and 280

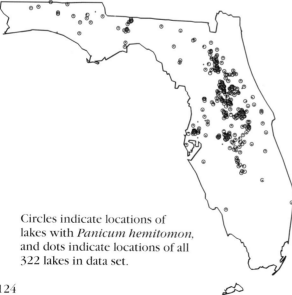

Circles indicate locations of lakes with *Panicum hemitomon*, and dots indicate locations of all 322 lakes in data set.

and 1710 (µg/L), respectively. The water chemistry averages of the 300 lakes with maidencane showed no significant differences from those of all 322 lakes. The 300 lakes also had water chemistry ranges similar to those in all 322 lakes. This suggests that maidencane can occur in a wide range of Florida's aquatic systems.

Selected references from a total of 195 maidencane citations in the APIRS database:

Callahan, J.L. and C.D. Morris. 1987. Survey of 13 Polk County, Florida lakes for mosquito (Diptera: Culicidae) and midge (Diptera: Chironomidae) production. Florida Entomologist 70(4):471-476.

Canfield, D.E., M.J. Maceina, L.M. Hodgson, and K.A. Langeland. 1983. Limnological features of some northwestern Florida lakes. Journal of Freshwater Ecology 2(1):67-79.

Colle, D.E., J.V. Shireman, W.T. Haller, et al. 1987. Influence of hydrilla on harvestable sport-fish populations, angler use, and angler expenditures at Orange Lake, Florida. North American Journal of Fisheries Management 7:410-417.

Hujik, B. 1994. Invasion of the tussocks. Aquatics 16(2):4,6,8.

Hulon, M.W., E.J. Moyer, R.S. Butler, and V.P. Williams. 1992. Aquatic plant response to the 1987 drawdown/muck removal project on Lake Tohopekaliga, Florida. Aquatics 14(3):18-21.

Schramm, H.L., K.J. Jirka, and M.V. Hoyer. 1987. Epiphytic macroinvertebrates on dominant macrophytes in two central Florida lakes. Journal of Freshwater Ecology 4(2):151-161.

Tarver, D.P. 1980. Water fluctuation and the aquatic flora of Lake Miccosukee. Journal of Aquatic Plant Management 18:19-23.

Panicum hemitomon

Variables	Mean all lakes (n=322)	Number of lakes	Mean	10th percentile	Median	90th percentile
pH	6.7	300	6.6	4.7	6.7	8.6
Alkalinity (mg/L as CaCO₃)	23.9	300	22.7	0.8	7.3	67.0
Conductance (µS/cm @ 25°C)	149	300	143	32	100	286
Color (Pt-Co units)	52	300	51	5	24	127
Total phosphorus (µg/L)	45	299	40	9	17	82
Total nitrogen (µg/L)	870	299	830	280	640	1710
Chlorophyll a (µg/L)	20	300	17	1	6	39
Secchi (m)	1.8	265	1.8	0.5	1.5	3.9
Calcium (mg/L)	17.6	299	16.9	0.9	8.0	46.0
Magnesium (mg/L)	8.2	299	8.2	0.8	3.7	21.3
Sodium (mg/L)	13.2	275	12.7	2.9	7.7	19.8
Potassium (mg/L)	2.6	299	2.5	0.2	1.6	6.8
Sulfate (mg/L)	15.2	275	14.8	3.3	9.7	34.7
Chloride (mg/L)	23.4	299	22.4	5.8	14.0	36.0
Iron (mg/L)	0.2	202	0.2	0.0	0.10	0.4
Silicon (mg/L)	1.5	202	1.4	0.1	0.6	3.7

Panicum repens (torpedograss)

Kerry Dressler

Alison Fox

Description and distribution

Torpedograss is a perennial with long creeping rhizomes that can form extensive colonies. The stems are rigid and usually 40–80 mm tall. The leaf blades are flat or folded, 2–7 mm wide, and surrounded basely by a sparsely pubescent sheath. The panical varies in size but usually is not large. It is mostly obpyramidal, 30–80 mm tall, loose but with the branches generally strongly ascending (sometimes diverging-ascending). This plant is often confused with maidencane, but torpedograss has very narrow leaves and spikelets that often have a purple tinge. It is native to Australia and is now common in the Gulf Coast states from Florida to Texas (Godfrey and Wooten 1981). The Florida distribution map shows that torpedograss was found in lakes throughout the state with no apparent geographical pattern.

Biology

Torpedograss flowers from May through October in Florida (Dressler et al. 1987). It reproduces readily vegetatively and by seed germination. The rapid vegetative reproduction from the shoreline habitats toward open water allows torpedograss to form extremely thick stands, which can impair navigational and recreational uses of some aquatic systems. Torpedograss is also difficult to control with today's technology, making it a significant problem in the state of Florida.

Florida data

Torpedograss was identified in 213 lakes. The 10th and 90th percentiles for pH, alkalinity, total phosphorus, and total nitrogen values in these lakes show that 80% of the lakes with torpedograss had levels between 5.3 and 8.7, 1.5 and 74.7 (mg/L as $CaCO_3$), 10 and 112 (µg/L), and 320 and 1930 (µg/L), respectively. The 213 lakes collectively averaged significantly higher pH, calcium, magnesium, and potassium values than those of all 322 lakes. Thus torpedograss can occur in a range of lake types, but slight evidence suggests it tends to occur in alkaline, hardwater lakes.

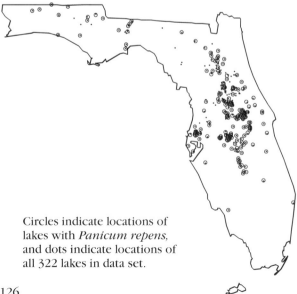

Circles indicate locations of lakes with *Panicum repens,* and dots indicate locations of all 322 lakes in data set.

Selected references from a total of 216 torpedograss citations in the APIRS database:

Bowman, W.D. 1991. Effect of nitrogen nutrition on photosynthesis and growth in *Panicum* species. Plant Cell Environment 14:295–301.

Chandrasena, J.P.N.R. and H.C.P. Peiris. 1989. Studies on the biology of *Panicum repens* L. II. Intraspecific competition and resource-allocation. Tropical Pest Management 35(3):316–320.

Chandrasena, J.P.N.R. 1990. Torpedograss (*Panicum repens* L.) control with lower rates of glyphosate. Tropical Pest Management 36(4):336–342.

Hilda, A. and S. Suryanarayanan. 1976. Cross-protection in the blast disease of *Panicum repens* L. Proceedings of the Indian Academy of Sciences 84B(6):215–225.

Peng, S.Y. and L.T. Twu. 1979. Studies on the regenerative capacity of rhizomes of torpedograss (*Panicum repens* Linn.). Part 2. Eradicative effects of ploughings and herbicides. Journal of the Agricultural Association of China. 105:67–82.

Smith, B.E., D.G. Shilling, and W.T. Haller. 1992. Torpedograss biology and control in a draw-down situation—1992. Aquatics 14(3):15–17.

Smith, B.E., D.G. Shilling, W.T. Haller, and G.E. MacDonald. 1993. Factors influencing the efficacy of glyphosate on torpedograss (*Panicum repens* L.). Journal of Aquatic Plant Management 31;199–202.

Tarver, D.P. 1979. Torpedograss (*Panicum repens* L.). Aquatics 1(2):5–6.

Wilcut, J.W., B. Truelove, D.E. Davis, and J.C. Williams. 1988. Temperature factors limiting the spread of cogongrass (*Imperata cylindrica*) and torpedograss (*Panicum repens*). Weed Science 36:49–55.

Wilcut, J.W., R.R. Dute, B. Truelove, and D.E. Davis. 1988. Factors limiting the distribution of cogongrass, *Imperata cylindrica*, and torpedograss, *Panicum repens*. Weed Science 36:577–582.

Panicum repens

Variables	Mean all lakes (n=322)	Number of lakes	Mean	10th percentile	Median	90th percentile
pH*	6.7	213	7.1	5.3	7.1	8.7
Alkalinity (mg/L as CaCO$_3$)	23.9	213	29.2	1.5	16.7	74.7
Conductance (µS/cm @ 25°C)	149	213	182	41	137	344
Color (Pt-Co units)	52	213	46	5	24	112
Total phosphorus (µg/L)	45	212	53	10	22	112
Total nitrogen (µg/L)	870	212	950	320	720	1930
Chlorophyll a (µg/L)	20	213	25	2	9	67
Secchi (m)	1.8	182	1.7	0.4	1.3	3.6
Calcium (mg/L)*	17.6	213	22.8	2.5	13.2	61.2
Magnesium (mg/L)*	8.2	213	11.0	1.7	6.7	29.6
Sodium (mg/L)	13.2	202	16.4	3.7	9.5	25.8
Potassium (mg/L)*	2.6	213	3.2	0.3	2.2	8.4
Sulfate (mg/L)	15.2	202	18.1	4.7	11.8	42.3
Chloride (mg/L)	23.4	213	29.3	6.9	17.4	42.7
Iron (mg/L)	0.2	168	0.2	0.0	0.10	0.4
Silicon (mg/L)	1.5	168	1.6	0.1	0.7	3.8

* Denotes a significant difference (p<0.05) from mean of all lakes.

Paspalidium geminatum (Egyptian paspalidium)

Jefi Schardt

Jefi Schardt

Description and distribution

Egyptian paspalidium is a perennial grass that forms rhizomes. The stems are slender or up to 10 mm wide basely and somewhat succulent; the lower segments are commonly bent over to the substrate, rooted, and elongated. The ligule is a ring of hairs. Leaf blades are 10–40 mm long, flat in the middle, usually with long-tapering tips. The inflorescence is unbranched and bearing alternately relatively short-ascending or appressed-ascending, flattish, spikelike, fertile branches. Spikelets alternate in two rows on one side of the sharply three-angled stalk whose apex is usually pointed and free beyond the seating of the uppermost spikelet. Egyptian paspalidium is common in Florida, Louisiana, Texas, Oklahoma, and other warmer areas of both hemispheres (Godfrey and Wooten 1981). The Florida distribution map shows that Egyptian paspalidium was found primarily in central and south Florida. Lakes are progressively more alkaline and nutrient rich as one moves from northwestern to southern Florida (Canfield and Hoyer 1988). Thus the distribution of Egyptian paspalidium in Florida suggests that it may tend to occur in alkaline, hardwater, nutrient-rich lakes.

Biology

Egyptian paspalidium reproduces by seed germination and vegetatively through rhizome production. It tends to occur in moist soil and shoreline habitats, often growing toward open water, and sometimes in floating islands. These stands can often be thick and extensive, impairing navigational and recreational uses of some aquatic systems.

Florida data

Egyptian paspalidium was identified in 108 lakes. The 10th and 90th percentiles for pH, alkalinity, total phosphorus, and total nitrogen values in these lakes show that 80% of the lakes with Egyptian paspalidium had levels between 5.8 and

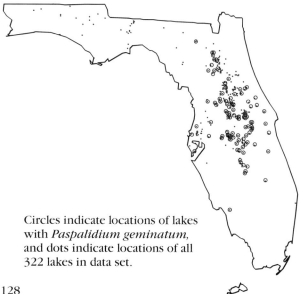

Circles indicate locations of lakes with *Paspalidium geminatum,* and dots indicate locations of all 322 lakes in data set.

8.8, 2.3 and 103.6 (mg/L as $CaCO_3$), 7 and 132 (µg/L), and 400 and 2030 (µg/L), respectively. These 108 lakes also collectively averaged significantly higher pH, alkalinity, specific conductance, total phosphorus, total nitrogen, calcium, magnesium, sodium, potassium, and chloride values than those of all 322 lakes. Average Secchi depth was also significantly less than in all 322 lakes. Thus while Egyptian paspalidium can occur in a range of lake types, it definitely tends to occur in alkaline, hardwater, nutrient-rich lakes.

Selected references from a total of 23 Egyptian paspalidium citations in the APIRS database:

Billore, D.K. and L.N. Vyas. 1981. Distribution and production of macrophytes in Pichhola Lake, Udaipur (India). International Journal of Ecology and Environmental Sciences 7:45-54.

Lock, J.M. 1973. The aquatic vegetation of Lake Gevige, Uganda. Phytocoenologia 1(2):250-262.

Misra, R. 1946. A study in the ecology of the low-lying lands. Indian Ecologist 1:27-47.

Petr, T. 1987. Fish, fisheries, aquatic macrophytes and water quality in inland waters. Water Quality Bulletin 12(3):103-106,128-129.

Rodgers, J.A. 1983. Identifying Florida's most common aquatic grasses. Aquatics 5(3):4,9.

Schardt, J. 1983. The 1982 aquatic plant survey. Aquatics 5(2):4,5,8,9.

Schramm, H.L. and K.J. Jirka. 1989. Epiphytic macroinvertebrates as a food resource for bluegill in Florida lakes. Transactions of the American Fisheries Society 118:416-426.

Schramm, H.L., K.J. Jirka, and M.V. Hoyer. 1987. Epiphytic macroinvertebrates on dominant macrophytes in two central Florida lakes. Journal of Freshwater Ecology 4(2):151-161.

Welsh, R.P.H. and P. Denny. 1978. The vegetation of Nyumba ya Mungu reservoir, Tanzania. Biological Journal of the Linnean Society 10:67-92.

Paspalidium geminatum

Variables	Mean all lakes (n=322)	Number of lakes	Mean	10th percentile	Median	90th percentile
pH*	6.7	108	7.4	5.8	7.4	8.8
Alkalinity (mg/L as $CaCO_3$)*	23.9	108	34.7	2.3	22.7	103.6
Conductance (µS/cm @ 25°C)*	149	108	211	63	133	459
Color (Pt-Co units)	52	108	61	7	40	132
Total phosphorus (µg/L)*	45	108	55	12	29	112
Total nitrogen (µg/L)*	870	108	1090	400	890	2030
Chlorophyll a (µg/L)	20	108	27	3	11	74
Secchi (m)*	1.8	98	1.3	0.4	1.0	2.9
Calcium (mg/L)*	17.6	108	31.5	4.1	20.1	86.0
Magnesium (mg/L)*	8.2	108	15.8	2.9	9.7	43.4
Sodium (mg/L)*	13.2	104	20.5	5.6	10.4	64.3
Potassium (mg/L)*	2.6	108	3.3	0.4	2.3	8.5
Sulfate (mg/L)	15.2	104	20.6	5.1	12.7	50.0
Chloride (mg/L)*	23.4	108	36.8	9.7	18.7	101.4
Iron (mg/L)	0.2	92	0.2	0.0	0.1	0.4
Silicon (mg/L)	1.5	92	2.1	0.2	1.3	5.1

* Denotes a significant difference (p<0.05) from mean of all lakes.

Paspalum distichum (knotgrass)

Mark Hoyer

Description and distribution

Knotgrass is a perennial herb with branches bending over at the base rooting at the nodes or creeping branches rooting at the node from which flowering branches arise to 500 mm tall. The leaves are relatively short, 600–800 mm long, and 3–8 mm wide, usually folded below, strongly tapered to a rolled tip. The inflorescence is a terminal pair of divergent to ascending seed heads (occasionally 1–3) 20–80 mm long, with flowers occurring only on the lower side. The spikelets are solitary, 2.5–30 mm long, in two rows on the flower stalk, and appressed almost parallel to it. Knotgrass is semicosmopolitan in warm temperate and tropical areas (Godfrey and Wooten 1981). The Florida distribution map shows that knotgrass was found primarily in central Florida.

Biology

Knotgrass flowers from May through November (Dressler et al. 1987). It commonly occurs in thick mats on shoreline habitats, growing toward open water. These mats sometimes impair navigational and recreational uses of some aquatic systems. Knotgrass has been useful as a soil binder, decreasing some erosion.

Florida data

Knotgrass was identified in 36 lakes. The 10th and 90th percentiles for pH, alkalinity, total phosphorus, and total nitrogen values in these lakes show that 80% of the lakes with knotgrass had levels between 5.7 and 8.9, 1.4 and 115.8 (mg/L as $CaCO_3$), 7 and 110 (µg/L), and 380 and 3230 (µg/L), respectively. The water chemistry averages of the 36 lakes with knotgrass showed no significant differences from those of all 322 lakes. The 36 lakes also had water chemistry ranges similar to those in all 322 lakes. This suggests that knotgrass can occur in a wide range of aquatic systems.

Circles indicate locations of lakes with *Paspalum distichum,* and dots indicate locations of all 322 lakes in data set.

Selected references from a total of 103 knotgrass citations in the APIRS database:

Hsiao, A.I. and W.Z. Huang. 1989. Effects of flooding on rooting and sprouting of isolated stem segments and on plant growth of *Paspalum distichum* L. Weed Research 29:335-344 (in English with French and German summaries).

Hsiao, A.I. and W.Z. Huang. 1989. Apical dominance in the shoot and its possible role in the survival of *Paspalum distichum* L. Weed Research 29:327-334.

Huang, W.Z. and A.I. Hsiao. 1987. Factors affecting seed dormancy and germination of *Paspalum distichum*. Weed Research 27(6):405-415.

Huang, W.Z., A.I. Hsiao, and L. Jordan. 1987. The effects of temperature, light and certain growth regulation substances on sprouting, rooting and growth of single-node rhizome and shoot segments of *Paspalum distichum* L. Weed Research 27(1):57-67.

Liu, S.H., A.I. Hsiao, and W.A. Quick. 1991. The influence of leaf blade, nutrients, water and light on the promotion of axillary bud growth of isolated single-node stem segments of *Paspalum distichum* L. Weed Research 31:385-394.

Manuel, J.S. and B.L. Mercado. 1977. Biology of *Paspalum distichum*. I. Pattern of growth and asexual reproduction. Philippine Agriculturalist 61:192-198.

Middleton, B.A., A.G. Van der Valk, D.H. Mason, et al. 1991. Vegetation dynamics and seed banks of a monsoonal wetland overgrown with *Paspalum distichum* L. in northern India. Aquatic Botany 40:239-259.

Middleton, B.A., A.G. Van der Valk, R.L. Williams, et al. 1992. Litter decomposition in an Indian monsoonal wetland overgrown with *Paspalum distichum*. Wetlands 12(1):37-44.

Rogers, K.H. and J. de Bruyn. 1988. Decomposition of *Paspalum distichum* L.: Methodology in seasonally inundated systems. Verhandlungen Internationale Vereinigung fuer Theoretische und Angewandte Limnologie 23(4):1945-1948.

Paspalum distichum

Variables	Mean all lakes (n=322)	Number of lakes	Mean	10th percentile	Median	90th percentile
pH	6.7	36	7.5	5.7	7.7	8.9
Alkalinity (mg/L as CaCO$_3$)	23.9	36	42.8	1.4	27.8	115.8
Conductance (µS/cm @ 25°C)	149	36	206	60	141	407
Color (Pt-Co units)	52	36	58	6	24	137
Total phosphorus (µg/L)	45	36	46	7	23	110
Total nitrogen (µg/L)	870	36	1310	380	1080	3230
Chlorophyll a (µg/L)	20	36	43	2	15	166
Secchi (m)	1.8	29	1.1	0.3	0.8	2.6
Calcium (mg/L)	17.6	36	20.1	3.3	13.8	41.5
Magnesium (mg/L)	8.2	36	8.3	1.2	6.1	16.5
Sodium (mg/L)	13.2	31	16.4	4.5	9.0	26.0
Potassium (mg/L)	2.6	36	3.7	0.3	2.2	10.0
Sulfate (mg/L)	15.2	31	16.2	1.0	10.0	34.2
Chloride (mg/L)	23.4	36	29.1	10.5	18.0	41.3
Iron (mg/L)	0.2	23	0.1	0.0	0.10	0.3
Silicon (mg/L)	1.5	23	2.2	0.2	1.0	7.9

Paspalum repens (water paspalum)

Alison Fox

Kerry Dressler

Description and distribution

Water paspalum is an annual plant, aquatic or subaquatic, with sprawling, often elongated spongy stems. The stems are often submersed with the upper portions sparsely branched and the inflorescence emersed. This species is distinguished from other species of *Paspalum* by the stiff, coarse hairs on the loose leaf sheaths. The leaf blades are flat, entire, 100-200 mm long, about 15-25 mm wide, and gradually tapering at both sides. The seed heads are 90-200 mm long, with 20 to 60 branches, and the branches are 25-100 mm long. The flowers are 1.5 mm long and are on the underside of the branches. Water paspalum is a native plant common from Florida to Texas (Godfrey and Wooten 1981). The Florida distribution map shows that water paspalum was found primarily in central and south Florida. Lakes are progressively more alkaline and nutrient rich as one moves from northwestern to southern Florida (Canfield and Hoyer 1988). Thus the distribution of water paspalum in Florida suggests that it may tend to occur in alkaline, hardwater, nutrient-rich lakes.

Biology

Water paspalum flowers from May through November in Florida (Dressler et al. 1987). It is described as a perennial, but mats are seldom found in the early spring. They apparently die back each fall after the plants flower, then reestablish from isolated mats or from seed germination during May and June. The mats can be thick and extensive, causing impairment of navigational and recreational uses of some aquatic systems. The seeds are used to some extent by water fowl and songbirds, and the mats are refuge and habitat for invertebrates and fish populations.

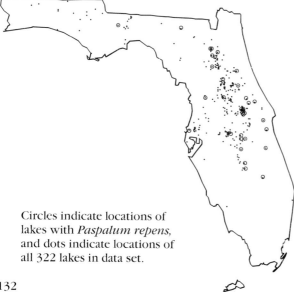

Circles indicate locations of lakes with *Paspalum repens*, and dots indicate locations of all 322 lakes in data set.

Florida data

Water paspalum was identified in 34 lakes. The 10th and 90th percentiles for pH, alkalinity, total phosphorus, and total nitrogen values in these lakes show that 80% of the lakes with water paspalum had levels between 6.4 and 8.6, 5.3 and 70.2 (mg/L as $CaCO_3$), 14 and 119 (µg/L), and 420 and 1310 (µg/L), respectively. These 34 lakes also collectively averaged significantly higher pH, alkalinity, specific conductance, total phosphorus, calcium, magnesium, sodium, sulfate and chloride values than all 322 lakes. Thus while water paspalum can occur in a range of lake types, it definitely tends to occur in alkaline, hardwater, nutrient-rich lakes.

Selected references from a total of 52 water paspalum citations in the APIRS database:

Bodle, M. 1986. Water paspalum. Aquatics 8(4):4,6.

Junk, W. 1970. Investigations on the ecology and production-biology of the "floating meadows" (Paspalo-Echinochloetum) on the middle Amazon. Part 1: The floating vegetation and its ecology. Amazoniana 2(4):449–495.

Junk, W.J. 1973. Investigations on the ecology and production-biology of the "floating meadows" (Paspalo-Echinochloetum) on the middle Amazon. Part 2: The aquatic fauna in the root zone of floating vegetation. Amazoniana 4:9–102.

Vegetti, A.C. 1987. Typological analysis of the inflorescence of Paspalum Poaceae. Kurtziana 19:155–160.

Paspalum repens

Variables	Mean all lakes (n=322)	Number of lakes	Mean	10th percentile	Median	90th percentile
pH*	6.7	34	7.5	6.4	7.6	8.6
Alkalinity (mg/L as $CaCO_3$)*	23.9	34	34.9	5.3	27.1	70.2
Conductance (µS/cm @ 25°C)*	149	34	283	64	174	762
Color (Pt-Co units)	52	34	72	5	56	121
Total phosphorus (µg/L)*	45	34	63	14	44	119
Total nitrogen (µg/L)	870	34	930	420	860	1310
Chlorophyll a (µg/L)	20	34	20	3	14	41
Secchi (m)	1.8	33	1.4	0.4	0.8	3.8
Calcium (mg/L)*	17.6	34	45.5	5.1	38.3	98.1
Magnesium (mg/L)*	8.2	34	20.8	3.0	10.8	53.7
Sodium (mg/L)*	13.2	34	32.3	5.3	10.0	108.5
Potassium (mg/L)	2.6	34	3.0	0.3	2.2	6.6
Sulfate (mg/L)*	15.2	34	29.6	4.5	18.4	67.9
Chloride (mg/L)*	23.4	34	57.9	8.3	15.6	201.9
Iron (mg/L)	0.2	33	0.2	0.0	0.2	0.5
Silicon (mg/L)	1.5	33	2.7	0.1	2.4	6.6

* Denotes a significant difference (p<0.05) from mean of all lakes.

Peltandra virginica (arrow arum)

Kerry Dressler

Kerry Dressler

Description and distribution

Arrow arum is a perennial herb with fibrous rootstocks and long stalked leaves. The leaves are light green, narrowly sagittate, with long acute basal lobes. They are usually 200–750 mm long with three conspicuous palmate primary veins. The inflorescence is an elongated, cylindrical spike containing many light-yellow unisexual flowers. The spathe enveloping the inflorescence is 100–180 mm long and is green with pale margins. It is convoluted at the base and then spreads outward with wavy margins. The fruit is a green or light-brown berry 6–15 mm long that contains many viable seeds. Arrow arum is a native plant common throughout the eastern United States (Godfrey and Wooten 1981). The Florida distribution map shows that arrow arum was found scattered throughout Florida but primarily in central Florida.

Biology

Arrow arum flowers from February through September in Florida (Dressler et al. 1987). It reproduces by seed germination and vegetatively. It grows primarily on shoreline habitats and rarely into any significantly large mats. The large berries, which contain numerous seeds, are consumed by several species of aquatic birds.

Florida data

Arrow arum was identified in 29 lakes. The 10th and 90th percentiles for pH, alkalinity, total phosphorus, and total nitrogen values in these lakes show that 80% of the lakes with arrow arum had levels between 5.0 and 8.8, 1.3 and 110.8 (mg/L as $CaCO_3$), 8 and 129 (µg/L), and 300 and 2010 (µg/L), respectively. These 29 lakes with arrow arum had water chemistry averages similar to those of all 322 lakes.

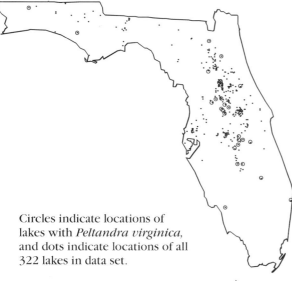

Circles indicate locations of lakes with *Peltandra virginica,* and dots indicate locations of all 322 lakes in data set.

Selected references from a total of 122 arrow arum citations in the APIRS database:

Boland, W. and C.J. Burk. 1992. Some effects of acid growing conditions on three emergent macrophytes: *Zizania aquatica, Leersia oryzoides* and *Peltandra virginica*. Environmental Pollution 76:211-217.

Chambers, R.M. and J.W. Fourqurean. 1991. Alternative criteria for assessing nutrient limitation of a wetland macrophyte (*Peltandra virginica* (L.) Kunth). Aquatic Botany 40:305-320.

Edwards, T.I. 1933. The germination and growth of *Peltandra virginica* in the absence of oxygen. Bulletin of the Torrey Botanical Club 60:573-581.

Frye, J.P., A.L. Mills, and W.E. Odum. 1994. Methane flux in *Peltandra virginica* (Araceae) wetlands: Comparison of field data with a mathematical model. American Journal of Botany 81(4):407-413.

Hart, H.T. 1928. Delayed germination in seeds of *Peltandra virginica* and *Celastrus scandens*. Publications of the Puget Sound Biological Station, University of Washington 6:255-261.

West, D. and D.F. Whigham. 1976. Seed germination of arrow arum (*Peltandra virginica* L.). Bartonia 44:44-49.

Whigham, D.F., R.L. Simpson, and M.A. Leck. 1979. The distribution of seeds, seedlings, and established plants of arrow arum (*Peltandra virginica* (L.) Kunth) in a freshwater tidal wetland. Bulletin of the Torrey Botanical Club 106(3):193-199.

Peltandra virginica

Variables	Mean all lakes (n=322)	Number of lakes	Mean	10th percentile	Median	90th percentile
pH	6.7	29	7.1	5.0	7.1	8.8
Alkalinity (mg/L as CaCO$_3$)	23.9	29	34.6	1.3	22.0	110.8
Conductance (µS/cm @ 25°C)	149	29	153	35	101	347
Color (Pt-Co units)	52	29	58	8	36	129
Total phosphorus (µg/L)	45	29	41	10	28	105
Total nitrogen (µg/L)	870	29	1050	300	920	2010
Chlorophyll a (µg/L)	20	29	23	2	11	62
Secchi (m)	1.8	27	1.3	0.4	0.9	2.8
Calcium (mg/L)	17.6	29	26.3	0.9	17.3	73.3
Magnesium (mg/L)	8.2	29	12.0	0.8	9.7	32.0
Sodium (mg/L)	13.2	29	12.5	3.4	7.9	20.4
Potassium (mg/L)	2.6	29	2.2	0.2	1.5	5.1
Sulfate (mg/L)	15.2	29	13.0	3.0	7.8	26.4
Chloride (mg/L)	23.4	29	22.2	6.0	14.4	37.0
Iron (mg/L)	0.2	24	0.2	0.10	0.2	0.5
Silicon (mg/L)	1.5	24	2.3	0.3	1.9	5.0

Pennisetum purpureum (napier grass)

Jesse Van Dyke

Jesse Van Dyke

Description and distribution

Napier grass is a robust perennial that commonly occurs in large clumps or clones. The stems are erect and stiff, growing tall to almost 4 m. The leaf blades have fine-toothed margins and are linear below, long tapering above, 20–40 mm at the widest point. They also have a whitish midrib above and are strongly keeled below. The densely flowered panicles are tawny, 150–300 mm long, and 10–30 mm wide with sparsely plumose bristles 10–12 mm long. The spikelets are 4–6 mm long, having 2 to 3 in a cluster with the middle spikelet usually larger than the others. Napier grass is native to Africa and now is naturalized in southern Florida (Godfrey and Wooten 1981). The Florida distribution map shows that napier grass was found primarily from south-central to south Florida.

Biology

Napier grass was originally introduced into Texas and southern Florida from Africa as a forage crop for cattle. It is more of a moist soil or terrestrial plant than an aquatic one. It does, however, grow well in shoreline habitats and wetland areas. The seeds are used by aquatic bird and songbird species. Some songbird species also use napier grass as nesting habitat.

Florida data

Napier grass was identified in only 15 lakes. The 10th and 90th percentiles for pH, alkalinity, total phosphorus, and total nitrogen values in these lakes show that 80% of the lakes with napier grass had levels between 6.0 and 8.7, 6.6 and 101.7 (mg/L as $CaCO_3$), 7 and 201 (µg/L), and 310 and 2160 (µg/L), respectively. These 15 lakes collectively averaged similar water chemistry values compared to those of all 322 lakes with the exception that average calcium and magnesium values for lakes with napier grass were significantly higher. Thus napier grass can occur in a wide variety of lake systems but may prefer hardwater lakes.

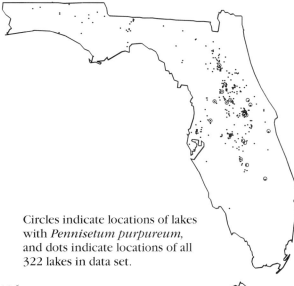

Circles indicate locations of lakes with *Pennisetum purpureum*, and dots indicate locations of all 322 lakes in data set.

Selected references from a total of 40 napier grass citations in the APIRS database:

Austin, D.F. 1978. Exotic plants and their effects in southeastern Florida. Environmental Conservation 5(1):25-34.

Chandler, S.F. and I.K. Vasil. 1984. Optimization of plant regeneration from term embryogenic callus cultures of *Pennisetum purpureum* Schum. (napier grass). Journal of Plant Physiology 117(2):147-156.

Ferraris, R. 1980. Effect of harvest interval, nitrogen rates and application times on *Pennisetum purpureum* grown as an agro-industrial crop. Field Crops Research 3:109-120.

Ferraris, R. 1978. The effect of photoperiod and temperature on the first crop and ratoon growth of *Pennisetum purpureum* Schum. Australian Journal of Agricultural Research 29:941-950.

Ferraris, R. and D.F. Sinclair. 1980. Factors affecting the growth of *Pennisetum purpureum* in the wet tropics. I. Short-term growth and regrowth. Australian Journal of Agricultural Research 31:899-913.

Lantz, P.S. 1993. Florida's most invasive species. Palmetto 13(3):6-7.

Schmitz, D.C. 1990. The invasion of exotic aquatic and wetland plants in Florida: History and efforts to prevent new introductions. Aquatics 12(2):6-13,24.

Pennisetum purpureum

Variables	Mean all lakes (n=322)	Number of lakes	Mean	10th percentile	Median	90th percentile
pH	6.7	15	7.8	6.0	8.2	8.7
Alkalinity (mg/L as CaCO$_3$)	23.9	15	50.7	5.6	44.8	101.7
Conductance (µS/cm @ 25°C)	149	15	315	80	244	818
Color (Pt-Co units)	52	15	49	3	47	97
Total phosphorus (µg/L)	45	15	57	7	31	201
Total nitrogen (µg/L)	870	15	1030	310	990	2160
Chlorophyll a (µg/L)	20	15	27	3	15	96
Secchi (m)	1.8	13	1.0	0.4	0.7	2.6
Calcium (mg/L)*	17.6	15	55.1	7.3	51.0	102.9
Magnesium (mg/L)*	8.2	15	26.5	3.4	17.0	59.0
Sodium (mg/L)	13.2	15	34.8	5.6	10.5	122.7
Potassium (mg/L)	2.6	15	3.2	0.6	2.5	6.6
Sulfate (mg/L)	15.2	15	27.8	7.8	20.3	63.8
Chloride (mg/L)	23.4	15	63.2	10.2	19.7	223.2
Iron (mg/L)	0.2	14	0.2	0.0	0.1	0.7
Silicon (mg/L)	1.5	14	3.0	0.2	2.6	8.3

* Denotes a significant difference (p<0.05) from mean of all lakes.

Phragmites australis (common reed)

Kerry Dressler

Kerry Dressler

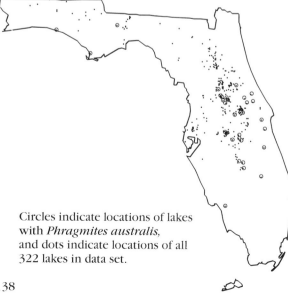

Circles indicate locations of lakes with *Phragmites australis,* and dots indicate locations of all 322 lakes in data set.

Description and distribution

Common reed is a coarse perennial plant with stout rhizomes deeply seated in the substrate. The stiff erect stems are 2–4.5 m tall with flat leaves throughout. The leaves gradually taper to long-attenuate tips and are smooth except for the lower portions; the ligule is a dense ring of short, stiff hairs. The panicle is 150–450 mm long, light brown to purplish and densely branched, with spikelets that are several-flowered. An important characteristic of common reed is the hairs along the flowering axis, which extend about 10 mm below each floret, giving the inflorescence a silky appearance. Common reed is semicosmopolitan (Godfrey and Wooten 1981). The Florida distribution map shows that common reed was found primarily in central and south Florida. Lakes are progressively more alkaline and nutrient rich as one moves from northwestern to southern Florida (Canfield and Hoyer 1988). Thus the distribution of common reed in Florida suggests that it may tend to occur in alkaline, hardwater, nutrient-rich lakes.

Biology

Common reed flowers year-round in Florida (Dressler et al. 1987). It is found in swamps and shoreline habitats in both fresh and brackish water. It is capable of establishing in deep water or in moist soil habitats. The stands can be thick and extensive, impairing navigational and recreational uses of some aquatic habitats. Many species of birds use it as a food source and cover. It has several commercial uses, including reed pulp for making wood products such as printing paper, cardboard, and compressed fiberboard; fishing poles; and mouthpieces for musical instruments.

Florida data

Common reed was identified in 30 lakes. The 10th and 90th percentiles for pH, alkalinity, total phosphorus, and total nitrogen values in these lakes show that 80% of the lakes with common reed had levels between 6.9 and 8.7, 10.8 and 108.4 (mg/L as $CaCO_3$), 15 and 169 (µg/L), and 500 and 2390 (µg/L), respectively. These 39 lakes also collectively averaged significantly higher pH, alkalinity, specific conductance, total phosphorus, calcium, magnesium, sodium, potassium, chloride, and silicon values than all 322 lakes. Average Secchi depth was also significantly less than in all 322 lakes. Thus while common reed can occur in a range of lake types, it definitely tends to occur in alkaline, hardwater, nutrient-rich lakes.

Selected references from a total of 2075 common reed citations in the APIRS database:

Best, E.P.H., M. Zippin, and J.H.A. Dassen. Growth and production of *Phragmites australis* in Lake Vechten (The Netherlands). Hydrobiological Bulletin 15(3):165-173.

Bornkamm, R. and F. Raghi-Atri. 1986. On the effects of different nitrogen and phosphorus concentrations on the development of *Phragmites australis* (Cav.) Trin. ex Steudel. Archiv fuer Hydrobiologie 105(4):423-441.

Cizkova-Koncalova, H., J. Kvet, and K. Thompson. 1992. Carbon starvation: A key to reed decline in eutrophic lakes. Aquatic Botany 43:105-113.

Fiala, K. 1970. Growth and production of underground organs of *Typha angustifolia* L., *Typha latifolia* L. and *Phragmites communis* Trin. Polskie Archiwum Hydrobiologii 20(1):59-66.

Hara, T., J. van der Toorn, and J.H. Mook. 1993. Growth dynamics and size structure of shoots of *Phragmites australis*, a clonal plant. Journal of Ecology 81(1):47-60.

Haslam, S.M. 1972. Biological flora of the British Isles: *Phragmites communis*. Journal of Ecology 60:585-610.

Haslam, S.M. 1973. Some aspects of the life history and autecology of *Phragmites communis* Trin. A review. Polskie Archiwum Hydrobiologii 20(1):79-100.

Kvet, J. 1971. Growth analysis approach to the production ecology of reedswamp plant communities. Hydrobiologia 12:15-40.

Mook, J.H. and J. van der Toorn. 1982. The influence of environmental factors and management of stands of *Phragmites australis*. II. Effects on yield and its relationships with shoot density. Journal of Applied Ecology 19:501-517.

Ostendorp, W. 1989. "Die-back" of reeds in Europe—a critical review of literature. Aquatic Botany 35:5-26.

Rezk, M.R. and T.Y. Edany. 1981. Ecology of *Phragmites australis* (Cav.) Trin. ex Steud. in Shattalarab, Iraq. Part II. Reed growth as affected by the chemical composition of its beds. Polskie Archiwum Hydrobiologii 28(1):19-31.

Szczepanska, W. and A. Szczepanski. 1982. Interactions between *Phragmites australis* (Cav.) Trin. ex Steud. and *Typha latifolia* L. Ekologia Polska 30(1-2):165-186.

Ulrich, K.E. and T.M. Burton. 1985. The effects of nitrate, phosphate and potassium fertilization on growth and nutrient uptake patterns of *Phragmites australis* (Cav.) Trin. ex Steudel. Aquatic Botany 21:53-62.

Phragmites australis

Variables	Mean all lakes (n=322)	Number of lakes	Mean	10th percentile	Median	90th percentile
pH*	6.7	30	7.9	6.9	7.9	8.7
Alkalinity (mg/L as CaCO$_3$)*	23.9	30	51.9	10.8	45.9	108.4
Conductance (µS/cm @ 25°C)*	149	30	316	83	241	790
Color (Pt-Co units)	52	30	66	14	58	127
Total phosphorus (µg/L)*	45	30	68	15	45	169
Total nitrogen (µg/L)	870	30	1190	500	1080	2390
Chlorophyll a (µg/L)	20	30	29	4	15	85
Secchi (m)*	1.8	29	0.8	0.4	0.7	1.3
Calcium (mg/L)*	17.6	30	49.3	9.7	40.1	98.2
Magnesium (mg/L)*	8.2	30	23.6	6.6	10.7	55.5
Sodium (mg/L)*	13.2	29	34.9	6.9	14.7	122.0
Potassium (mg/L)*	2.6	30	3.9	1.2	3.4	8.1
Sulfate (mg/L)	15.2	29	25.7	6.4	13.7	56.7
Chloride (mg/L)*	23.4	30	62.4	12.6	26.7	218.7
Iron (mg/L)	0.2	28	0.3	0.0	0.2	0.7
Silicon (mg/L)*	1.5	28	3.0	0.4	2.6	6.0

* Denotes a significant difference (p<0.05) from mean of all lakes.

Pistia stratiotes (water lettuce)

Alison Fox

Kerry Dressler

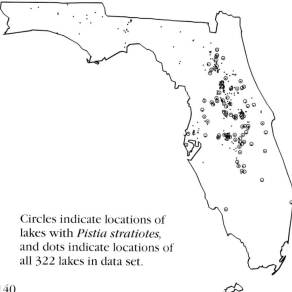

Circles indicate locations of lakes with *Pistia stratiotes,* and dots indicate locations of all 322 lakes in data set.

Description and distribution

Water lettuce is a floating stoloniferous aquatic herb with numerous dusty green leaves and feather-like roots. The 30- to 150-mm-long leaves are spongy with dense fine hairs and are spirally arranged around a central axis. They have conspicuous veins running their length, which tend to be even more obvious on the underside. The small unisexual flowers are embedded within the fleshy axis of the spike and are seldom seen. The green fruit is ovoid and has many seeds that have a thick wrinkled covering. Water lettuce can be found throughout peninsular Florida and westward to Texas (Godfrey and Wooten 1981). The Florida distribution map shows that water lettuce was found primarily in central and south Florida. Lakes are progressively more alkaline and nutrient rich as one moves from northwestern to southern Florida (Canfield and Hoyer 1988). Thus the distribution of water lettuce in Florida suggests that it may tend to occur in alkaline, hardwater, nutrient-rich lakes.

Biology

Water lettuce flowers year round in Florida (Dressler et al. 1987). It reproduces primarily by budding from the main plant or from the stolons. It forms dense mats in lakes and other waterways. Although its origins are not clear, it is an exotic plant in the United States. It can be an aquatic weed problem in Florida because it can cover the surface of a lake and impede recreational use of the waterway. Water lettuce provides cover and shade for fish and other aquatic life.

Florida data

Water lettuce was identified in 84 lakes. The 10th and 90th percentiles for pH, alkalinity, total phosphorus, and total nitrogen values in these lakes show that 80% of the lakes with water lettuce had levels between 5.4 and 8.8, 2.2 and 98.4 (mg/L as $CaCO_3$), 10 and 129 (μg/L), and 280 and 1960 (μg/L), respectively. These

84 lakes also collectively averaged significantly higher pH, alkalinity, specific conductance, total phosphorus, calcium, magnesium, sodium, and chloride values than all 322 lakes. Thus while water lettuce can occur in a range of lake types, it tends to occur in alkaline, hardwater, nutrient-rich lakes.

Selected references from a total of 832 water lettuce citations in the APIRS database:

Aliotta, G., P. Monaco, G. Pinto, et al. 1991. Potential allelochemicals from *Pistia stratiotes* L. Journal of Chemical Ecology 17(11):2223-2234.

Bruner, M.C. 1982. Water-lettuce, *Pistia stratiotes* L. Aquatics 4(3):4,14.

Chadwick, M.J. and M. Obeid. 1966. Comparative study of the growth of *Eichhornia crassipes* Solms and *Pistia stratiotes* L. in water-culture. Journal of Ecology 54(3):563-575.

Chan, K.L. and J.R. Linley. 1990. Distribution of the immature *Atrichopogon wirthi* (Diptera: Ceratopogonidae) on leaves of the water lettuce, *Pistia stratiotes*. Environmental Entomology 19(2):286-292.

Deloach, C.J., A.D. Deloach, and H.A. Cordo. 1976. *Neohydronomous pulchellus*, a weevil attacking *Pistia stratiotes* in South America: Biology and host specificity. Annals of the Entomological Society of America 69(5):830-834.

DeWald, L.B. and L.P. Lounibos. 1990. Seasonal growth of *Pistia stratiotes* L. in south Florida. Aquatic Botany 36:263-275.

Roa, P.N. and A.S. Reddy. 1984. Studies on the population biology of water lettuce: *Pistia stratiotes* L. Hydrobiologia 119(1):15-19.

Sharma, B.M. and M.K.C. Sridhar. 1989. Growth characteristics of water lettuce (*Pistia stratiotes* L.) in southwest Nigeria. Archiv fuer Hydrobiologie 115(2):305-312.

Stoddard, A.A. 1989. The phytogeography and paleofloristics of *Pistia stratiotes* L. Aquatics 11(3):21-24.

Tucker, C.S. 1983. Culture density and productivity of *Pistia stratiotes*. Journal of Aquatic Plant Management 21:40-41 (notes).

Pistia stratiotes

Variables	Mean all lakes (n=322)	Number of lakes	Mean	10th percentile	Median	90th percentile
pH*	6.7	84	7.3	5.4	7.3	8.8
Alkalinity (mg/L as CaCO$_3$)*	23.9	84	33.8	2.2	22.7	98.4
Conductance (µS/cm @ 25°C)*	149	84	214	58	134	519
Color (Pt-Co units)	52	84	66	5	44	121
Total phosphorus (µg/L)*	45	84	68	10	31	129
Total nitrogen (µg/L)	870	84	1030	280	970	1960
Chlorophyll a (µg/L)	20	84	24	2	11	66
Secchi (m)	1.8	76	1.4	0.4	0.9	3.6
Calcium (mg/L)*	17.6	84	30.4	3.6	18.9	90.6
Magnesium (mg/L)*	8.2	84	15.0	2.2	10.1	40.2
Sodium (mg/L)*	13.2	82	21.6	5.0	10.4	71.5
Potassium (mg/L)	2.6	84	3.3	0.2	2.2	8.8
Sulfate (mg/L)	15.2	82	20.3	3.5	12.2	50.6
Chloride (mg/L)*	23.4	84	38.0	8.4	18.0	129.0
Iron (mg/L)	0.2	72	0.2	0.0	0.1	0.4
Silicon (mg/L)	1.5	72	2.1	0.2	1.5	4.8

* Denotes a significant difference (p<0.05) from mean of all lakes.

Polygonum hydropiperoides (smartweed)

Description and distribution

Smartweed is an herbaceous slender plant with decumbent lower stems. It is 500 mm tall or slightly taller with creeping rhizomes and pubescent stems. The nodes are swollen and can have roots forming from them. The alternate leaves are lanceolate and 70–100 mm long and 10 mm wide. Smartweed has a thin sheath around the stem just above the base of the leaf. The inflorescence is a raceme that is 5 mm wide and 20–60 mm long. The flowers of the raceme are whitish to pink in color. The fruit is a flattened to triangular nutlet 2–3 mm long and is dark brown to black. Smartweed is commonly found throughout the United States (Godfrey and Wooten 1981). The Florida distribution map shows that smartweed was found primarily in the central regions of Florida, but occasionally it can be found in the panhandle.

Biology

Smartweed flowers throughout the year in Florida (Dressler et al. 1987). It reproduces by seed germination and vegetative rooting from the nodes. It grows in thick dense colonies along lake shorelines and other marshy habitats. Many bird and small mammal species feed upon the seeds. When crushed or handled, the leaves and stems can cause eye irritation.

Florida data

Smartweed was identified in 54 lakes. The 10th and 90th percentiles for pH, alkalinity, total phosphorus, and total nitrogen values in these lakes show that 80% of the lakes with smartweed had levels between 5.8 and 8.8, 1.9 and 68.7 (mg/L as $CaCO_3$), 10 and 121 (μg/L), and 470 and 1960 (μg/L), respectively. The water chemistry averages of the 54 lakes with smartweed showed no significant differences from those in all 322 lakes. The 54 lakes also had water chemistry ranges similar to those in all 322 lakes. This suggests that smartweed can occur in a wide range of Florida aquatic systems.

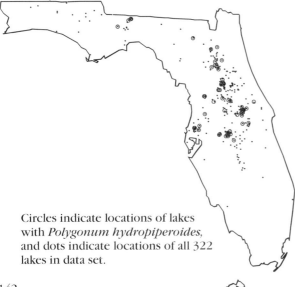

Circles indicate locations of lakes with *Polygonum hydropiperoides,* and dots indicate locations of all 322 lakes in data set.

Selected references from a total of 946 smartweed citations in the APIRS database:

Banthorpe, D.V., C.J.W. Brooks, J.T. Brown, et al. 1989. Synthesis and accumulation of polygodial by tissue cultures of *Polygonum hydropiper*. Phytochemistry 28(6):1631-1633.

Britton, C.E. 1933. British *Polygona*, section *persicaria*. Journal of Botany, London 71:90-98.

Carter, M.F. and J.B. Grace. 1990. Relationships between flooding tolerance, life history, and short term competitive performance in three species of *Polygonum*. American Journal of Botany 77(3):381-387.

Coulter, S. 1892. Cleistogamy in the genus *Polygonum*. Botanical Gazette 17:91-92.

Furuta, T., Y. Fukuyama, and Y. Asakawa. 1986. Polygonolide, an isocoumarin from *Polygonum hydropiper* possessing anti-inflammatory activity. Phytochemistry 25(2):517-520.

Justice, O.L. 1944. Viability and dormancy in seeds of *Polygonum amphibium*. American Journal of Botany 31:369-377.

Kulakkattolickal, A.T. 1989. Piscicidal plants of Nepal: Ripe fruit of *Catunaregam spinosa* (Thunb.) (Rubiaceae) and leaves of *Polygonum hydropiper* L. (Polygonaceae) as fish poisons. Aquaculture 78(3/4):293-301.

Mitchell, R.S. 1971. Comparative leaf structure of aquatic *Polygonum* species. American Journal of Botany 58(4):342-360.

Sell, P.D. and J.R. Akeroyd. 1988. *Polygonum hydropiper* L. var. *densiflorum* A. Braun. Watsonia 17(2):178-179.

Yagi, A., T. Uemura, N. Okamura, et al. 1994. Antioxidative sulphated flavonoids in leaves of *Polygonum hydropiper*. Phytochemistry 35(4):885-887.

Polygonum hydropiperoides

Variables	Mean all lakes (n=322)	Number of lakes	Mean	10th percentile	Median	90th percentile
pH	6.7	54	7.3	5.8	7.4	8.8
Alkalinity (mg/L as $CaCO_3$)	23.9	54	30.0	1.9	23.0	68.7
Conductance (µS/cm @ 25°C)	149	54	172	53	136	323
Color (Pt-Co units)	52	54	49	9	24	102
Total phosphorus (µg/L)	45	53	59	10	26	121
Total nitrogen (µg/L)	870	53	1080	470	900	1960
Chlorophyll a (µg/L)	20	54	28	2	14	73
Secchi (m)	1.8	43	1.4	0.4	1.4	2.2
Calcium (mg/L)	17.6	54	15.9	2.0	10.1	37.7
Magnesium (mg/L)	8.2	54	6.2	1.0	3.6	13.9
Sodium (mg/L)	13.2	49	14.3	3.6	8.8	25.7
Potassium (mg/L)	2.6	54	3.4	0.2	2.1	9.3
Sulfate (mg/L)	15.2	49	14.4	0.7	7.8	25.3
Chloride (mg/L)	23.4	53	25.8	8.2	17.8	42.9
Iron (mg/L)	0.2	36	0.1	0.0	0.10	0.3
Silicon (mg/L)	1.5	36	1.8	0.1	0.5	7.7

Pontederia cordata (pickerelweed)

Kerry Dressler

Kerry Dressler

Description and distribution

Pickerelweed is a perennial herb with creeping rhizomes rooted in the substrate. Erect leaves grow from the rhizomes in clusters. The leaves may be up to 120 mm wide and twice as long, varying in shape from lanceolate to ovate, with heart-shaped bases. Each stem has a leaf with a terminal spike of numerous violet-blue flowers. The fruit is a one seeded utricle. Pickerelweed is a common plant found in the eastern United States and Canada (Godfrey and Wooten 1981). The Florida distribution map shows that pickerelweed was found in lakes across the whole state, with no apparent geographical pattern.

Biology

Pickerelweed flowers throughout the year in Florida (Dressler et al. 1987). It reproduces by seed germination but primarily vegetatively. The plant is found mostly in shoreline habitats and rarely in quantities that would impair use of aquatic systems. Some aquatic bird species use pickerelweed as a secondary food source.

Florida data

Pickerelweed was identified in 254 lakes. The 10th and 90th percentiles for pH, alkalinity, total phosphorus, and total nitrogen values in these lakes show that 80% of the lakes with pickerelweed had levels between 4.9 and 8.7, 1.2 and 69.0 (mg/L as $CaCO_3$), 10 and 92 (µg/L), and 310 and 1780 (µg/L), respectively. The water chemistry averages of the 254 lakes with pickerelweed showed no significant differences from those in all 322 lakes. The 254 lakes also had water chemistry ranges similar to those in all 322 lakes. This suggests that pickerelweed can occur in a wide range of aquatic systems.

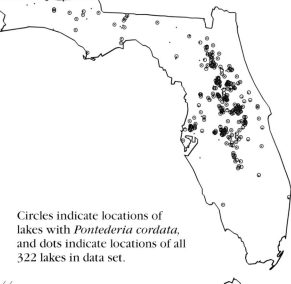

Circles indicate locations of lakes with *Pontederia cordata,* and dots indicate locations of all 322 lakes in data set.

Selected references from a total of 318 pickerelweed citations in the APIRS database:

Anderson, J.M. and S.C.H. Barrett. 1986. Pollen tube growth in tristylous *Pontederia cordata* (Pontederiaceae). Canadian Journal of Botany 64(11):2602-2607.

Charlton, W.A. 1975. Distribution of lateral roots and pattern of lateral initiation in *Pontederia cordata*. Botanical Gazette 136(3):225-235.

Deloach, C.J. and H.A. Cordo. 1981 Biology and host range of the weevil *Neochetina affinis*, which feeds on Pontederiaceae in Argentina. Annals of the Entomological Society of America 74(1):14-19.

Melton, F. and D.L. Sutton. 1991. Pickerelweed. Aquatics 13(2):4-5,8.

Richards, J.H. and S.C.H. Barrett. 1987. Development of tristyly in *Pontederia cordata* (Pontederiaceae). I. Mature floral structures and patterns of relative growth of reproductive organs. American Journal of Botany 74(12):1831-1841.

Schonland, S. 1887. The apical meristem in the roots of Pontederiaceae. Annals of Botany 1:179-182.

Silveira-Guido, A. 1971. Preliminary data on biology and specificity of *Acigona ignitalis* Hamps (Lep. Pyralidae) of the host plant *Eichhornia crassipes* Mart. Solms-Laubach (Pontederiaceae). Revista de la Sociedad Entomologica Argentina 33(1-4):137-145.

Smith, W.R. 1898. A contribution to the life history of the Pontederiaceae. Botanical Gazette 25:324-337.

Sutton, D.L. 1990. A method for germination of arrowhead, pickerelweed and spikerush seeds. Aquatics 12(4):8-10.

Sutton, D.L. 1991. Culture and growth of pickerelweed from seedlings. Journal of Aquatic Plant Management 29:39-42.

Pontederia cordata

Variables	Mean all lakes (n=322)	Number of lakes	Mean	10th percentile	Median	90th percentile
pH	6.7	254	6.9	4.9	6.9	8.7
Alkalinity (mg/L as $CaCO_3$)	23.9	254	25.5	1.2	11.1	69.0
Conductance (µS/cm @ 25°C)	149	254	161	39	116	311
Color (Pt-Co units)	52	254	51	6	26	125
Total phosphorus (µg/L)	45	253	44	10	20	92
Total nitrogen (µg/L)	870	253	870	310	680	1780
Chlorophyll a (µg/L)	20	254	19	1	7	45
Secchi (m)	1.8	221	1.7	0.4	1.4	3.6
Calcium (mg/L)	17.6	254	19.2	1.6	10.2	50.8
Magnesium (mg/L)	8.2	254	9.3	1.0	5.2	23.7
Sodium (mg/L)	13.2	237	14.2	3.6	8.5	20.9
Potassium (mg/L)	2.6	254	2.9	0.2	2.0	8.0
Sulfate (mg/L)	15.2	237	16.4	4.2	11.0	39.7
Chloride (mg/L)	23.4	254	25.3	7.0	15.8	39.4
Iron (mg/L)	0.2	184	0.2	0.0	0.10	0.4
Silicon (mg/L)	1.5	184	1.5	0.1	0.6	3.8

Potamogeton diversifolius (variable-leaf pondweed)

Kerry Dressler

Kerry Dressler

Description and distribution

Variable-leaf pondweed is a perennial plant arising from delicate branching rhizomes. It has two leaf forms, both dark green. The floating leaves are elliptical or ovate, 10–40 mm long, 10–20 mm wide, with a petiole one to two times the length of the blade. The submersed leaves are narrowly linear, 20–60 mm long, 0.5–1.5 mm wide, acute at the tip, and tapering to a sessile base. Emersed spikes are elongated, 5–20 mm long, arising from the axils of the floating leaves, and with up to 50 flowers. Submersed spikes are one- to four-flowered, usually shorter than slender, having recurved stalks and arising from the axils of the submersed leaves. The fruit is a nutlet, usually green with a toothed dorsal keel. Variable-leaf pondweed is a native plant common throughout the United States (Godfrey and Wooten 1981). The Florida distribution map shows that variable-leaf pondweed was found scattered throughout Florida with no apparent geographical pattern.

Biology

Potamogeton species flower from January through October in Florida (Dressler et al. 1987). Variable-leaf pondweed reproduces primarily by seed germination. It is not competitive compared to *Egeria*, *Najas*, or *Hydrilla*, but occasionally it can produce extensive stands that impair navigational and recreational activities in some aquatic systems. Several species of aquatic birds eat the seed heads. The plant can also serve as refuge and habitat for invertebrates and fish populations.

Florida data

Variable-leaf pondweed was identified in 40 lakes. The 10th and 90th percentiles for pH, alkalinity, total phosphorus, and total nitrogen values in these lakes show that 80% of the lakes with variable-leaf pondweed had levels between 5.2 and 7.7, 1.3 and 43.5 (mg/L as $CaCO_3$), 9 and 40 (µg/L), and 280 and 900 (µg/L),

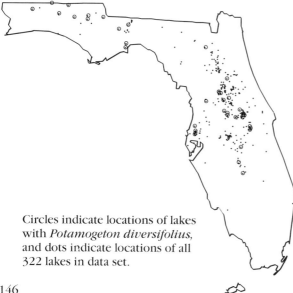

Circles indicate locations of lakes with *Potamogeton diversifolius*, and dots indicate locations of all 322 lakes in data set.

respectively. The water chemistry averages of the 40 lakes with variable-leaf pondweed showed no significant differences from those in all 322 lakes. The 40 lakes also had water chemistry ranges similar to those in all 322 lakes. This suggests that variableleaf pondweed can occur in a wide range of aquatic systems.

Selected references from a total of 78 variableleaf pondweed citations in the APIRS database:

Haynes, R.R. 1968. *Potamogeton* in Louisiana. Proceedings of the Louisiana Academy of Sciences 31:82-90.

Kadono, Y. 1982. Distribution and habitat of Japanese *Potamogeton*. Botanical Magazine of Tokyo 95:63-76.

Klekowski, E.J. and E.O. Beal. 1965. A study of variations in the *Potamogeton capillaceus diversifolius* complex (Potamogetonaceae). Brittonia 17(2):175-181.

Ogden, E.C. 1966. *Potamogeton* L. Texas Research Foundation, Hoblitzelle Agriculture Laboratory, Bulletin 1(3):369-382.

Ogden, E.C. 1974. *Potamogeton* spp. in New York, USA. New York State Museum and Science Service, Bulletin, Albany, N.Y.

Wohler, J.R., D.B. Robertson, and H.R. Laube. 1975. Studies on the decomposition of *Potamogeton diversifolius*. Bulletin of the Torrey Botanical Club 102(2):76-78.

Potamogeton diversifolius

Variables	Mean all lakes (n=322)	Number of lakes	Mean	10th percentile	Median	90th percentile
pH	6.7	40	6.3	5.2	6.3	7.7
Alkalinity (mg/L as CaCO$_3$)	23.9	40	11.6	1.3	3.6	43.5
Conductance (µS/cm @ 25°C)	149	40	96	18	89	182
Color (Pt-Co units)	52	40	41	6	15	121
Total phosphorus (µg/L)	45	40	21	9	14	40
Total nitrogen (µg/L)	870	40	540	280	480	900
Chlorophyll a (µg/L)	20	40	7	2	5	19
Secchi (m)	1.8	37	2.3	0.8	2.2	3.9
Calcium (mg/L)	17.6	40	11.8	2.0	6.3	39.5
Magnesium (mg/L)	8.2	40	6.8	1.2	3.0	14.6
Sodium (mg/L)	13.2	40	8.8	1.8	8.7	17.0
Potassium (mg/L)	2.6	40	1.7	0.2	1.2	3.7
Sulfate (mg/L)	15.2	40	10.8	3.6	8.2	18.0
Chloride (mg/L)	23.4	40	15.7	2.8	15.9	28.0
Iron (mg/L)	0.2	37	0.2	0.0	0.10	0.6
Silicon (mg/L)	1.5	37	0.8	0.1	0.4	1.9

Potamogeton illinoensis (Illinois pondweed)

Jesse Van Dyke

Alison Fox

Description and distribution

Illinois pondweed is a dark green, submersed plant arising from a network of slender horizontal rhizomes, which are spotted or streaked with red. The stems are more or less erect, simple or branched, with floating and submersed leaves. The floating leaves are elliptic to oblong-elliptic, 30–190 mm long, and 15–65 mm wide, but often absent. The submersed leaves are lanceolate to elliptic, 40–200 mm long, and 20–30 mm wide. The stems of the floating leaves are up to 90 mm long, while the submersed leaves are sessile. The inflorescence is a spike 20–80 mm long, borne at the tip of the stem, and usually fruiting densely. The fruit is greenish, 2–4 mm wide, with two conspicuous lateral keels. Illinois pondweed is common in much of Canada and the United States (Godfrey and Wooten 1981). The Florida distribution map shows that Illinois pondweed was found primarily in central and south Florida. Lakes are progressively more alkaline and nutrient rich as one moves from northwestern to southern Florida (Canfield and Hoyer 1988). Thus the distribution of Illinois pondweed in Florida suggests that it may tend to occur in alkaline, hardwater, nutrient-rich lakes.

Biology

Potamogeton species flower from January through October (Dressler et al. 1987). Illinois pondweed reproduces by seed germination and growth from rhizome production. Its growth can be extensive and thick, causing aquatic weed problems. However, it is good refuge and habitat for invertebrates and fish populations.

Florida data

Illinois pondweed was identified in 47 lakes. The 10th and 90th percentiles for pH, alkalinity, total phosphorus, and total nitrogen values in these lakes show that 80% of the lakes with Illinois pondweed had levels between 6.8 and 8.7, 10.6 and 104.6 (mg/L as $CaCO_3$), 10 and 94 (μg/L),

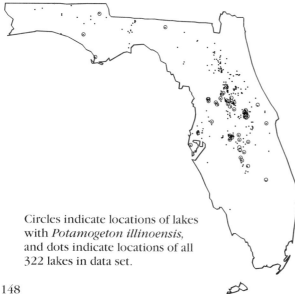

Circles indicate locations of lakes with *Potamogeton illinoensis,* and dots indicate locations of all 322 lakes in data set.

and 430 and 1900 (µg/L), respectively. These 47 lakes also collectively averaged significantly higher pH, alkalinity, specific conductance, calcium, and magnesium values than those of all 322 lakes. Thus, while Illinois pondweed can occur in a range of lake types, it tends to occur in alkaline, hardwater lakes.

Selected references from a total of 12 Illinois pondweed citations in the APIRS database:

Gutierrez, M.G. 1987. The lectotype of *Potamogeton illinoensis* (Potamogetonaceae). Taxon 36(1):112-113.

Langeland, K.A. and B.E. Smith. 1993. Investigations into the propagation and growth requirements of Illinois pondweed. In New and improved methods for the control of aquatic weeds, Semi-annual Report, Center for Aquatic Plants, USDA/ ARS, Institute of Food and Agricultural Sciences, University of Florida, Gainesville.

Les, D.H. and D.J. Sheridan. 1990. Biochemical heterophylly and flavonoid evolution in North American *Potamogeton* (Potamogetonaceae). American Journal of Botany 77(4):453-465.

Ogden, E. C. 1943. Broad-leaved species of *Potamogeton* of North America north of Mexico. Rhodora 45(531):57-105, 45(532):119-163, 45(533):171-214.

Ogden, E.C. 1953. Key to the North American species of *Potamogeton*. Circular of the New York State Museum, Albany, N.Y.

Ogden, E.C. 1974. *Potamogeton* spp. in New York, USA. New York State Museum and Science Service, Bulletin, Albany, N.Y.

Stern, K.R. 1961. Chromosome numbers in nine taxa of *Potamogeton*. Bulletin of the Torrey Botanical Club 88:411-414.

Potamogeton illinoensis

Variables	Mean all lakes (n=322)	Number of lakes	Mean	10th percentile	Median	90th percentile
pH*	6.7	47	7.8	6.8	7.9	8.7
Alkalinity (mg/L as CaCO$_3$)*	23.9	47	49.4	10.6	40.0	104.6
Conductance (µS/cm @ 25°C)*	149	47	238	99	183	473
Color (Pt-Co units)	52	47	30	4	17	94
Total phosphorus (µg/L)	45	47	30	10	17	76
Total nitrogen (µg/L)	870	47	1010	430	810	1900
Chlorophyll a (µg/L)	20	47	18	2	8	52
Secchi (m)	1.8	39	1.7	0.5	1.4	3.6
Calcium (mg/L)*	17.6	47	38.7	7.7	26.8	93.0
Magnesium (mg/L)*	8.2	47	17.5	2.5	11.8	46.0
Sodium (mg/L)	13.2	45	20.1	4.9	10.5	50.1
Potassium (mg/L)	2.6	47	3.5	0.2	3.3	7.4
Sulfate (mg/L)	15.2	45	21.0	3.2	15.5	48.0
Chloride (mg/L)	23.4	47	35.3	9.0	19.1	76.2
Iron (mg/L)	0.2	40	0.1	0.0	0.10	0.2
Silicon (mg/L)	1.5	40	2.3	0.2	1.6	5.8

* Denotes a significant difference (p<0.05) from mean of all lakes.

Potamogeton pectinatus (sago pondweed)

Jesse Van Dyke

Brian Nelson

Description and distribution

Sago pondweed is a submersed plant with no floating leaves that arise from thick matted rhizomes that have terminal tuberous bulbs. The branching stems are long and slender, up to 4 m long. The leaf blades are entire, filiform, 0.5–1.5 mm wide, and 50–350 mm long and originate at the apex of a sheath. The leaf tapers to a point, and numerous strong cross-veins are present throughout the plant. The inflorescence is a spike that is conspicuously interrupted by two to four unequally remote whorls. The spike is 5–25 mm long and becomes lax at maturity. The fruit is a plump nutlet 2.5–5 mm long and 2–3 mm wide. Sago pondweed is a native plant found in the eastern half of the United States southwest to Arizona and from Quebec to Alaska (Godfrey and Wooten 1981). The Florida distribution map shows that sago pondweed was found scattered throughout Florida with no apparent geographical pattern.

Biology

Potamogeton species flower from January through October in Florida (Dressler et al. 1987). Sago pondweed reproduces by seed germination, by bulb growth, and vegetatively through rhizome growth. Its growth often is extensive, impairing navigational and recreational activities in many aquatic systems. Several species of aquatic birds use the fruit, roots, and bulbs as food. The plant can also serve as refuge and habitat for invertebrates and fish populations.

Florida data

Sago pondweed was identified in only 26 lakes. The 10th and 90th percentiles for pH, alkalinity, total phosphorus, and total nitrogen values in these lakes show that 80% of the lakes with sago pondweed had levels between 5.7 and 8.4, 2.3 and 80.7 (mg/L as $CaCO_3$), 12 and 52 (µg/L), and 370 and 1620 (µg/L), respectively. The water chemistry averages of the 26 lakes with sago pondweed showed no

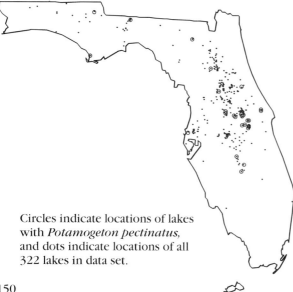

Circles indicate locations of lakes with *Potamogeton pectinatus*, and dots indicate locations of all 322 lakes in data set.

significant differences from those in all 322 lakes. The 26 lakes also had water chemistry ranges similar to those in all 322 lakes. This suggests that sago pondweed can occur in a wide range of aquatic systems.

Selected references from a total of 241 sago pondweed citations in the APIRS database:

Anderson, L.W.J. 1981. Effect of light on the phytotoxicity of fluridone in American pondweed (*Potamogeton nodosus*) and sago pondweed (*P. pectinatus*). Weed Science 29:723-728.

Anderson, M.G. 1978. Distribution and production of sago pondweed (*Potamogeton pectinatus* L.) on a northern prairie marsh. Ecology 59:154-160.

Dawes, C.J. and J.M. Lawrence. 1989. Allocations of energy resources in the freshwater angiosperms *Vallisneria americana* Michx. and *Potamogeton pectinatus* L. in Florida. Florida Scientist 52(1):58-63.

Howard-Williams, C. and B.R. Allanson. 1981. Phosphorus cycling in a dense *Potamogeton pectinatus* L. bed. Oecologia (Berlin) 49:56-66.

Huebert, D.B. and P.R. Gorham. 1983. Biphasic mineral nutrition of the submersed aquatic macrophyte *Potamogeton pectinatus* L. Aquatic Botany 16(3):269-284.

Moen, R.A. and Y. Cohen. 1989. Growth and competition between *Potamogeton pectinatus* L. and *Myriophyllum exalbescens* Fern. in experimental ecosystems. Aquatic Botany 33:257-270.

Ozimek, T., K. Prejs, and A. Prejs. 1986. Biomass and growth rate of *Potamogeton pectinatus* L. in lakes of different trophic state. Ekologia Polska 34(1):125-132.

Purohit, R. and S.P. Singh. 1987. Germination and growth of *Potamogeton pectinatus* L. at different water depths in Lake Nainital, Uttar Pradesh, India. Internationale Revue der Gesamten Hydrobiologie 72(2):251-256.

Spencer, D.F. 1987. Tuber size and planting depth influence growth of *Potamogeton pectinatus* L. American Midland Naturalist 118(1):77-84.

Van Wijck, C., C.J. De Groot, and P. Grillas. 1992. The effects of anaerobic sediment on the growth of *Potamogeton pectinatus* L.: The role of organic matter, sulphide and ferrous iron. Aquatic Botany 44:31-49.

Potamogeton pectinatus

Variables	Mean all lakes (n=322)	Number of lakes	Mean	10th percentile	Median	90th percentile
pH	6.7	26	7.0	5.7	7.1	8.4
Alkalinity (mg/L as CaCO₃)	23.9	26	25.4	2.3	15.1	80.7
Conductance (µS/cm @ 25°C)	149	26	238	68	115	789
Color (Pt-Co units)	52	26	59	4	41	147
Total phosphorus (µg/L)	45	26	38	12	23	52
Total nitrogen (µg/L)	870	26	870	370	680	1620
Chlorophyll a (µg/L)	20	26	15	2	6	40
Secchi (m)	1.8	19	1.7	0.5	1.4	3.6
Calcium (mg/L)	17.6	26	23.5	4.4	11.1	72.5
Magnesium (mg/L)*	8.2	26	14.3	2.5	9.6	39.6
Sodium (mg/L)	13.2	25	28.5	4.6	10.0	102.9
Potassium (mg/L)	2.6	26	2.8	0.6	2.0	7.2
Sulfate (mg/L)	15.2	25	18.9	4.2	12.7	56.9
Chloride (mg/L)	23.4	26	51.5	9.1	22.1	187.3
Iron (mg/L)	0.2	19	0.3	0.0	0.2	0.9
Silicon (mg/L)	1.5	19	1.7	0.1	1.0	5.1

* Denotes a significant difference (p<0.05) from mean of all lakes.

Rhynchospora inundata (inundated beak-rush)

Kerry Dressler

Kerry Dressler

Description and distribution

Inundated beak-rush is a perennial herb with long scaly stolons. It tends to form dense colonies, the individual plants being about 1 m tall. The leaves are 10 mm wide or slightly less. The inflorescence is a narrow spikelet that is loosely clustered at the tip of the branch. The brown, lanceolate spikelets are about 250 mm long including the beak. The achenes are obovate, flat, and 4–5 mm long with a 10–12 mm tubercle at the tip. Inundated beak-rush is found along the eastern part of the United States from Massachusetts to Florida (Godfrey and Wooten 1981). The Florida distribution map shows that inundated beak-rush is found primarily in north-central Florida.

Biology

Inundated beak-rush flowers from February through October in Florida (Dressler et al. 1987). It reproduces by seed germination and vegetatively. It is found along lake margins and other areas that tend to have wet soils such as swamps, bogs, and wet flatwoods. The nutlets are eaten by many species of birds as well as small rodents.

Florida data

Inundated beak-rush was identified in only 15 lakes. The 10th and 90th percentiles for pH, alkalinity, total phosphorus, and total nitrogen values in these lakes show that 80% of the lakes with inundated beak-rush had levels between 4.4 and 8.0, 0.3 and 50.0 (mg/L as $CaCO_3$), 7 and 36 (µg/L), and 310 and 1730 (µg/L), respectively. These 15 lakes collectively averaged similar water chemistry values than those of all 322 lakes except that average calcium and magnesium values for lakes with inundated beak-rush were significantly lower. Thus inundated beak-rush can occur in lakes with a variety of water chemistry conditions, but it may tend to favor softwater lakes.

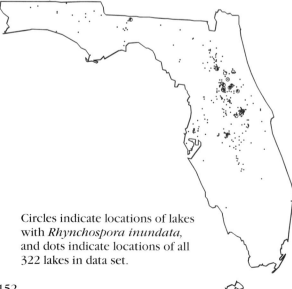

Circles indicate locations of lakes with *Rhynchospora inundata,* and dots indicate locations of all 322 lakes in data set.

Selected references from a total of 139 inundated beak-rush citations in the APIRS database:

Carr, D.W. and B. Rushton. 1994. Treatment of stormwater by a native herbaceous marsh. Pp. 31–44 in Proceedings of the twentieth annual conference on wetlands restoration and creation, F.J. Webb, editor. Hillsborough Community College, Institute of Florida Studies, Tampa, Fla.

Clough, K.S. and G.R. Best. 1991. Wetland macrophyte production and hydrodynamics in Hopkins Prairie, Ocala National Forest, Fla., March 1989–December 1990. 1990 Annual Report, Special Publication SJ91-SP10, prepared for St. Johns River Water Management Distract, Center for Wetlands, University of Florida, Gainesville, 87pp.

Clough, K.S., G.R. Best, and S. Schmid. 1992. Hydrology, plant community structure and nutrient dynamics of Hopkins Prairie, Ocala National Forest, Fla., May 1990–December 1991. Final Report, 1992, Special Publication SJ93-SP3, St. Johns River Water Management District, Center for Wetlands, University of Florida, Gainesville, 123pp.

Gomez-Laurito, J. 1989. The systematics of *Rhynchospora vahl* subgenus rhynchospora cyperaceae in Costa Rica. Brenesia 32:33–72.

Lodge, T.E. 1994. The Everglades handbook: Understanding the ecosystem. St. Lucie Press, Delray Beach, Fla., 228 pp.

Ohlson, M. and N. Malmer. 1990. Total nutrient accumulation and seasonal variation in resource allocation in the bog plant *Rhynchospora alba*. Oikos 58:100–108.

Stalter, R. and E.E. Lamont. 1990. The vascular flora of Assateague Island, Virginia. Bulletin of the Torrey Botanical Club 117(1):48–56.

Toth, L.A. 1993. The ecological basis of the Kissimmee River restoration plan. Florida Scientist 56(1):25–51.

Ueno, O. and T. Koyama. 1987. Distribution and evolution of C4 syndrome in *Rhynchospora* (Rhynchosporeae-Cyperaceae). Bot. Mag. Tokyo 100(1057):63–85.

Rhynchospora inundata

Variables	Mean all lakes (n=322)	Number of lakes	Mean	10th percentile	Median	90th percentile
pH	6.7	15	5.7	4.4	5.1	8.0
Alkalinity (mg/L as CaCO$_3$)	23.9	15	12.1	0.3	1.8	50.0
Conductance (µS/cm @ 25°C)	149	15	70	30	45	153
Color (Pt-Co units)	52	15	49	5	29	162
Total phosphorus (µg/L)	45	14	17	7	13	36
Total nitrogen (µg/L)	870	14	850	310	720	1730
Chlorophyll a (µg/L)	20	15	8	1.0	4	25
Secchi (m)	1.8	12	2.0	0.8	1.6	4.1
Calcium (mg/L)*	17.6	15	6.3	0.5	1.5	26.6
Magnesium (mg/L)*	8.2	15	1.9	0.5	0.9	6.0
Sodium (mg/L)	13.2	14	5.3	2.1	4.1	10.5
Potassium (mg/L)	2.6	15	0.9	0.10	0.3	2.7
Sulfate (mg/L)	15.2	14	6.2	0.6	5.0	13.2
Chloride (mg/L)	23.4	15	10.1	5.2	8.3	20.8
Iron (mg/L)	0.2	2	0.0	0.0	0.0	0.0
Silicon (mg/L)	1.5	2	0.7	0.2	0.7	1.3

* Denotes a significant difference ($p < 0.05$) from mean of all lakes.

Rhynchospora tracyi (Tracy's beak-rush)

Kerry Dressler

Kerry Dressler

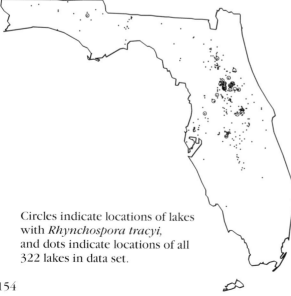

Circles indicate locations of lakes with *Rhynchospora tracyi*, and dots indicate locations of all 322 lakes in data set.

Description and distribution

Tracy's beak-rush is a perennial herb that forms thick colonies and has slender scaly stolons. The stems are 1.2 m tall with in-rolled leaves that are 8 mm wide and as long as or slightly shorter than the stems. The inflorescence is one or two spherical balls of light brown lanceolate spikelets, about 10–20 mm across. The flat achenes are obovate and 2.5–3.0 mm long with a thin beaked tubercle that is 4–5 mm long. The achene is ringed by six finely toothed bristles that are longer than the achene. Tracy's beak-rush is found along the Coastal Plain from South Carolina to Florida and west to Mississippi (Godfrey and Wooten 1981). The Florida distribution map shows that Tracy's beak-rush was found primarily in north-central and central Florida.

Biology

Tracy's beak-rush reproduces by seed germination and vegetatively. It flowers throughout the year in Florida (Dressler et al. 1987). It commonly grows in shallow water along lake shores. The seeds can be used by birds and small mammals.

Florida data

Tracy's beak-rush was identified in only 28 lakes. The 10th and 90th percentiles for pH, alkalinity, total phosphorus, and total nitrogen values in these lakes show that 80% of the lakes with Tracy's beak-rush had levels between 4.4 and 7.0, 0.0 and 20.8 (mg/L as $CaCO_3$), 6 and 20 (µg/L), and 200 and 1430 (µg/L), respectively. These 28 lakes collectively averaged significantly lower pH, alkalinity, specific conductance, total phosphorus, calcium, magnesium, and potassium values than all 322 lakes. The average Secchi disc depth measurement for the 28 lakes was also significantly higher than for all 322 lakes. Thus Tracy's beak-rush tends to occur in acid, softwater, nutrient-poor lakes.

Selected references from a total of 139 Tracy's beak-rush citations in the APIRS database:

Beal, E.O. and T.L. Quay. 1968. Review of *Utricularia olivacea* Wright ex Grisebach (Lentibulariaceae). Journal of Elisha Mitchell Scientific Society 84(4):462–466.

Dierberg, F.E. 1992. The littoral zone of Lake Okeechobee as a source of phosphorus after drawdown. Environmental Management 16(3):371–380.

Gunderson, L.H. 1994. Vegetation of the Everglades: Determinants of community composition. Pp. 323–340 in Everglades: The ecosystem and its restoration, S.M. Davis and J.C. Ogden, editors. St. Lucie Press, Delray Beach, Fla.

Myers, R.L. 1983. Site susceptibility to invasion by the exotic tree *Melaleuca quinquenervia* in southern Florida. Journal of Applied Ecology 20(2):645–658.

Rader, R.B. and C.J. Richardson. 1992. The effects of nutrient enrichment on algae and macroinvertebrates in the Everglades: A review. Wetlands 12(2):121–135.

Rhynchospora tracyi

Variables	Mean all lakes (n=322)	Number of lakes	Mean	10th percentile	Median	90th percentile
pH*	6.7	28	5.3	4.4	4.9	7.0
Alkalinity (mg/L as $CaCO_3$)*	23.9	28	5.9	0.0	1.5	20.8
Conductance (µS/cm @ 25°C)*	149	28	65	31	44	138
Color (Pt-Co units)	52	28	42	3	14	161
Total phosphorus (µg/L)*	45	27	12	6	10	20
Total nitrogen (µg/L)	870	27	700	200	540	1430
Chlorophyll a (µg/L)	20	28	3	1.0	1	13
Secchi (m)*	1.8	26	2.7	1.0	2.6	4.6
Calcium (mg/L)*	17.6	28	4.4	0.6	1.2	16.8
Magnesium (mg/L)*	8.2	28	2.7	0.6	0.9	8.3
Sodium (mg/L)	13.2	28	5.4	2.4	4.1	11.6
Potassium (mg/L)*	2.6	28	0.8	0.2	0.3	2.6
Sulfate (mg/L)	15.2	28	7.3	2.6	5.2	13.0
Chloride (mg/L)	23.4	28	10.8	6.0	8.3	21.8
Iron (mg/L)	0.2	7	0.1	0.0	0.10	0.2
Silicon (mg/L)	1.5	7	0.4	0.10	0.4	0.9

* Denotes a significant difference ($p < 0.05$) from mean of all lakes.

Sacciolepis striata (American cupscalegrass)

Jeff Schardt

Jeff Schardt

Description and distribution

American cupscalegrass is a perennial with creeping stolons and bent stems rooting at the nodes with weak, branching, vertical stems 0.5–1.5 m long. The stems and leaves are glabrous, and only the margins of the leaf sheaths are hairy. The leaf sheaths and blades are striated; the blades are flat, tapering from the base, 40–200 mm long and 3–20 mm wide. Spikelets are 3.5–5 mm long on stems of unequal length, borne rather loosely or fairly compactly on solitary, elongated, almost cylindrical panicles that are 60–200 mm long. American cupscalegrass occurs in the Coastal Plain of south New Jersey to Florida, west to Texas, Tennessee, Oklahoma, and Wisconsin (Godfrey and Wooten 1981).The Florida distribution map shows that American cupscalegrass is found throughout the state with no apparent geographical pattern.

Biology

American cupscalegrass can form extensive stands, which can impair navigational and recreational uses of some aquatic systems. Several species of aquatic and songbirds use the seeds as a secondary food source.

Florida data

American cupscalegrass was identified in 106 lakes. The 10th and 90th percentiles for pH, alkalinity, total phosphorus, and total nitrogen values in these lakes show that 80% of the lakes with American cupscalegrass had levels between 5.3 and 8.6, 1.5 and 83.5 (mg/L as $CaCO_3$), 8 and 166 (µg/L), and 330 and 1730 (µg/L), respectively. Most of the water chemistry averages of the 106 lakes with American cupscalegrass showed no significant differences from those for all 322 lakes. Average magnesium and calcium values, however, were significantly higher than those in all 322 lakes. This suggests that American cupscalegrass can occur in a wide range of aquatic systems in Florida but it may favor hardwater lakes.

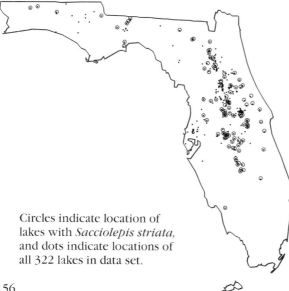

Circles indicate location of lakes with *Sacciolepis striata*, and dots indicate locations of all 322 lakes in data set.

Selected references from a total of 24 American cupscalegrass citations in the APIRS database:

Hestand, R.S. and C.C. Carter. 1974. The effects of winter drawdown on aquatic vegetation in a shallow water reservoir. Hyacinth Control Journal 12:9-12.

Howard-Williams, C. 1977. A checklist of the vascular plants of Lake Chilwa, Malawi, with special reference to the influence of environmental factors on the distribution of taxa. Kirkia 10(2):563-579.

Hujik, B. 1994. Invasion of the tussocks. Aquatics 16(2):4, 6, 8.

Hunt, K.W. 1943. Floating mats on a southeastern coastal plain reservoir. Bulletin of the Torrey Botanical Club 70(5):481-488.

Obot, E.A. 1986. Ecological comparison of the pre- and post-impoundment macrophyte flora of the River Niger and Lake Kainji, Nigeria. Vegetatio 68:67-70.

Obot, E.A. and J.S.O. Ayeni. 1987. Conservation and utilization of aquatic macrophytes in Lake Kainji, Nigeria. Environmental Conservation 14(2):168-170.

Obot, E.A. and I.G. Mbagwu. 1988. Successional patterns of aquatic macrophytes in Jebba Lake, Nigeria. African Journal of Ecology 26:295-299.

Palmisano, A.W. 1972. The effect of salinity on the germination and growth of plants important to wildlife in the Gulf Coast marshes. Proceedings of the Annual Conference of the Southeastern Association of Game and Fish Commissioners 25:215-223.

Partington, W.M. 1968. Florida Audubon's viewpoint on aquatic weed control. Hyacinth Control Journal 7:21-22.

Ramey, V. 1992. Grasses, sedges and rushes: Part I. *Sacciolepis striata*. Aquatic plant management series, Aquatic plant identification. Center for Aquatic Plants Information Office, Institute of Food and Agricultural Sciences, University of Florida, Gainesville. 55 mins. (Video).

Schmalzer, P.A., C.R. Hinkle, and J.L. Mailander. 1991. Changes in community composition and biomass in *Juncus roemerianus* Scheele and *Spartina bakeri* Merr. marshes one year after a fire. Wetlands 11(1):67-86.

Sacciolepis striata

Variables	Mean all lakes (n=322)	Number of lakes	Mean	10th percentile	Median	90th percentile
pH	6.7	106	6.9	5.3	7.0	8.6
Alkalinity (mg/L as CaCO$_3$)	23.9	106	27.6	1.5	10.7	83.5
Conductance (µS/cm @ 25°C)	149	106	177	36	100	422
Color (Pt-Co units)	52	106	68	8	39	166
Total phosphorus (µg/L)	45	106	46	12	24	108
Total nitrogen (µg/L)	870	106	910	330	710	1730
Chlorophyll a (µg/L)	20	106	20	3	9	44
Secchi (m)	1.8	95	1.4	0.4	1.1	3.0
Calcium (mg/L)*	17.6	106	24.8	2.8	13.2	83.2
Magnesium (mg/L)*	8.2	106	12.9	1.8	8.2	35.2
Sodium (mg/L)	13.2	104	17.2	3.4	8.2	42.4
Potassium (mg/L)	2.6	106	2.8	0.2	1.7	7.1
Sulfate (mg/L)	15.2	104	17.4	4.0	11.4	46.0
Chloride (mg/L)	23.4	106	30.9	6.4	14.6	54.8
Iron (mg/L)	0.2	92	0.2	0.0	0.1	0.6
Silicon (mg/L)	1.5	92	1.9	0.2	1.3	4.4

* Denotes a significant difference (p<0.05) from mean of all lakes.

Sagittaria kurziana (strap-leaf sagittaria)

Alison Fox

Jesse Van Dyke

Description and distribution

Strap-leaf sagittaria is a submersed aquatic plant that forms dense stands from rhizomes. The dark green leaves are flat, ribbon- or strap-like, and up to 2500 mm long and 14 mm wide. Each leaf has three to five prominent veins running the length and ending at the pointed tip. The white flowers are in whorls of four to 10 and arise to the surface of the water on a long leafless stalk. The flowers are 9–14 mm long and 4–8 m wide. The fruiting heads are 8–10 mm across with seeds that have five lateral crests that are deeply indented in between. Strap-leaf sagittaria is a native plant found throughout north and central Florida (Godfrey and Wooten 1981). The Florida distribution map shows that strap-leaf sagittaria was found scattered throughout but primarily in central Florida.

Biology

Strap-leaf sagittaria flowers throughout the year in Florida (Godfrey and Wooten 1981). It reproduces by seed germination and vegetatively. This species of sagittaria tends to be found in clear cool waters of many of Florida's rivers and springs. It forms very dense stands, which at times can impede boat traffic, but generally it is considered beneficial to waterfowl and fish.

Florida data

Strap-leaf sagittaria was identified in 15 lakes. The 10th and 90th percentiles for pH, alkalinity, total phosphorus, and total nitrogen values in these lakes show that 80% of the lakes with strap-leaf sagittaria had levels between 4.4 and 8.7, 0.8 and 106.4 (mg/L as $CaCO_3$), 7 and 86 (μg/L), and 240 and 1600 (μg/L), respectively. These 15 lakes with strap-leaf sagittaria had water chemistry averages similar to those of all 322 lakes.

Circles indicate locations of lakes with *Sagittaria kurziana*, and dots indicate locations of all 322 lakes in data set.

Selected references from a total of 15 strap-leaf sagittaria citations in the APIRS database:

Adams, P. and R.K. Godfrey. 1961. Observations on the *Sagittaria subulata* complex. Rhodora 63(753):247–266.

Andrew, W. 1992. Going with the flow or why some aquatic plants "prefer" flowing water habitats. Aquatics 14(2):9–10.

Brown, W.V. 1942. A note on *Sagittaria kurziana.* Rhodora 44:211–213.

Demort, C.L. 1991. The St. Johns River system. Pp. 97-120 in The rivers of Florida, R.J. Livingston, editor. Springer-Verlag, New York.

Silverberg, D.J. and J.G. Morris. 1987. The role of nutrients and energy in the diet selection of the West Indian manatee (*Trichechus manatus*) in the winter refuge at Homosassa Springs, Citrus County, Florida. American Zoologist 27(4):44A.

Sutton, D.L. 1989. The arrowhead plants. Aquatics 11(2):4–9.

Wooten, J.W. 1986. Edaphic factors associated with eleven species of *Sagittaria* (Alismataceae). Aquatic Botany 24(1):35–41.

Sagittaria kurziana

Variables	Mean all lakes (n=322)	Number of lakes	Mean	10th percentile	Median	90th percentile
pH	6.7	15	6.9	4.4	7.0	8.7
Alkalinity (mg/L as $CaCO_3$)	23.9	15	36.2	0.8	18.6	106.4
Conductance (µS/cm @ 25°C)	149	15	263	36	70	878
Color (Pt-Co units)	52	15	54	2	47	143
Total phosphorus (µg/L)	45	15	34	7	20	86
Total nitrogen (µg/L)	870	15	860	240	840	1600
Chlorophyll a (µg/L)	20	15	17	1.0	10	59
Secchi (m)	1.8	15	1.6	0.5	1.2	3.8
Calcium (mg/L)	17.6	15	39.1	1.2	17.3	101.0
Magnesium (mg/L)	8.2	15	18.4	0.7	5.8	59.6
Sodium (mg/L)	13.2	15	31.6	2.8	7.1	130.6
Potassium (mg/L)	2.6	15	2.2	0.2	1.0	6.1
Sulfate (mg/L)	15.2	15	21.8	3.2	7.0	74.9
Chloride (mg/L)	23.4	15	57.6	4.1	12.2	235.7
Iron (mg/L)	0.2	13	0.1	0.0	0.2	0.2
Silicon (mg/L)	1.5	13	2.1	0.10	2.1	6.0

Sagittaria lancifolia (duck potato)

Kerry Dressler

Description and distribution

Duck potato is an amphibious perennial with coarse, stout rhizomes. The elliptic to oblong-elliptic leaves are on a spongy thick stem. The leaves tend to be thick and rather large, from 300–600 mm long and 40–100 mm wide. The flowers, in whorls of three or more, are attached to a leafless stem up to 1500 mm long, which can be branched. The lower whorls are the postulate flowers, and the uppermost whorls are the staminated flowers. The flowers are white. The 15 mm long fruiting heads contain many small beaked or curved seeds. Duck potato is common throughout the Coastal Plain states north from Delaware and Maryland south to Florida and west to Texas and Oklahoma (Godfrey and Wooten 1981). The Florida distribution map shows that duck potato was found throughout the state.

Biology

Duck potato flowers throughout the year in Florida (Dressler et al. 1987). It reproduces by seed germination and vegetatively through rhizome production. It is a very common emergent aquatic plant that tends to grow along marshy lake shores and in deep water, as well as in ditches and canals throughout the state. It can impede water flow in those ditches and canals. The seeds sometimes are used by several bird species.

Florida data

Duck potato was identified in 176 lakes. The 10th and 90th percentiles for pH, alkalinity, total phosphorus, and total nitrogen values in these lakes show that 80% of the lakes with duck potato had levels between 5.3 and 8.7, 1.6 and 92.4 (mg/L as $CaCO_3$), 10 and 108 (µg/L), and 390 and 1960 (µg/L), respectively. These 176 lakes also collectively averaged significantly higher pH, alkalinity, specific conductance, calcium, and magnesium values than all 322 lakes. Thus while duck potato can occur in a range of lake types, it tends to occur in alkaline, hardwater lakes.

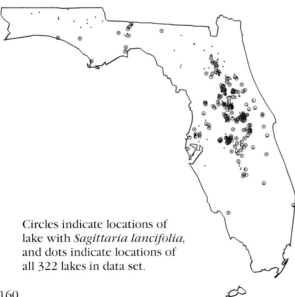

Circles indicate locations of lake with *Sagittaria lancifolia,* and dots indicate locations of all 322 lakes in data set.

Selected references from a total of 96 duck potato citations in the APIRS database:

Argue, C.L. 1972. Pollen of the Alismataceae and Butomaceae. Development of the nexine in *Sagittaria lancifolia* L. Pollen Spores 14:5-16.

Collon, E.G. and J. Velasquez. 1989. Dispersion, germination and growth of seedlings of *Sagittaria lancifolia* L. Folia Geobotanica et Phytotaxonomica 24:37-49.

Cook, M.T. 1907. The embryology of *Sagittaria lancifolia* L. Ohio Naturalist 7:97-101.

Delaune, R.D. and C.W. Lindau. 1990. Fate of added ^{15}N-labeled nitrogen in a *Sagittaria lancifolia* L. Gulf Coast marsh. Journal of Freshwater Ecology 5(3):265-268.

Pezeshki, S.R., R.D. Delaune, and W.H. Patrick. 1987. Effects of flooding and salinity on photosynthesis of *Sagittaria lancifolia*. Marine Ecology Progress Series 41(1):87-91.

Singh, V. and R. Sattler. 1973. Nonspiral androecium and gynoecium of *Sagittaria latifolia*. Canadian Journal of Botany 51:1093-1095.

Wooten, J.W. 1986. Variations in leaf characteristics of six species of *Sagittaria* (Alismataceae) caused by various water levels. Aquatic Botany 23(4):321-327.

Wooten, J.W. 1986. Edaphic factors associated with eleven species of *Sagittaria* (Alismataceae). Aquatic Botany 24(1):35-41.

Sagittaria lancifolia

Variables	Mean all lakes (n=322)	Number of lakes	Mean	10th percentile	Median	90th percentile
pH*	6.7	176	7.2	5.3	7.3	8.7
Alkalinity (mg/L as CaCO$_3$)*	23.9	176	32.9	1.6	21.8	92.4
Conductance (µS/cm @ 25°C)*	149	176	190	46	140	390
Color (Pt-Co units)	52	176	61	7	29	154
Total phosphorus (µg/L)	45	176	44	10	22	108
Total nitrogen (µg/L)	870	176	1020	390	820	1960
Chlorophyll a (µg/L)	20	176	23	2	9	67
Secchi (m)	1.8	157	1.5	0.4	1.3	3.2
Calcium (mg/L)*	17.6	176	23.9	2.5	14.8	68.3
Magnesium (mg/L)*	8.2	176	11.6	1.5	7.5	32.1
Sodium (mg/L)	13.2	163	17.2	3.9	9.6	30.5
Potassium (mg/L)	2.6	176	3.4	0.2	2.3	8.8
Sulfate (mg/L)	15.2	163	17.1	3.7	11.5	43.6
Chloride (mg/L)	23.4	176	30.8	8.0	17.4	43.8
Iron (mg/L)	0.2	133	0.2	0.0	0.10	0.4
Silicon (mg/L)	1.5	133	1.9	0.1	0.9	5.0

* Denotes a significant difference (p<0.05) from mean of all lakes.

Sagittaria latifolia (common arrowhead)

Alison Fox

Description and distribution

Common arrowhead is an emergent aquatic to subaquatic plant that has slender rhizomes and three-lobed, arrowhead-shaped leaves. The leaves are on a long spongy stalk and are 50–250 mm long and 20–200 mm wide. The basal lobes are as long as or longer than the terminal lobe of each leaf, and the lobes are nearly linear to broadly ovate-triangular. The inflorescence arises from a leafless stalk that is 800 mm tall. The white flowers are in racemes that are in whorls of fewer than 10. The fruiting heads tend to be 25 mm across with achenes that are cuneate to obovate and winged. Common arrowhead is widespread throughout the United States (Godfrey and Wooten 1981). The Florida distribution map shows that common arrowhead is scattered throughout the state but primarily in central Florida.

Biology

Common arrowhead reproduces sexually by seed and vegetatively by rhizomes. It tends to grow along the shorelines of lakes in shallow water. This species of *Sagittaria* is considered a beneficial aquatic plant and rarely becomes an aquatic plant problem. It is a valuable food source for many species of aquatic birds and other wildlife.

Florida data

Common arrowhead was identified in only 67 lakes. The 10th and 90th percentiles for pH, alkalinity, total phosphorus, and total nitrogen values in these lakes show that 80% of the lakes with common arrowhead had levels between 5.5 and 8.9, 1.8 and 101.2 (mg/L as $CaCO_3$), 12 and 124 (μg/L), and 380 and 2470 (μg/L), respectively. These 67 lakes also collectively averaged significantly higher pH, total phosphorus, calcium, and magnesium values than all 322 lakes. Thus while common arrowhead can occur in a range of lake types, it tends to occur in alkaline, hardwater, nutrient-rich lakes.

Circles indicate locations of lakes with *Sagittaria latifolia,* and dots indicate locations of all 322 lakes in data set.

Selected references from a total of 281 common arrowhead citations in the APIRS database:

Bloedel, C.A. and A.M. Hirsch. 1979. Developmental studies of the leaves of *Sagittaria latifolia* and their relationship to the leaf-base theory of monocotyledonous leaf morphology. Canadian Journal of Botany 57:420-432.

Clark, W.R. and R.T. Clay. 1985. Standing crop of *Sagittaria* in the upper Mississippi River. Canadian Journal of Botany 63(8):1453-1457.

Delesalle, V.A. and G.E. Muenchow. 1992. Opportunities for selfing and inbreeding depression in *Sagittaria* congeners (Alismataceae) with contrasting sexual systems. Evolutionary Trends in Plants 6(2):81-91.

Garbisch, E. and S. McLininch. 1994. The establishment of *Sagittaria latifolia* from large and small tubers as a function of water depth. Wetland Journal 6(3):19-21.

Grubaugh, J.W., R.V. Anderson, D.M. Day, K.S. Lubinski, and R.E. Sparks. 1986. Production and fate of organic material from *Sagittaria latifolia* and *Nelumbo lutea* on pool 19, Mississippi River. Journal of Freshwater Ecology 3(4):477-484.

Kaul, R.B. 1967. Development and vasculature of the flowers of *Lophotocarpus calycinus* and *Sagittaria latifolia*. American Journal of Botany 54:914-920.

Muenchow, G. and V. Delesalle. 1994. Pollinator response to male floral display size in two *Sagittaria* (Alismataceae) species. American Journal of Botany 81(5):568-573.

Muenchow, G., and V. Delesalle. 1992. Patterns of weevil herbivory on male, monoecious and female inflorescences of *Sagittaria latifolia*. American Midland Naturalist 127(2):355-367.

Rataj, K. 1972. Revision of the genus *Sagittaria*. Part I. (Old World Species). Annotationes Zoologicae et Botanicae, Bratislava 76:1-31.

Wooten, J.W. 1971. The monoecious and dioecious conditions in *Sagittaria latifolia* L. (Alismataceae). Evolution 25:549-553.

Sagittaria latifolia

Variables	Mean all lakes (n=322)	Number of lakes	Mean	10th percentile	Median	90th percentile
pH*	6.7	67	7.3	5.5	7.3	8.9
Alkalinity (mg/L as CaCO$_3$)	23.9	67	34.2	1.8	21.7	101.2
Conductance (µS/cm @ 25°C)	149	67	156	27	111	356
Color (Pt-Co units)	52	67	57	9	39	112
Total phosphorus (µg/L)*	45	67	59	12	28	124
Total nitrogen (µg/L)	870	67	1140	380	920	2470
Chlorophyll a (µg/L)	20	67	30	3	11	89
Secchi (m)	1.8	62	1.4	0.4	1.0	2.9
Calcium (mg/L)*	17.6	67	29.0	2.3	19.9	82.9
Magnesium (mg/L)*	8.2	67	12.3	1.7	8.2	31.8
Sodium (mg/L)	13.2	65	12.4	2.1	8.6	17.8
Potassium (mg/L)	2.6	67	2.6	0.2	1.9	6.4
Sulfate (mg/L)	15.2	65	13.6	3.1	9.2	28.4
Chloride (mg/L)	23.4	67	22.7	3.2	15.2	38.0
Iron (mg/L)	0.2	59	0.2	0.0	0.2	0.6
Silicon (mg/L)	1.5	59	2.2	0.1	1.1	7.0

* Denotes a significant difference (p<0.05) from mean of all lakes.

Sagittaria subulata (dwarf arrowhead)

Jesse Van Dyke

Jesse Van Dyke

Description and distribution

Dwarf arrowhead is a small, rhizomatous perennial herb that tends to form dense mats along the bottoms of lakes. The leaves are linear and tend to taper from the base to the apex. They are 20–300 mm long, 3–8 mm wide, thickish, and lenticular. The white, three-petaled flowers are on a long leafless stalk 60–400 mm long with two to eight whorls. The fruiting head has an obovate achene 1.5–2.0 mm long with a thin wing along the margin. Dwarf arrowhead is common in the eastern United States (Godfrey and Wooten 1981). The Florida distribution map shows that dwarf arrowhead was found from the northwest to south-central regions of the state.

Biology

Dwarf arrowhead reproduces primarily vegetatively but also by seed germination. It grows along the bottoms of clear sand-bottom lakes, often in dense stands forming a carpet-like mat. The seeds and rhizomes occasionally are used by waterfowl.

Florida data

Dwarf arrowhead was identified in 73 lakes. The 10th and 90th percentiles for pH, alkalinity, total phosphorus, and total nitrogen values in these lakes show that 80% of the lakes with dwarf arrowhead had levels between 4.8 and 8.3, 0.4 and 56.4 (mg/L as $CaCO_3$), 7 and 52 (µg/L), and 160 and 1450 (µg/L), respectively. The water chemistry averages of the 73 lakes with dwarf arrowhead showed no significant differences from those of all 322 lakes. The 73 lakes also had water chemistry ranges similar to those in all 322 lakes. This suggests that dwarf arrowhead can occur in a wide range of aquatic systems.

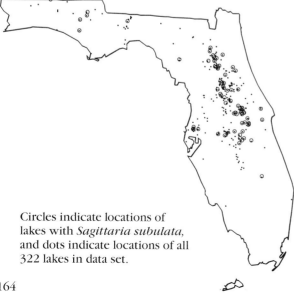

Circles indicate locations of lakes with *Sagittaria subulata,* and dots indicate locations of all 322 lakes in data set.

Selected references from a total of 40 dwarf arrowhead citations in the APIRS database:

Adams, P. and R.K. Godfrey. 1961. Observations on the *Sagittaria subulata* complex. Rhodora 63(753):247-266.

Brewis, A. 1975. *Sagittaria subulata* (L.) Buch. in the British Isles. Watsonia 10(4):411.

Clausen, R.T. 1941. The variations of *Sagittaria subulata*. Torreya 41:161-162.

Lieu, S.M. 1980. Growth forms in the Alismatales. I. *Alisma triviale* and species of *Sagittaria* with upright vegetative axes. Canadian Journal of Botany 57(21):2325-2352.

Rataj, K. 1972. Revision of the genus *Sagittaria*. Part I. (Old World Species). Annotationes Zoologicae et Botanicae, Bratislava 76:1-31.

Sutton, D.L. 1990. Growth of *Sagittaria subulata* and interaction with hydrilla. Journal of Aquatic Plant Management 28:20-22.

Wooten, J.W. 1986. Edaphic factors associated with eleven species of *Sagittaria* (Alismataceae). Aquatic Botany 24(1):35-41.

Sagittaria subulata

Variables	Mean all lakes (n=322)	Number of lakes	Mean	10th percentile	Median	90th percentile
pH	6.7	73	6.6	4.8	6.6	8.3
Alkalinity (mg/L as CaCO$_3$)	23.9	73	18.5	0.4	4.3	56.4
Conductance (µS/cm @ 25°C)	149	73	147	35	100	297
Color (Pt-Co units)	52	73	34	4	14	98
Total phosphorus (µg/L)	45	72	24	7	15	52
Total nitrogen (µg/L)	870	72	700	160	500	1450
Chlorophyll a (µg/L)	20	73	12	1	5	34
Secchi (m)	1.8	63	2.3	0.6	1.9	5.1
Calcium (mg/L)	17.6	73	16.3	1.3	6.8	38.9
Magnesium (mg/L)	8.2	73	8.6	0.8	3.2	24.1
Sodium (mg/L)	13.2	68	14.3	3.3	8.3	17.3
Potassium (mg/L)	2.6	73	2.4	0.2	1.5	6.4
Sulfate (mg/L)	15.2	68	16.4	5.0	10.9	50.2
Chloride (mg/L)	23.4	73	25.5	6.2	15.2	35.2
Iron (mg/L)	0.2	54	0.1	0.0	0.10	0.4
Silicon (mg/L)	1.5	54	1.2	0.10	0.5	3.8

Salix spp. (willow)

Brian Nelson

Brian Nelson

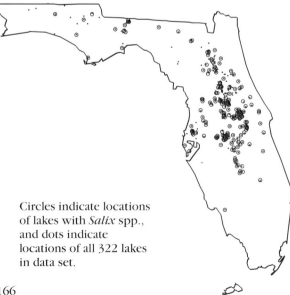

Circles indicate locations of lakes with *Salix* spp., and dots indicate locations of all 322 lakes in data set.

Description and distribution

Willows are deciduous shrubs and trees occasionally reaching heights of 35 m. They have irregular crowns and usually several trunk stems arising from the base. The bark is dark brown to black, heavily furrowed, aromatic, and bitter to taste. The leaves are simple, alternate, deciduous, short petioled, with finely serrated margins, usually 100–160 mm long, and more than three times as long as broad. The flowers are individually small and borne in erect to spreading catkins, which usually develop in the spring before or as the leaves are developing. The fruit is an ovoid-conical capsule, about 10 mm long, containing many small, hairy seeds. About 200 species of willow are widely distributed in northern temperate and arctic regions; a few are located in the southern temperate zone (Tarver et al. 1986). The Florida distribution map shows that willow was found scattered throughout the state but primarily in central and south Florida. Lakes are progressively more alkaline and nutrient rich as one moves from northwestern to southern Florida (Canfield and Hoyer 1988). Thus the distribution of willow in Florida suggests that it may tend to occur in alkaline, hardwater, nutrient-rich lakes.

Biology

Willow flowers from February through April in Florida (Dressler et al. 1987). It reproduces primarily by seed germination. It can form dense thickets in moist soil areas, along streams and rivers, but generally grows only on lake shorelines. These growths rarely cause impairment to navigational or recreational activities in lakes. The twigs, buds, and foliage are eaten by several mammal and bird species. Several aquatic and songbird species also use them as refuge and nesting habitat. Willows growing on lakeshores occasionally fall or grow out into the lake where several species of fish use them as refuge and spawning habitat.

Florida data

Willow was identified in 207 lakes. The 10th and 90th percentiles for pH, alkalinity, total phosphorus, and total nitrogen values in these lakes show that 80% of the lakes with willow had levels between 5.5 and 8.8, 1.6 and 80.2 (mg/L as $CaCO_3$), 10 and 116 (µg/L), and 390 and 1990 (µg/L), respectively. These 207 lakes also collectively averaged significantly higher pH, alkalinity, specific conductance, total phosphorus, calcium, magnesium, and potassium values than those of all 322 lakes. Thus while willow can occur in a range of lake types, it definitely tends to occur in alkaline, hardwater, nutrient-rich lakes.

Selected references from a total of 189 willow citations in the APIRS database:

Bacchus, S.T. 1991. Looking beyond hydrology: The creation and restoration of wetlands, Part 2. Palmetto 11(4):9–12.

Bauer, V. 1988. Estimation of production in a wetland willow stand on the basis of CO_2 exchange measurements. Ekologia 7(4):345–361.

Davies, T.D. and A.D. Cohen. 1989. Composition and significance of the peat deposits of Florida Bay. Bulletin of Marine Science 44(1):387–398.

Eisner, W.R. and P.A. Colinvaux. 1990. A long pollen record from Ahaliorak Lake, Arctic Alaska. Review of Palaeobotany and Palynology 63:35–52.

Farone, S.M. and T.N. McNabb. 1993. Changes in nontarget wetland vegetation following a large-scale fluridone application. Journal of Aquatic Plant Management 31:185–189.

Hanlon, R.D.G. 1982. The breakdown and decomposition of allochthonous and autochthonous plant litter in an oligotrophic lake (Llyn Frongoch). Hydrobiologia 88:281–288.

Howell, H.H. 1975. A study of some of the ecological factors affecting the occurence of water willow (*Justicia americana* L.) in Jessamine Creek, Kentucky. N. Am. Benthol. Soc. titles & abstr. or. V.

Iacobelli, A. and R.L. Jefferies. 1991. Inverse salinity gradients in coastal marshes and the death of stands of *Salix*: The effects of grubbing by geese. Journal of Ecology 79:61–73.

Klosowski, S. 1992. Temporal and spatial variation of habitat conditions in the zonation of littoral plant communities. Aquatic Botany 43:199–208.

Koncalova, M.N. and D. Jicinska. 1982. Reproduction strategy in two wetland willow species. Pp. 215–222 in Wetlands: Ecology and management, B. Gopal, R.E. Turner, R.G. Wetzel, and D.F. Whigham, editors. National Institute of Ecology and International Science Publications.

Mandossian, A. and R.P. McIntosh. 1960. Vegetation zonation on the shore of a small lake. American Midland Naturalist 64(2):301–308.

Reid, G.K. 1952. Some considerations and problems in the ecology of floating islands. Journal of the Florida Academy of Science 15(1):63–66.

Winchester, B.H., J.S. Bays, J.C. Higman, and R. L. Knight. 1985. Physiography and vegetation zonation of shallow emergent marshes in southwest Florida. Wetlands 5:99–118.

Salix spp.

Variables	Mean all lakes (n=322)	Number of lakes	Mean	10th percentile	Median	90th percentile
pH*	6.7	207	7.3	5.5	7.4	8.8
Alkalinity (mg/L as $CaCO_3$)*	23.9	207	32.6	1.6	22.0	80.2
Conductance (µS/cm @ 25°C)*	149	207	186	54	143	348
Color (Pt-Co units)	52	207	52	7	27	129
Total phosphorus (µg/L)*	45	206	59	10	24	116
Total nitrogen (µg/L)	870	206	1010	390	790	1990
Chlorophyll a (µg/L)	20	207	27	2	11	73
Secchi (m)	1.8	169	1.5	0.4	1.1	3.3
Calcium (mg/L)*	17.6	207	24.3	2.8	14.7	65.0
Magnesium (mg/L)*	8.2	207	11.1	1.7	7.3	28.0
Sodium (mg/L)	13.2	195	16.3	4.1	9.5	25.8
Potassium (mg/L)*	2.6	207	3.3	0.3	2.2	8.6
Sulfate (mg/L)	15.2	195	17.8	4.2	11.7	43.4
Chloride (mg/L)	23.4	206	29.1	8.2	17.1	41.3
Iron (mg/L)	0.2	155	0.2	0.0	0.1	0.4
Silicon (mg/L)	1.5	155	1.9	0.2	0.9	5.0

* Denotes a significant difference (p<0.05) from mean of all lakes.

Salvinia spp. (water fern)

Kerry Dressler

Kerry Dressler

Description and distribution

Water fern is a free-floating fern composed of floating leaf-like fronds and submersed root-like leaves. The floating leaves are bluish-green, sessile, suborbicular with a cordate base, and 10–15 mm long. They have a distinct ventral midrib, giving a folded appearance down the center of the leaf. Stiff, dense, water-resistant hairs are found on the upper leaf surface, and wet, dark hairs are on the under surface. Salvinia has no roots, but a third leaf located under the surface leaves is divided into many thread-like segments. All three leaves are joined at a central axis, which can be several centimeters long with other sets of leaves attached. Sporocarps are formed at the base of the floating leaves. Water fern is an exotic plant, brought into the country from Africa or South America and naturalized primarily in the southeastern United States (Tarver et al. 1986). The Florida distribution map shows that water fern was primarily found in lakes from north-central to southern Florida but not frequently in northwestern Florida. Lakes are progressively more alkaline and nutrient rich as one moves from northwestern to southern Florida (Canfield and Hoyer 1988). Thus the distribution of salvinia in Florida suggests that water fern may tend to occur in alkaline, hardwater, nutrient-rich lakes.

Biology

Water fern ally with its two spore types encased in special capsules called sporocaps, which actually are outgrowths of several fertile leaves. Reproduction occurs by spores, but leaves breaking away at the axis portion add greatly to the spread of water fern. It can grow into extensive mats, shading out other forms of aquatic vegetation, but only in sheltered areas. In lakes with much wind-fetch, water fern plants are usually blown onto shore and desiccated. When water fern completely covers a pond or lake, it can impair navigational and recreational activities. Wildlife use of water fern is minimal; however, it can be habitat for some aquatic invertebrates.

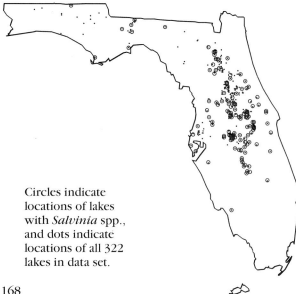

Circles indicate locations of lakes with *Salvinia* spp., and dots indicate locations of all 322 lakes in data set.

Florida data

Water fern was identified in 136 lakes. The 10th and 90th percentiles for pH, alkalinity, total phosphorus, and total nitrogen values in these lakes showed that 80% of the lakes with water fern had levels between 5.5 and 8.8, 1.9 and 97.9 (mg/L as CaCO$_3$), 12 and 124 (µg/L), and 380 and 1960 (µg/L), respectively. These 136 lakes also collectively had significantly higher pH, specific conductance, total phosphorus, calcium, magnesium, and chloride levels than the averages of all 322 lakes. Thus while water fern can occur in a range of lakes types, it tends to occur in alkaline, hardwater, nutrient-rich lakes.

Selected references from a total of 1021 water fern citations in the APIRS database:

Agami, M. and K.R. Reddy. 1989. Inter-relationships between *Salvinia rotundifolia* and *Spirodela polyrhiza* at various interaction stages. Journal of Aquatic Plant Management 27:96-102.

Cordo, H.A., C.J. Deloach, and R. Ferrer. 1982. The weevils *Lixellus*, *Tanysphiroideus*, and *Cytrobagous* that feed on *Hydrocotyle* and *Salvinia* in Argentina. Coleopterists Bulletin 36(2):279-286.

DeBusk, W.F. and K.R. Reddy. 1987. Growth and nutrient uptake potential of *Azolla caroliniana* Willd. and *Salvinia rotundifolia* Willd. as a function of temperature. Environmental Experimental Botany 27(2):215-221.

Gaudet, J.J. and D.V. Koh. 1967. Effect of various growth regulators on *Salvinia rotundifolia* in sterile culture. Bulletin of the Torrey Botanical Club 95(1):91-102.

Johnstone, I.M. 1969. A note on the taxonomy of *Salvinia* in New Zealand. Tane 15:97-98.

Little, E.C.S. 1967. Occurrence of *Salvinia auriculata* on the Congo River. Nature 208(5015):1111-1112.

Nelson, B. 1984. *Salvinia molesta* Mitchell—Does it threaten Florida? Aquatics 6(3):6-8.

Outridge, P.M., W.E. Rauser, and T.C. Hutchinson. 1991. Changes in metal-binding peptides due to acclimation to cadmium transferred between ramets of *Salvinia minima*. Oecologia 88:109-115.

Reddy, K.R. and W.F. DeBusk. 1985. Growth characteristics of aquatic macrophytes cultured in nutrient-enriched water: II. Azolla, duckweed and salvinia. Economic Botany 39(2):200-208.

Weatherby, C.A. 1937. A further note on *Salvinia*. American Fern Journal 27:98-102.

Salvinia spp.

Variables	Mean all lakes (n=322)	Number of lakes	Mean	10th percentile	Median	90th percentile
pH*	6.7	136	7.2	5.5	7.1	8.8
Alkalinity (mg/L as CaCO$_3$)	23.9	136	31.3	1.9	18.7	97.9
Conductance (µS/cm @ 25°C)*	149	136	199	56	118	422
Color (Pt-Co units)	52	136	63	7	41	135
Total phosphorus (µg/L)*	45	136	56	12	28	124
Total nitrogen (µg/L)	870	136	1010	380	800	1960
Chlorophyll a (µg/L)	20	136	24	3	9	68
Secchi (m)	1.8	123	1.5	0.4	1.0	3.1
Calcium (mg/L)*	17.6	136	28.7	3.8	16.0	77.4
Magnesium (mg/L)*	8.2	136	14.6	2.7	9.5	39.1
Sodium (mg/L)*	13.2	132	19.5	5.0	9.5	43.5
Potassium (mg/L)	2.6	136	3.2	0.3	2.2	8.4
Sulfate (mg/L)	15.2	132	19.7	4.7	12.0	48.6
Chloride (mg/L)*	23.4	136	34.8	8.5	17.4	67.7
Iron (mg/L)	0.2	116	0.2	0.0	0.1	0.5
Silicon (mg/L)	1.5	116	2.0	0.2	1.1	5.0

* Denotes a significant difference (p<0.05) from mean of all lakes.

Sambucus canadensis (elderberry)

Description and distribution

Elderberry is a soft-stemmed shrub that sometimes reaches 4 m tall. The roots spread underground runners that form thickets. The bark is grayish-brown with small corky spots. The leaves are opposite, pinnately once compound, with the lower leaves again divided into three segments. The leaves have a rank odor when crushed. The small white flowers are 3–5 mm across and occur in flat heads 100–300 mm across. The fruit is a blue-black fleshy berry with 3–5 stones. Elderberry commonly occurs from Nova Scotia and Quebec to Manitoba and South Dakota generally south to Florida and Texas (Godfrey and Wooten 1981). The Florida distribution map shows that the few lakes with elderberry were scattered throughout the state with no apparent geographical pattern.

Biology

Elderberry flowers April through June in Florida (Dressler et al. 1987). The plants form extensive thickets in some moist soil areas but grow mostly on shoreline habitats of lake systems. Elderberry growth on lakes rarely if ever impairs navigational or recreational activities. The blossoms and fruits are used extensively by aquatic and songbird species. The bushes are also used as refuge and nesting habitat for several bird species. Elderberry plants when growing on lakeshores occasionally fall or grow out into a lake where several species of fish use them as refuge and spawning habitat. The blossoms and fruits are also used for pies, preserves, and sweet down-home elderberry wine. (Try some.)

Florida data

Elderberry plants were identified in only 22 lakes. The 10th and 90th percentiles for pH, alkalinity, total phosphorus, and total nitrogen values in these lakes show that 80% of the lakes with elderberry had levels between 6.4 and 8.9, 1.6 and 106 (mg/L as $CaCO_3$), 6 and 106 (µg/L), and 380 and 1970 (µg/L), respectively. Most of the water chemistry averages of the 22 lakes with elderberry showed no significant differences from those of all 322 lakes. Average pH values, however,

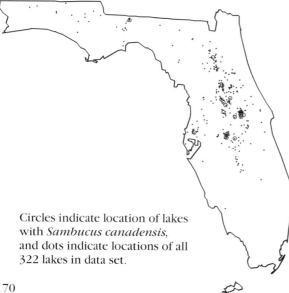

Circles indicate location of lakes with *Sambucus canadensis,* and dots indicate locations of all 322 lakes in data set.

were significantly higher than those of all 322 lakes. This suggests that while elderberry can occur in a wide range of aquatic systems in Florida, there is some evidence that it may prefer alkaline soils.

Selected references from a total of 7 elderberry citations in the APIRS database:

Birkaya, A.G. and N.I. Gudzhabicze. 1957. Application of herbicides to control weeds in drainage canals in Colchis. Gidrotekhnika i Melioratsiia 9(4):41-48.

Brown, S. 1981. A comparison of the structure, primary productivity, and transpiration of cypress ecosystems in Florida. Ecological Monographs 51(4):403-427.

Haslam, S.M. 1965. Ecological studies in the Breck Fens. I. Vegetation in relation to habitat. Journal of Ecology 53:599-619.

Hill, S.R. 1974. An annotated checklist of the vascular flora of Assateague Island (Maryland and Virginia). Castanea 51(4):265-305.

Morton, J.F. 1974. Wild plants for survival in south Florida. Trend House, Tampa, Fla. 80 pp.

Sambucus canadensis

Variables	Mean all lakes (n=322)	Number of lakes	Mean	10th percentile	Median	90th percentile
pH*	6.7	22	7.9	6.4	8.2	8.9
Alkalinity (mg/L as CaCO$_3$)	23.9	22	45.0	1.6	47.9	106.4
Conductance (µS/cm @ 25°C)	149	22	202	79	189	295
Color (Pt-Co units)	52	22	24	7	17	50
Total phosphorus (µg/L)	45	22	34	6	26	106
Total nitrogen (µg/L)	870	22	1070	380	1020	1970
Chlorophyll a (µg/L)	20	22	29	2	23	73
Secchi (m)	1.8	12	0.8	0.3	0.8	1.6
Calcium (mg/L)	17.6	21	19.2	5.3	18.0	37.6
Magnesium (mg/L)	8.2	21	6.4	2.7	5.2	11.6
Sodium (mg/L)	13.2	20	12.9	6.5	10.6	25.6
Potassium (mg/L)	2.6	21	4.8	1.7	4.4	8.8
Sulfate (mg/L)	15.2	20	17.4	7.3	15.6	32.5
Chloride (mg/L)	23.4	22	22.5	11.8	19.7	39.9
Iron (mg/L)	0.2	11	0.10	0.0	0.10	0.3
Silicon (mg/L)	1.5	11	1.8	0.3	1.7	4.1

* Denotes a significant difference (p<0.05) from mean of all lakes.

Saururus cernuus (lizard's tail)

Description and distribution

Lizard's tail is a perennial herb that has rhizomes and forms colonies. Hairy stems are erect, reaching about 120 mm. They are unbranched below, simple or with a few ascending branches above. The green leaves are alternate lanceolate to heart-shaped, 50–120 mm long, 20–80 mm wide, and aromatic. Opposite the uppermost leaf on a long hairy stem is an arching inflorescence consisting of numerous small, fragrant, whitish flowers in a dense spike 200 mm long and 10 mm wide. The fruit consists of a few one-seeded nutlets that separate at maturity. Lizard's tail is a native plant generally found in the eastern half of the United States (Godfrey and Wooten 1981). The Florida distribution map shows that lizard's tail was found scattered throughout Florida with no apparent geographical pattern.

Biology

Lizard's tail flowers from December through May in Florida (Dressler et al. 1987). It reproduces by seed germination and vegetatively through rhizome growth. It grows in moist soil areas and lake shoreline habitats. The plant rarely grows to the extent that it causes aquatic weed problems. Lizard's tail has little wildlife value.

Florida data

Lizard's tail was identified in only 41 lakes. The 10th and 90th percentiles for pH, alkalinity, total phosphorus, and total nitrogen values in these lakes show that 80% of the lakes with lizard's tail had levels between 5.4 and 8.7, 1.9 and 102.9 (mg/L as $CaCO_3$), 12 and 120 (μg/L), and 390 and 2380 (μg/L), respectively. The water chemistry averages and water chemistry ranges of the 41 lakes with lizard's tail showed no significant differences from those of all 322 lakes. This suggests that lizard's tail can occur in a wide range of aquatic systems.

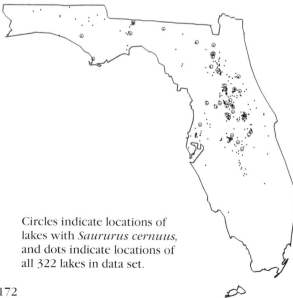

Circles indicate locations of lakes with *Saururus cernuus,* and dots indicate locations of all 322 lakes in data set.

172

Selected references from a total of 69 lizard's tail citations in the APIRS database:

Baldwin, J.T. and B.M. Speese. 1949. Cytogeography of *Saururus cernuus*. Bulletin of the Torrey Botanical Club 76(3):213-216.

Boyd, C.E. 1922. Production and chemical composition of *Saururus cernuus* L. at sites of differing fertility. Ecology 53(3):927-32.

Hall, T.F. 1940. The biology of *Saururus cernuus* L. American Midland Naturalist 24:253-260.

Johnson, D.S. 1900. On the development of *Saururus cernuus*. Bulletin of the Torrey Botanical Club 27:365-72.

Speirs, D. 1992. Growing emersed plants. Aquatic Gardener 5(2):47-48.

Wiersema, J.H. and R.R. Haynes. 1983. Aquatic and marsh plants of Alabama. III. Magnolidae. Castanea 48(2):99-108.

Saururus cernuus

Variables	Mean all lakes (n=322)	Number of lakes	Mean	10th percentile	Median	90th percentile
pH	6.7	41	7.2	5.4	7.1	8.7
Alkalinity (mg/L as CaCO$_3$)	23.9	41	34.7	1.9	21.3	102.9
Conductance (µS/cm @ 25°C)	149	41	156	36	117	335
Color (Pt-Co units)	52	41	53	13	29	109
Total phosphorus (µg/L)	45	41	53	12	26	120
Total nitrogen (µg/L)	870	41	1060	390	710	2380
Chlorophyll a (µg/L)	20	41	27	3	10	84
Secchi (m)	1.8	38	1.3	0.4	1.2	2.7
Calcium (mg/L)	17.6	41	25.6	2.6	14.8	63.6
Magnesium (mg/L)	8.2	41	11.9	2.1	7.4	32.3
Sodium (mg/L)	13.2	39	12.6	3.1	8.5	20.1
Potassium (mg/L)	2.6	41	2.6	0.2	1.7	7.7
Sulfate (mg/L)	15.2	39	13.8	2.5	8.2	47.2
Chloride (mg/L)	23.4	40	21.7	6.0	16.0	36.5
Iron (mg/L)	0.2	36	0.2	0.0	0.1	0.4
Silicon (mg/L)	1.5	36	1.8	0.2	1.0	5.1

Scirpus californicus (giant bulrush)

Kerry Dressler

Kerry Dressler

Description and distribution

Giant bulrush is a tall perennial plant with short knotty rhizomes. The round to triangular stems attain heights of up to 3 m and measure 10-30 mm wide at the base, gradually tapering to 2-4 mm at the inflorescence. The stems are dark green and smooth. Leaf blades are absent, but there are several brown basal leaf sheaths. The inflorescence is 40-120 mm long with 50-150 spikelets on long drooping branches. The spikelets are 6-10 mm long and ovoid and consist of 30-50 small chestnut-colored flowers. The fruit is a gray or grayish brown nutlet, 2 mm long, smooth with two to four feathery bristles. Giant bulrush has a sporadic occurrence in the Gulf Coast states (Godfrey and Wooten 1981). The Florida distribution map shows that the few lakes with giant bulrush were located primarily in south-central Florida.

Biology

Giant bulrush flowers from April through September in Florida (Dressler et al. 1987). It reproduces by seed germination and vegetatively through rhizome growth. It grows mostly in near-shore habitats and rarely causes problems to navigational and recreational activities. The seeds are used by several species of aquatic and songbirds. Stands of giant bulrush are also refuge and habitat for invertebrate and fish populations.

Florida data

Giant bulrush was identified in only 30 lakes. The 10th and 90th percentiles for pH, alkalinity, total phosphorus, and total nitrogen values in these lakes show that 80% of the lakes with giant bulrush had levels between 5.8 and 8.8, 1.6 and 119.4 (mg/L as $CaCO_3$), 12 and 113 (μg/L), and 410 and 2480 (μg/L), respectively. Most of the water chemistry averages of the 30 lakes with giant bulrush showed no significant differences from those for all 322 lakes. Average pH, alkalinity, specific conductance, and potassium values,

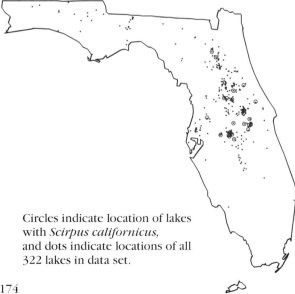

Circles indicate location of lakes with *Scirpus californicus,* and dots indicate locations of all 322 lakes in data set.

however, were significantly higher than those for all 322 lakes. This suggests that while giant bulrush can occur in a wide range of aquatic systems in Florida, it may prefer alkaline, hardwater lakes.

Selected references from a total of 80 giant bulrush citations in the APIRS database:

Berkelhamer, R.C. and T.J. Bradley. 1989. Mosquito larval development in container habitats: The role of rotting *Scirpus californicus*. Journal of the American Mosquito Control Association 5(2):258-260.

Heiser, C.B. Jr. 1979. The totora (*Scirpus californicus*) in Ecuador and Peru. Economic Botany 32:222-236.

Koyama, T. 1963. The genus *Scirpus* Linn.: Critical species of the section pterolepis. Canadian Journal of Botany 41:1107-1131.

Marshall, S. 1986. Transplanting bulrush to enhance fisheries and aquatic habitat. Aquatics 8(4):16-17.

Smith, L.L. 1979. Productivity and nutrient uptake in a tropical *Scirpus/Brachiara* marsh. Tropical Ecology 20(1):49-55.

Smith, S.G. 1973. Ecology of the *Scirpus lacustris* complex in North America. Polish Archives of Hydrobiology 20(1):215-216.

Thayer, D.D. and J.C. Joyce. 1990. The impact of herbicides on bulrush communities—an evaluation of water hyacinth control effects within native plants. Aquatics 12(4):12-19.

Scirpus californicus

Variables	Mean all lakes (n=322)	Number of lakes	Mean	10th percentile	Median	90th percentile
pH*	6.7	30	7.6	5.8	7.8	8.8
Alkalinity (mg/L as $CaCO_3$)*	23.9	30	44.4	1.6	47.1	119.4
Conductance (µS/cm @ 25°C)*	149	30	241	62	183	566
Color (Pt-Co units)	52	30	45	6	23	130
Total phosphorus (µg/L)	45	30	43	12	30	113
Total nitrogen (µg/L)	870	30	1100	410	940	2480
Chlorophyll a (µg/L)	20	30	25	3	14	74
Secchi (m)	1.8	20	1.4	0.3	1.0	2.9
Calcium (mg/L)	17.6	30	19.5	3.6	17.6	39.0
Magnesium (mg/L)	8.2	30	8.4	2.4	4.7	17.0
Sodium (mg/L)	13.2	24	23.3	6.6	11.4	69.1
Potassium (mg/L)*	2.6	30	4.3	0.6	3.7	9.5
Sulfate (mg/L)	15.2	24	20.4	5.9	14.0	38.6
Chloride (mg/L)	23.4	30	37.1	10.1	22.1	92.8
Iron (mg/L)	0.2	15	0.2	0.0	0.1	0.5
Silicon (mg/L)	1.5	15	1.7	0.1	1.0	4.5

* Denotes a significant difference (p<0.05) from mean of all lakes.

Scirpus cubensis (burhead sedge)

Kerry Dressler

Description and distribution

Burhead sedge is a perennial herb, with slender, reddish rhizomes. The slender, triangular stems reach 1 m in height, but often are shorter. The leaves are all near the base and often are longer than the stem. The inflorescence, with two to six leaf-like bracts, consists of one to several dense spherical heads, 10–20 mm in diameter. A single head is sessile; several heads occur on stalks of varying lengths. The fruit is an olive nutlet about 3 mm long, with the base tip and edges covered with a white, bony material. Burhead sedge occurs sporadically in the Gulf Coast states from Florida to Texas (Godfrey and Wooten 1981). The Florida distribution map shows that the few lakes with burhead sedge were located primarily in south-central Florida.

Biology

Burhead sedge flowers throughout the year in Florida (Dressler et al. 1987). It reproduces by seed germination and vegetatively through rhizome growth. It grows mostly in near-shore habitats and rarely causes problems to navigational and recreational activities. The seeds are used by several species of aquatic and songbirds. Stands of burhead sedge are also refuge and habitat for invertebrate and fish populations.

Florida data

Burhead sedge was identified in 91 lakes. The 10th and 90th percentiles for pH, alkalinity, total phosphorus, and total nitrogen values in these lakes show that 80% of the lakes with burhead sedge had levels between 5.6 and 8.6, 2.2 and 74.6 (mg/L as $CaCO_3$), 12 and 103 (μg/L), and 370 and 1780 (μg/L), respectively. Most of the water chemistry averages of the 91 lakes with burhead sedge showed no significant differences from those for all 322 lakes. Average calcium and magnesium values, however, were significantly higher than those of all 322 lakes. This suggests that while burhead sedge can occur in a wide range of aquatic systems in Florida, it may prefer hardwater lakes.

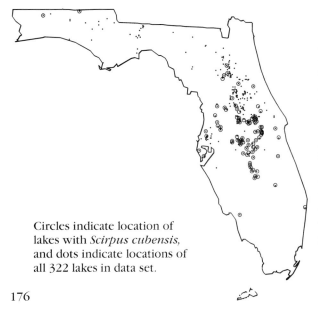

Circles indicate location of lakes with *Scirpus cubensis,* and dots indicate locations of all 322 lakes in data set.

Selected references from a total of 80 burhead sedge citations in the APIRS database:

Holm, L.G., D.L. Plucknett, J.V. Pancho, and J.P. Herberger. 1977. The world's worst weeds: Distribution and biology. University Press Hawaii, Honolulu. 609 pp.

Hotchkiss, N. 1965. Bulrushes and bulrush-like plants of eastern North America. U.S. Dept. of the Interior, Fish and Wildlife Services., Bureau of Sport Fisheries and Wildlife, Washington, D.C., Circular 221,19 pp.

Howard-Williams, C. and W.J. Junk. 1976. The decomposition of aquatic macrophytes in the floating meadows of a central Amazonian varzea lake. Biogeographica 7:115-123.

Hujik, B. 1994. Invasion of the tussocks. Aquatics 16(2):4,6,8.

Lubke, R.A., P.E. Reavell, and P.J. Dye. 1984. The effects of dredging on the macrophytic vegetation of the Bo Ro River, Okavango Delta, Botswana. Biological Conservation 30(3):211-236.

Mitchell, D.S. 1969. The ecology of vascular hydrophytes on Lake Kariba. Hydrobiologia 34(3)(4): 448-464.

Obeng, L.E. 1969. The invertebrate fauna of aquatic plants of the Volta Lake in relation to the spread of helminth parasites. Accra International Symposium on Man-Made Lakes, Accra, Ghana, 1966. Pp. 320-325.

Okali, D.U.U. and J.B. Hall. 1974. Colonization of *Pistia stratiotes* L. mats by *Scirpus cubensis* Poeppig and Kunth on the Volta Lake. Ghana Journal of Agricultural Science 7:31-36.

Schelpe, E.A. 1961. The ecology of *Salvinia auriculata* and associated vegetation on Kariba Lake. Journal of South African Botany 27:181-187.

Scirpus cubensis

Variables	Mean all lakes (n=322)	Number of lakes	Mean	10th percentile	Median	90th percentile
pH	6.7	91	7.2	5.6	7.2	8.6
Alkalinity (mg/L as CaCO$_3$)	23.9	91	28.6	2.2	17.0	74.6
Conductance (µS/cm @ 25°C)	149	91	182	63	116	317
Color (Pt-Co units)	52	91	59	7	38	131
Total phosphorus (µg/L)	45	90	42	12	24	103
Total nitrogen (µg/L)	870	90	920	370	820	1780
Chlorophyll a (µg/L)	20	91	17	3	8	37
Secchi (m)	1.8	81	1.5	0.4	1.1	2.9
Calcium (mg/L)*	17.6	91	28.4	4.6	13.7	85.0
Magnesium (mg/L)*	8.2	91	13.7	2.7	9.4	34.7
Sodium (mg/L)	13.2	87	16.8	5.6	9.2	28.1
Potassium (mg/L)	2.6	91	3.0	0.6	2.2	6.7
Sulfate (mg/L)	15.2	87	19.3	5.1	12.4	47.9
Chloride (mg/L)	23.4	91	30.9	10.1	17.4	43.0
Iron (mg/L)	0.2	77	0.2	0.0	0.1	0.5
Silicon (mg/L)	1.5	77	1.7	0.1	1.0	3.7

* Denotes a significant difference (p<0.05) from mean of all lakes.

Spartina bakeri (cordgrass)

Kerry Dressler

Kerry Dressler

Description and distribution

Cordgrass produces stout clumps from basal offshoots or short rhizomes. Long ascending leaves 100–200 mm long and 4–8 mm wide are rolled to somewhat flattened in shape, giving a cylindrical appearance. The inflorescence is 120–200 mm long with five to 12 appressed spikes from 30–60 mm long. Spikelets are 6–8 mm long and one flowered. The fruit is 2–4 mm long and flattened. Cordgrass occurs in the coastal states from South Carolina to Texas (Tarver et al. 1986). The Florida distribution map shows that lakes with cordgrass were located primarily in central and south Florida.

Biology

Cordgrass flowers throughout the year in Florida (Dressler et al. 1987). It reproduces by seed germination and vegetatively through rhizome growth. It grows mostly in near-shore habitats and rarely causes problems to navigational and recreational activities. The seeds are used by several species of aquatic and songbirds. Stands of cordgrass are also refuge and habitat for invertebrate and fish populations.

Florida data

Cordgrass was identified in 63 lakes. The 10th and 90th percentiles for pH, alkalinity, total phosphorus, and total nitrogen values in these lakes show that 80% of the lakes with cordgrass had levels between 5.0 and 8.6, 1.5 and 102.3 (mg/L as $CaCO_3$), 10 and 89 (μg/L), and 310 and 1720 (μg/L), respectively. Most of the water chemistry averages of the 63 lakes with cordgrass showed no significant differences from those for all 322 lakes. Average specific conductance, calcium, magnesium, sodium, and chloride values, however, were significantly higher than those for all 322 lakes. This suggests that while cordgrass can occur in a range of aquatic systems in Florida, it may prefer hardwater lakes.

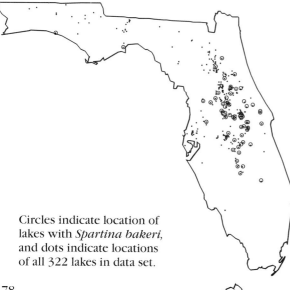
Circles indicate location of lakes with *Spartina bakeri*, and dots indicate locations of all 322 lakes in data set.

Selected references from a total of 18 cordgrass citations in the APIRS database:

Breiniger, D.R. and R.B. Smith. 1990. Waterbird use of coastal impoundments and management implications in east-central Florida. Wetlands 10(2): 223–241.

Burney, J.L. and J.M. Buhler. 1991. Wastewater treatment and habitat availability in a created freshwater wetland (Florida). Restoration Management Notes 9(1):43–44.

Garmann, G.C. and L.A. Nielsen. 1992. Medium-sized rivers of the Atlantic Coastal Plain. Pp. 315–350 in Biodiversity of the southeastern United States—Aquatic communities. John Wiley and Sons Inc., New York.

Kushlan, J.A. 1990. Freshwater marshes. Pp. 324–363 in Ecosystems of Florida, R.L. Myers and J.J. Ewel, editors. University of Central Florida Press, Orlando.

Loftin, J.P. 1994. On the waterfront. Water Magazine 3(2): 14–24.

Long, R.W. and O. Lakela. 1971. A flora of tropical Florida: A manual of the seed plants and ferns of southern peninsular Florida. University of Miami Press, Coral Gables.

Marchant, C.J. 1968. Evolution in *Spartina* (Gramineae). III. Species chromosome numbers and their taxonomic significance. Journal of the Linnean Society of London (Botany) 60:411–417.

Rochow, T.F. 1985. Hydrologic and vegetational changes resulting from underground pumping at the Cypress Creek Well Field, Pasco County, Florida. Florida Scientist 48(2): 65–80.

Schmalzer, P.A. and C.R. Hinkle. 1992. Soil dynamics following fire in *Juncus* and *Spartina* marshes. Wetlands 12(1):8–21.

Schmalzer, P.A., C.R. Hinkle, and J.L. Mailander. 1991. Changes in community composition and biomass in *Juncus roemerianus* Scheele and *Spartina bakeri* Merr. marshes one year after a fire. Wetlands 11(1):67–86.

Spartina bakeri

Variables	Mean all lakes (n=322)	Number of lakes	Mean	10th percentile	Median	90th percentile
pH	6.7	63	7.0	5.0	7.1	8.6
Alkalinity (mg/L as CaCO$_3$)	23.9	63	31.7	1.5	17.0	102.3
Conductance (µS/cm @ 25°C)*	149	63	233	57	128	708
Color (Pt-Co units)	52	63	57	4	42	151
Total phosphorus (µg/L)	45	63	37	10	22	89
Total nitrogen (µg/L)	870	63	920	310	800	1720
Chlorophyll a (µg/L)	20	63	20	2	7	57
Secchi (m)	1.8	56	1.6	0.5	1.2	3.6
Calcium (mg/L)*	17.6	63	29.9	2.9	20.2	91.9
Magnesium (mg/L)*	8.2	63	16.5	1.9	10.4	49.6
Sodium (mg/L)*	13.2	60	25.1	5.0	10.3	91.7
Potassium (mg/L)	2.6	63	3.4	0.2	2.3	8.4
Sulfate (mg/L)	15.2	60	21.3	5.4	12.8	56.6
Chloride (mg/L)*	23.4	63	45.3	9.3	19.7	171.2
Iron (mg/L)	0.2	52	0.2	0.0	0.10	0.5
Silicon (mg/L)	1.5	52	1.7	0.1	1.2	4.1

* Denotes a significant difference (p<0.05) from mean of all lakes.

Spirodela polyrhiza (giant duckweed)

Jesse Van Dyke

Jesse Van Dyke

Description and distribution

Giant duckweed is a small, free-floating plant 3–10 mm long, usually with two or more fronds, but sometimes with a single frond. The fronds are oblong or broadly elliptical, almost as wide as long, with five to 11 prominent veins, light green above, and reddish below. Each frond has several slender roots that end in long pointed rootcaps. The inflorescence consists of one pistillated flower and two or three staminated flowers arising from one of two reproductive pouches on either side of the basal end of the floating leaf. The fruit has one seed that is longitudinally ribbed. Giant duckweed is widespread in temperate and tropical latitudes but has limited distribution in Africa and is absent in South America (Godfrey and Wooten 1981). The Florida distribution map shows that giant duckweed was scattered throughout the state but primarily in central and south Florida. Lakes are progressively more alkaline and nutrient rich as one moves from northwestern to southern Florida (Canfield and Hoyer 1988). Thus the distribution of giant duckweed in Florida suggests that it may tend to occur in alkaline, hardwater, nutrient-rich lakes.

Biology

During adverse conditions of temperature or drought, giant duckweed produces turions that sink and remain dormant on the lake bottom until conditions improve. The starch-filled turion then expels a small gas bubble that carries the turion to the surface where it germinates rapidly. Giant duckweed also reproduces by budding. It has a tremendous growth potential and can yield mats several inches thick. These mats, which generally occur on smaller lakes and ponds, can interfere with navigational and recreational uses of some aquatic systems. Giant duckweed is a valuable food source for many species of aquatic birds and is also refuge and habitat for invertebrate populations.

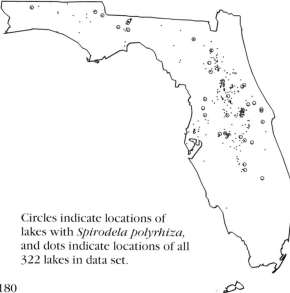

Circles indicate locations of lakes with *Spirodela polyrhiza,* and dots indicate locations of all 322 lakes in data set.

Florida data

Giant duckweed was identified in only 37 lakes. The 10th and 90th percentiles for pH, alkalinity, total phosphorus, and total nitrogen values in these lakes show that 80% of the lakes with giant duckweed had levels between 5.5 and 8.6, 2.3 and 96.5 (mg/L as $CaCO_3$), 12 and 234 (μg/L), and 430 and 1760 (μg/L), respectively. These 37 lakes also collectively averaged significantly higher pH, alkalinity, total phosphorus, calcium, and magnesium values than all 322 lakes. Thus while giant duckweed can occur in a range of lake types, it tends to occur in alkaline, hardwater, nutrient-rich lakes.

Selected references from a total of 514 giant duckweed citations in the APIRS database:

Borstlap, A.C. 1974. Antagonism between amino acids in the growth of *Spirodela polyrhiza* due to competitive amino acid uptake. Acta Botanica Nederlandica 23(5-6):723-738.

Bytniewska, K. and W. Potapczyk. 1981. Growth and contents of total and readily soluble protein in aseptic culture of *Spirodela polyrhiza*. Acta Physiologiae Plantarum 3(3):125-134.

Culley, D.D., E. Rejmankova, J. Kvet, and J.B. Frye. 1981. Production, chemical quality and use of duckweeds (Lemnaceae) in aquaculture, waste management, and animal feeds. Journal of World Mariculture Society 12(2):27-49.

Gorham, P.R. 1945. Growth factor studies with *Spirodela polyrhiza* (L.) Schleid. American Journal of Botany 32:496-505.

Jacobs, D.L. 1945. An ecological life-history of *Spirodela polyrhiza* (greater duck weed) with emphasis on the turion phase. Ecological Monograph 17:437-469.

Nelson, B. 1981. Duckweeds–nature's smallest flowering plants. Aquatics 3(1):4-16.

Sutton, D.L. and W.H. Ornes. 1977. Growth of *Spirodela polyrhiza* in state sewage effluent. Aquatic Botany 3:231-237.

Tatkowska, E. and J. Buczek. 1983. Effect of ammonium nutrition on the nitrate utilization, nitrate reductase activity and growth of *Spirodela polyrhiza*. Acta Societatis Botanicorum Poloniae 52(3-4):241-252.

Wang, W. 1990. Literature review on duckweed toxicity testing. Environmental Research 52:7-22.

Wolek, J. 1979. Experimental investigations of competition and allelopathy between *Spirodela polyrhiza* (L.) Schleid. and *Wolffia arrhiza* (L.) Wimm. Fragmenta Floristica et Geobotanica 25(2):282-350.

Spirodela polyrhiza

Variables	Mean all lakes (n=322)	Number of lakes	Mean	10th percentile	Median	90th percentile
pH*	6.7	37	7.4	5.5	7.7	8.6
Alkalinity (mg/L as $CaCO_3$)*	23.9	37	39.7	2.3	25.5	96.5
Conductance (μS/cm @ 25°C)	149	37	237	26	118	734
Color (Pt-Co units)	52	37	63	5	47	131
Total phosphorus (μg/L)*	45	37	80	12	42	234
Total nitrogen (μg/L)	870	37	1050	430	860	1760
Chlorophyll a (μg/L)	20	37	24	3	13	62
Secchi (m)	1.8	33	1.4	0.5	0.8	3.4
Calcium (mg/L)*	17.6	37	38.6	2.5	29.6	94.2
Magnesium (mg/L)*	8.2	37	15.6	2.1	9.6	46.5
Sodium (mg/L)	13.2	37	25.3	2.1	8.8	89.6
Potassium (mg/L)	2.6	37	2.3	0.2	1.7	5.5
Sulfate (mg/L)	15.2	37	20.9	3.2	11.2	60.2
Chloride (mg/L)	23.4	37	43.7	3.3	15.3	171.1
Iron (mg/L)	0.2	33	0.2	0.0	0.2	0.6
Silicon (mg/L)	1.5	33	2.5	0.1	1.6	7.0

* Denotes a significant difference (p<0.05) from mean of all lakes.

Thalia geniculata (fire flag)

Kerry Dressler

Kerry Dressler

Description and distribution

Fire flag is a robust, green, perennial herb growing from thick rhizomes, generally smooth throughout. The leaves are alternate, stalked (the stalk sheathing at the base), broadly lanceolate or ovate-lanceolate, 300–500 mm long, and 200 mm wide. The inflorescence is terminal and branching; the zigzagging internodes are short.The purple flowers are paired with two bracts, three sepals, three petals. The fruit is 4–6 mm across, ovoid, with one seed. Fire flag is found in Florida and Wisconsin (Godfrey and Wooten 1981). The Florida distribution map shows that fire flag was found primarily in south-central Florida. Lakes are progressively more alkaline and nutrient rich as one moves from northwestern to southern Florida (Canfield and Hoyer 1988). Thus the distribution of fire flag in Florida suggests that it may tend to occur in alkaline, hardwater, nutrient-rich lakes.

Biology

Fire flag reproduces by seed germination and vegetatively through rhizome production. It tends to occur in moist soil and shoreline habitats, often growing toward open water, sometimes in floating islands.

Florida data

Fire flag was identified in only 25 lakes. The 10th and 90th percentiles for pH, alkalinity, total phosphorus, and total nitrogen values in these lakes show that 80% of the lakes with fire flag had levels between 5.4 and 8.8, 2.0 and 114.5 (mg/L as $CaCO_3$), 16 and 139 (μg/L), and 480 and 2090 (μg/L), respectively. These 25 lakes also collectively averaged significantly higher pH, alkalinity, specific conductance, total phosphorus, calcium, magnesium, sodium, and chloride values than all 322 lakes. Average Secchi depth was also significantly less in lakes with fire flag. Thus while fire flag can occur in a range of lake types, it definitely tends to occur in alkaline, hardwater, nutrient-rich lakes.

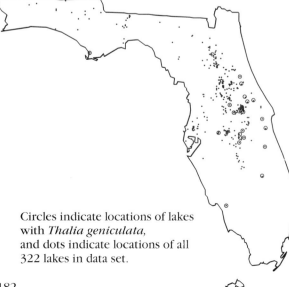

Circles indicate locations of lakes with *Thalia geniculata,* and dots indicate locations of all 322 lakes in data set.

Selected references from a total of 20 fire flag citations in the APIRS database:

Bjork, S. and G. Digerfeldt. 1991. Development and degradation, redevelopment and preservation of Jamaican wetlands. Ambio 20(7):276-284.

Cassani, J.R. 1983. Arrowroot *Thalia* spp. Aquatics 5(2):12-13.

Davis, M.A. 1987. The role of flower visitors in the explosive pollination of *Thalia geniculata* (Marantaceae), a Costa Rican marsh plant. Bulletin of the Torrey Botanical Club 114(2):134-138.

Kaul, R.B. 1973. Development of foliar diaphragms in *Sparganium eurycarpum.* American Journal of Botany 60(9):944-49.

Rejmankova, E., H.M. Savage, M.H. Rodriguez, D.R. Roberts, and M. Rejmanek. 1992. Aquatic vegetation as a basis for classification of *Anopheles albimanus* Weideman (Diptera: Culicidae) larval habitats. Environmental Entomology 21(3):598-603.

Thieret, J.W. 1972. Aquatic and marsh plants of Louisiana: A checklist. Louisiana Society of Horticultural Research Journal 13(1):1-45.

Thalia geniculata

Variables	Mean all lakes (n=322)	Number of lakes	Mean	10th percentile	Median	90th percentile
pH*	6.7	25	7.7	5.4	7.9	8.8
Alkalinity (mg/L as CaCO$_3$)*	23.9	25	50.0	2.0	49.3	114.5
Conductance (µS/cm @ 25°C)*	149	25	334	74	204	818
Color (Pt-Co units)	52	25	72	4	53	120
Total phosphorus (µg/L)*	45	25	64	16	42	139
Total nitrogen (µg/L)	870	25	1160	480	1110	2090
Chlorophyll a (µg/L)	20	25	29	3	15	99
Secchi (m)*	1.8	24	1.0	0.4	0.7	1.8
Calcium (mg/L)*	17.6	25	51.6	8.6	44.4	99.4
Magnesium (mg/L)*	8.2	25	23.4	2.8	11.3	55.0
Sodium (mg/L)*	13.2	24	38.4	6.7	15.0	122.9
Potassium (mg/L)	2.6	25	3.6	1.0	2.6	7.4
Sulfate (mg/L)	15.2	24	26.9	7.0	13.7	69.8
Chloride (mg/L)*	23.4	25	69.2	13.9	26.5	223.2
Iron (mg/L)	0.2	23	0.3	0.0	0.2	0.7
Silicon (mg/L)	1.5	23	2.7	0.3	3.1	5.2

* Denotes a significant difference (p<0.05) from mean of all lakes.

Typha spp. (cattail)

Kerry Dressler

Kerry Dressler

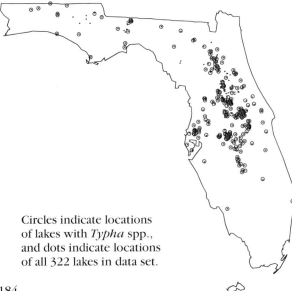

Circles indicate locations
of lakes with *Typha* spp.,
and dots indicate locations
of all 322 lakes in data set.

Description and distribution

The following four species of cattail are found in the United States: *Typha domingensis*, *T. glauca*, *T. angustifolia*, and *T. latifolia*. All four are perennial, erect, rhizomatous herbs with jointless stems. The numerous, extremely small flowers are in a dense cigar-shaped, brown spike, 150–500 mm long. The staminated portion of the spike is above the pistillated part. The distance between these two portions is the basis for determining species. The leaves are flat to slightly rounded, reaching heights up to 3 m and having a slight twist from base to tip. The fruit is a sausage-shaped cluster of nutlets surrounded by chaff. Cattail species are common throughout the southeastern United states (Godfrey and Wooten 1981). The Florida distribution map shows that cattail was found in lakes across the whole state, with no apparent geographical pattern.

Biology

Cattail flowers January through June in Florida (Dressler et al. 1987). It reproduces by seed germination and vegetatively from rhizomes. It is an aggressive invader of disturbed moist soil habitats and has a great growth potential. It is found primarily on shoreline habitats and can grow extensively, impairing navigational and recreational uses of some aquatic systems. Cattail is used as refuge and nesting habitat for several species of aquatic and songbirds. In some hypereutrophic lakes, where other plants are scarce, cattail is a major refuge and habitat for invertebrates and fish populations.

Florida data

Cattail was identified in 234 lakes. The 10th and 90th percentiles for pH, alkalinity, total phosphorus, and total nitrogen values in these lakes show that 80% of the lakes with cattail had levels between 5.6 and 8.7, 1.6 and 76.1

(mg/L as CaCO$_3$), 10 and 112 (µg/L), and 360 and 1950 (µg/L), respectively. These 234 lakes also collectively averaged significantly higher pH, alkalinity, specific conductance, calcium, magnesium, and potassium values than all 322 lakes. Thus while cattail can occur in a range of lake types, it tends to occur in alkaline, hardwater lakes.

Selected references from a total of 2694 cattail citations in the APIRS database:

Adriano, D.C., A. Fulenwider, R.R. Sharitz, T.G. Ciravolo, and G.D. Hoyt. 1980. Growth and mineral nutrition of cattail (*Typha*) as influenced by thermal alteration. Journal of Environmental Quality 9(4):649-653.

Bedish, J.W. 1967. Cattail moisture requirements and their significance to marsh management. American Midland Naturalist 78(2):288-300.

Cary, P.R. and P.G.J. Weerts. 1984. Growth and nutrient composition of *Typha orientalis* as affected by water temperature and nitrogen and phosphorus supply. Aquatic Botany 19:105-118.

Fiala, K. 1973. Growth and production of underground organs of *Typha angustifolia* L. Polish Archives of Hydrobiology 20(1):59-66.

Gilbert, K.M. 1987. The role of management of cattails in a lake ecosystem. Aquatics 9(1):9-11.

Grace, J.B. and R.G. Wetzel. 1982. Variations in growth and reproduction within populations of two rhizomatous plant species: *Typha latifolia* and *Typha angustifolia*. Oecologia 53:258-263.

McNaughton, S.J. 1966. Ecotype function in the *Typha* community-type. Ecological Monographs 36(4):298-325.

Reddy, K.R. and K.M. Portier. 1987. Nitrogen utilization by *Typha latifolia* L. as affected by temperature and rate of nitrogen application. Aquatic Botany 27(2):127-138.

Sharma, K.P. and B. Gopal. 1979. Effect of water regime on the growth and establishment of *Typha angustata* seedlings. International Journal of Ecology and Environmental Sciences 5:69-74.

Urban, N.H., S.M. Davis, and N.G. Aumen. 1993. Fluctuations in sawgrass and cattail densities in Everglades Water Conservation Area 2A under varying nutrient, hydrologic and fire regimes. Aquatic Botany 46:203-223.

Typha spp.

Variables	Mean all lakes (n=322)	Number of lakes	Mean	10th percentile	Median	90th percentile
pH*	6.7	234	7.2	5.6	7.2	8.7
Alkalinity (mg/L as CaCO$_3$)*	23.9	234	31.2	1.6	20.9	76.1
Conductance (µS/cm @ 25°C)*	149	234	184	54	145	340
Color (Pt-Co units)	52	234	47	7	25	111
Total phosphorus (µg/L)	45	233	55	10	22	112
Total nitrogen (µg/L)	870	233	970	360	730	1950
Chlorophyll a (µg/L)	20	234	25	3	10	67
Secchi (m)	1.8	194	1.5	0.4	1.3	2.9
Calcium (mg/L)*	17.6	234	23.0	2.8	13.4	59.7
Magnesium (mg/L)*	8.2	234	10.8	2.0	6.8	27.8
Sodium (mg/L)	13.2	217	16.1	4.3	9.6	23.5
Potassium (mg/L)*	2.6	234	3.3	0.3	2.2	8.6
Sulfate (mg/L)	15.2	217	18.2	4.4	11.7	44.1
Chloride (mg/L)	23.4	233	28.7	8.3	17.4	40.5
Iron (mg/L)	0.2	179	0.2	0.0	0.10	0.4
Silicon (mg/L)	1.5	179	1.7	0.2	0.7	4.2

* Denotes a significant difference (p<0.05) from mean of all lakes.

Utricularia biflora (tangled bladderwort)

Jesse Van Dyke

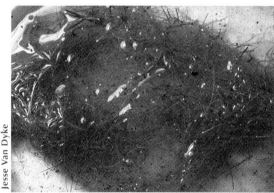

Jesse Van Dyke

Description and distribution

Tangled bladderwort is a free-floating, rootless plant that tends to form dense mats or bunches. It is a member of the genus *Utricularia*, which is known for having very specialized structures called bladders. These bladders trap small crustaceans and other animals, which are digested and the nutrients used for plant growth. The forked leaf-like lateral branches are small. A leafless flowering stem, 20–80 mm long, arises singly or in twos or threes from the main axes. On the axes below the flowering branch grow clawlike clusters of structures that are similar to rhizomes. The inflorescence is a raceme of one to three yellow flowers, streaked with red, that are 6-8 mm across. The fruit is a capsule about 4 mm across that contains a thin, brown, winged seed. Tangled bladderwort is found throughout the Coastal Plain states (Godfrey and Wooten 1981). The Florida distribution map shows that tangled bladderwort can be found from the northwest to southern regions of Florida.

Biology

Utricularia species flower throughout the year in Florida (Dressler et al. 1987). Tangled bladderwort reproduces by seed germination and fragmentation. It provides cover for small fish and aquatic invertebrates.

Florida data

Tangled bladderwort was identified in 89 lakes. The 10th and 90th percentiles for pH, alkalinity, total phosphorus, and total nitrogen values in these lakes show that 80% of the lakes with tangled bladderwort had levels between 5.4 and 8.6, 1.6 and 97.1 (mg/L as $CaCO_3$), 11 and 82 (μg/L), and 320 and 1840 (μg/L), respectively. Most water chemistry averages of the 89 lakes with tangled bladderwort showed no significant differences from those for all 322 lakes. Average calcium and magnesium values, however, were significantly higher than those of all 322 lakes. This suggests that while tangled bladderwort can occur in a wide range of aquatic systems, it may prefer hardwater lakes.

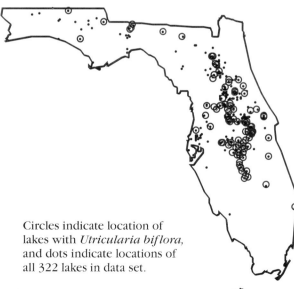

Circles indicate location of lakes with *Utricularia biflora,* and dots indicate locations of all 322 lakes in data set.

Selected references from a total of 937 *Utricularia* spp. citations in the APIRS database:

Brock, T.D. 1970. Photosynthesis by algal epiphytes of *Utricularia* in Everglades National Park. Bulletin of Marine Science 20(4):952–956.

Brown, M.S. 1940. *Utricularia inflata* in Canada. Canadian Field Naturalist 54:44

Cassani, J.R. 1988. Weed potential of cone-spur bladderwort *Utricularia biflora*. Aquatics 10(3):4–6.

Ceska, A. and O. Ceska. 1986. Noteworthy collections, Washington: *Utricularia inflata* Walt. (Lentibulariaceae). Madrono 33:80.

Fromm-Trinta, E. 1985. Lentibulariaceae of Brazil. Aquatic *Utricularia*. Bradea 4(29):188–210.

Haas, T.P. 1947. Observations on *Utricularia inflata* and *U. cleistogama*, a contribution to the biology of *Utricularia*. American Journal of Botany 34:583–584.

Hellquist, C.B. 1974. A white-flowered form of *Utricularia purpurea* from New Hampshire. Rhodora 76:805.

Kondo, K., M. Segawa, and K. Nehira. 1978. Anatomical studies on seeds and seedlings of some *Utricularia* (Lentibulariaceae). Brittonia 30:89–95.

Lloyd, F.E. 1937. Further notes on Australian *Utricularia* with a correction. Victorian Naturalist 53:163–166.

Lloyd, F.E. 1933. The structure and behavior of *Utricularia purpurea*. Canadian Journal of Research 8:234–252.

Lloyd, R.M. 1972. The traps of *Utricularia*. Proceedings of the International Congress Botany 6:51 73.

Lollar, A.Q., D.C. Coleman, and C.D. Boyd. 1971. Carnivorous pathway of phosphorus uptake by *Utricularia inflata*. Archiv fur Hydrobiologia 69(3):400–404.

Moeller, R.E. 1978. Carbon-uptake by the submerged hydrophyte *Utricularia purpurea*. Aquatic Botany 5(3):209–216.

Moeller, R.E. 1980. The temperature-determined growing season of a submerged hydrophyte: Tissue chemistry and biomass turnover of *Utricularia purpurea*. Freshwater Biology 10(5):391–400.

Mohan Ram, H.Y. and S. Dutta. 1966. *In vitro* culture of *Utricularia*. Current Science 35:48–50.

Rossbach, G.B. 1993. The developmental plasticity of *Utricularia aurea* (Lentibulariaceae) and its floats. Aquatic Botany 45:119–143.

Sorrie, B.A. 1992. *Utricularia inflata* Walter (Lentibulariaceae) in Massachusetts. Rhodora 94(880):391–392.

Utricularia biflora

Variables	Mean all lakes (n=322)	Number of lakes	Mean	10th percentile	Median	90th percentile
pH	6.7	89	7.0	5.4	7.0	8.6
Alkalinity (mg/L as $CaCO_3$)	23.9	89	27.0	1.6	11.5	97.1
Conductance (µS/cm @ 25°C)	149	89	175	40	106	384
Color (Pt-Co units)	52	89	62	6	37	133
Total phosphorus (µg/L)	45	89	37	11	22	82
Total nitrogen (µg/L)	870	89	920	320	750	1840
Chlorophyll a (µg/L)	20	89	18	3	7	40
Secchi (m)	1.8	79	1.5	0.4	1.1	3.4
Calcium (mg/L)*	17.6	89	23.8	3.2	14.9	60.3
Magnesium (mg/L)*	8.2	89	12.9	2.3	9.7	31.8
Sodium (mg/L)	13.2	84	16.9	3.7	8.3	32.8
Potassium (mg/L)	2.6	89	2.6	0.2	1.7	6.6
Sulfate (mg/L)	15.2	84	17.1	3.5	11.6	44.4
Chloride (mg/L)	23.4	89	30.3	6.8	15.8	42.4
Iron (mg/L)	0.2	74	0.2	0.0	0.1	0.6
Silicon (mg/L)	1.5	74	1.8	0.1	1.1	3.9

* Denotes a significant difference (p<0.05) from mean of all lakes.

Utricularia floridana (Florida bladderwort)

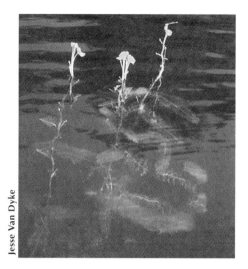

Jesse Van Dyke

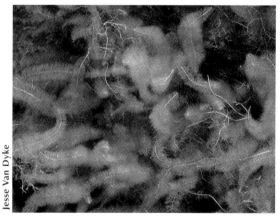

Jesse Van Dyke

Description and distribution

Florida bladderwort is a unique member of the Lentibulariaceae family in that this species has specialized structures called bladders. These bladders trap small crustaceans and other animals, which are digested and the nutrients used for plant growth. Although a portion of Florida bladderwort's plant body is "rooted" into the hydrosoil, this species of submersed aquatic plant has no true roots. This part of the plant tends to be whitish to light yellow. The upper part of the plant is green and branched and resembles a foxtail in shape. The branches are 20–50 mm across, and the leaf-like branches are forked several times. The flowering raceme arises from a leafless, flattened, flowering stem, which can be as long as 1 m. Its yellow flowers are red-streaked. The fruit is a capsule, 7-8 mm across with irregularly shaped brown seeds. Florida bladderwort is found primarily along the Coastal Plain states from South Carolina to central Florida (Godfrey and Wooten 1981). The Florida distribution map shows that Florida bladderwort occurs throughout the state.

Biology

Florida bladderwort reproduces by seed germination and fragmentation. *Utricularia* species flower throughout the year in Florida (Dressler et al. 1987). Florida bladderwort can form dense stands along the bottoms of lakes. This species can provide cover for fish and other aquatic animals.

Florida data

Florida bladderwort was identified in 90 lakes. The 10th and 90th percentiles for pH, alkalinity, total phosphorus, and total nitrogen values in these lakes show that 80% of the lakes with Florida bladderwort had levels that fell between 4.5 and 7.2, 0.8 and 22.3 (mg/L as $CaCO_3$), 7 and 27 (µg/L), and 184 and 1112 (µg/L), respectively. The 90 lakes collectively averaged significantly lower pH, alkalinity, specific conductance, total phosphorus,

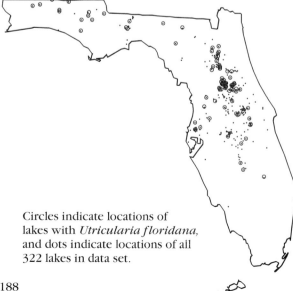

Circles indicate locations of lakes with *Utricularia floridana*, and dots indicate locations of all 322 lakes in data set.

total nitrogen, calcium, magnesium, sodium, potassium, sulfate, and chloride values than all 322 lakes. The average Secchi disc measurement for the 90 lakes was significantly higher than all 322 lakes. Thus Florida bladderwort tends to occur in acidic, softwater lakes with low nutrient concentrations.

Utricularia floridana: see references for *Utricularia biflora*

Utricularia floridana

Variables	Mean all lakes (n=322)	Number of lakes	Mean	10th percentile	Median	90th percentile
pH*	6.7	90	5.8	4.5	5.6	7.2
Alkalinity (mg/L as CaCO$_3$)*	23.9	90	8.0	0.8	2.2	22.3
Conductance (µS/cm @ 25°C)*	149	90	71	20	48	151
Color (Pt-Co units)	52	90	36	3	16	108
Total phosphorus (µg/L)*	45	89	16	7	11	27
Total nitrogen (µg/L)*	870	89	600	180	460	1110
Chlorophyll a (µg/L)	20	90	7	1.0	3	13
Secchi (m)*	1.8	84	2.6	0.8	2.3	4.5
Calcium (mg/L)*	17.6	90	7.0	0.7	3.0	18.6
Magnesium (mg/L)*	8.2	90	4.1	0.6	2.0	10.5
Sodium (mg/L)*	13.2	85	6.4	1.9	4.4	11.5
Potassium (mg/L)*	2.6	90	1.0	0.1	0.3	2.5
Sulfate (mg/L)*	15.2	85	8.6	3.0	5.8	13.5
Chloride (mg/L)*	23.4	90	11.7	2.9	8.5	22.9
Iron (mg/L)	0.2	53	0.2	0.0	0.10	0.4
Silicon (mg/L)*	1.5	53	0.7	0.10	0.3	1.6

* Denotes a significant difference (p<0.05) from mean of all lakes.

Utricularia foliosa (bladderwort)

Kerry Dressler

Description and distribution

Bladderwort is a free-floating submersed aquatic plant that tends to have a mucilaginous covering. A member of the Lentibulariaceae family, the genus *Utricularia* is known for having very specialized structures called bladders, which trap small crustaceans and other aquatic animals and use the nutrients for plant growth. Bladderwort is the most easily identified *Utricularia* species because it has a distinctive flat, strap-like main stem, which can be up to 10 mm wide and 1 m long. Bladderwort has three types of branches that extend from the primary stem. The first is very dissected and spreads laterally along a single plane. The second type is very long and cylindrical and has few dissections; this type is not oriented in only one plane. The third type is long and thread-like and tends to reach the surface of the water. This branch has no leaf-like structures below the surface, but has mussel-shaped bracts that lie on the water surface. Bladderwort has a leafless flowering stem 10–30 mm long. The flowers are yellow. The fruit is a capsule 5–7 mm across with a 3 mm seed. Bladderwort occurs from Florida to Louisiana (Godfrey and Wooten 1981). The Florida distribution map shows that bladderwort is found throughout the state.

Biology

Utricularia species flower throughout the year in Florida (Dressler et al. 1987). Bladderwort reproduces by seed germination and fragmentation. It grows in the near-shore and open water areas of lakes and ponds and provides good cover for fish and other aquatic invertebrates.

Florida data

Bladderwort was identified in 101 lakes. The 10th and 90th percentiles for pH, alkalinity, total phosphorus, and total nitrogen values in these lakes show that 80% of the lakes with bladderwort had levels between 5.5 and 8.5, 1.4 and 74.1 (mg/L as $CaCO_3$), 10 and 80 (µg/L), and

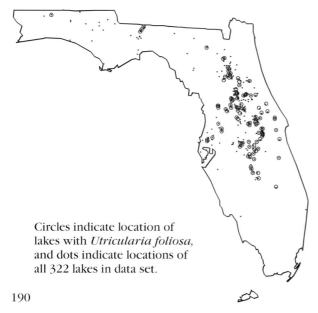

Circles indicate location of lakes with *Utricularia foliosa*, and dots indicate locations of all 322 lakes in data set.

320 and 1690 (µg/L), respectively. Most of the water chemistry averages of the 91 lakes with bladderwort showed no significant differences from those for all 322 lakes. Average magnesium values, however, were significantly higher than for all 322 lakes. This suggests that while bladderwort can occur in a wide range of aquatic systems, it may prefer hardwater lakes.

Utriculara foliosa: see references for *Utricularia biflora*

Utricularia foliosa

Variables	Mean all lakes (n=322)	Number of lakes	Mean	10th percentile	Median	90th percentile
pH	6.7	101	6.9	5.5	7.0	8.5
Alkalinity (mg/L as CaCO₃)	23.9	101	26.2	1.4	12.5	74.1
Conductance (µS/cm @ 25°C)	149	101	193	49	115	561
Color (Pt-Co units)	52	101	56	5	29	133
Total phosphorus (µg/L)	45	101	36	10	18	80
Total nitrogen (µg/L)	866	101	883	324	796	1691
Chlorophyll a (µg/L)	20	101	14	2	6	36
Secchi (m)	1.8	86	1.7	0.5	1.4	3.7
Calcium (mg/L)	17.6	101	23.9	2.1	14.3	66.9
Magnesium (mg/L)*	8.2	101	12.6	1.5	7.4	34.6
Sodium (mg/L)	13.2	100	19.5	4.6	9.4	54.9
Potassium (mg/L)	2.6	101	2.6	0.2	1.9	6.6
Sulfate (mg/L)	15.2	100	18.0	3.3	11.3	47.7
Chloride (mg/L)	23.4	101	35.5	8.5	17.5	97.6
Iron (mg/L)	0.2	80	0.2	0.0	0.1	0.5
Silicon (mg/L)	1.5	80	1.8	0.1	1.0	4.4

* Denotes a significant difference (p<0.05) from mean of all lakes.

Utricularia gibba (cone-spur bladderwort)

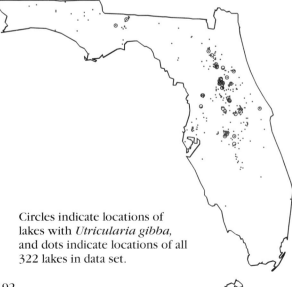

Description and distribution

Cone-spur bladderwort usually grows in shallow water and forms a dense mat of tangled stems and branches. The leaves are alternate and usually forked only once. Small bladders attached to scattered leaves act as traps for invertebrates. Slender flower stems, up to 150 mm high, hold one to three yellow flowers in which the upper and lower lips are about equal in length. Cone-spur bladderwort is a native species common in most parts of the United States (Tarver et al. 1986). The Florida distribution map shows that cone-spur bladderwort was found scattered throughout central Florida with no apparent geographical pattern.

Biology

Utricularia species flower throughout the year in Florida (Dressler et al. 1987). Cone-spur bladderwort reproduces by seed germination and vegetatively through fragmentation. It can grow extensively enough to impair navigational or recreational activities, but usually only in association with other aquatic plants. It has little wildlife value but can provide refuge and habitat for invertebrates and fish populations.

Florida data

Cone-spur bladderwort was identified in only 33 lakes. The 10th and 90th percentiles for pH, alkalinity, total phosphorus, and total nitrogen values in these lakes show that 80% of the lakes with cone-spur bladderwort had levels between 4.7 and 8.1, 0.4 and 52.3 (mg/L as $CaCO_3$), 8 and 54 (μg/L), and 380 and 1710 (μg/L), respectively. The water chemistry averages of the 33 lakes with cone-spur bladderwort showed no significant differences from those for all 322 lakes. The 33 lakes also had water chemistry ranges similar to those in all 322 lakes. This suggests that cone-spur bladderwort can occur in a wide range of aquatic systems.

Circles indicate locations of lakes with *Utricularia gibba,* and dots indicate locations of all 322 lakes in data set.

Utricularia gibba: see references for
Utricularia biflora

Utricularia gibba

Variables	Mean all lakes (n=322)	Number of lakes	Mean	10th percentile	Median	90th percentile
pH	6.7	33	6.3	4.7	6.4	8.1
Alkalinity (mg/L as CaCO$_3$)	23.9	33	19.4	0.4	7.3	52.3
Conductance (µS/cm @ 25°C)	149	33	141	30	71	334
Color (Pt-Co units)	52	33	62	7	24	147
Total phosphorus (µg/L)	45	32	23	8	11	54
Total nitrogen (µg/L)	870	32	850	380	620	1710
Chlorophyll a (µg/L)	20	33	11	1	3	21
Secchi (m)	1.8	28	1.8	0.6	1.9	2.9
Calcium (mg/L)	17.6	33	10.2	0.8	6.8	22.8
Magnesium (mg/L)	8.2	33	5.4	0.7	2.1	15.5
Sodium (mg/L)	13.2	31	11.5	2.8	6.4	14.7
Potassium (mg/L)	2.6	33	2.9	0.1	0.5	11.1
Sulfate (mg/L)	15.2	31	13.5	1.4	7.4	40.6
Chloride (mg/L)	23.4	33	22.1	6.2	12.3	33.4
Iron (mg/L)	0.2	15	0.2	0.0	0.10	0.9
Silicon (mg/L)	1.5	15	2.2	0.10	0.5	10.1

Utricularia inflata (big floating bladderwort)

Description and distribution

Big floating bladderwort is a large, free-floating bladderwort that has submersed, alternate leaves and four to nine whorled leaves with inflated petioles that serve as floats. The submersed leaves are forked four to five times and contain bladder-like structures that are used to trap small aquatic organisms. Flowering occurs in groups of 4–12 on scapes up to 400 mm long. The yellow flowers are about 20 mm wide. Big floating bladderwort is common in the Coastal Plain from New Jersey to Florida and west to east Texas (Godfrey and Wooten 1981). The Florida distribution map shows that big floating bladderwort was found scattered throughout the state but primarily in central Florida.

Biology

Utricularia species flower throughout the year in Florida (Dressler et al. 1987). Big floating bladderwort reproduces by seed germination and vegetatively through fragmentation. Its growth potential is sufficient for it to form extensive mats that can impair navigational and recreational activities. It is of little value to wildlife. It can, however, be good refuge and habitat for invertebrate and fish populations.

Florida data

Big floating bladderwort was identified in only 29 lakes. The 10th and 90th percentiles for pH, alkalinity, total phosphorus, and total nitrogen values in these lakes show that 80% of the lakes with big floating bladderwort had levels between 5.5 and 8.6, 1.7 and 99.6 (mg/L as $CaCO_3$), 10 and 52 (µg/L), and 340 and 2010(µg/L), respectively. The water chemistry averages of the 29 lakes with big floating bladderwort showed no significant differences from those for all 322 lakes. The 29 lakes also had water chemistry ranges similar to those for all 322 lakes. This suggests that big floating bladderwort can occur in a wide range of aquatic systems.

Alison Fox

Circles indicate locations of lakes with *Utricularia inflata*, and dots indicate locations of all 322 lakes in data set.

Utricularia inflata: **see references for**
Utricularia biflora

Utricularia inflata

Variables	Mean all lakes (n=322)	Number of lakes	Mean	10th percentile	Median	90th percentile
pH	6.7	29	7.3	5.5	7.3	8.6
Alkalinity (mg/L as CaCO$_3$)	23.9	29	35.5	1.7	23.9	99.6
Conductance (µS/cm @ 25°C)	149	29	230	57	165	613
Color (Pt-Co units)	52	29	38	4	25	91
Total phosphorus (µg/L)	45	29	28	10	17	52
Total nitrogen (µg/L)	870	29	950	340	800	2010
Chlorophyll a (µg/L)	20	29	16	3	8	42
Secchi (m)	1.8	26	1.7	0.5	1.4	3.6
Calcium (mg/L)	17.6	29	28.3	4.6	19.9	85.7
Magnesium (mg/L)	8.2	29	16.3	3.4	10.4	44.9
Sodium (mg/L)	13.2	28	23.5	5.2	12.3	89.8
Potassium (mg/L)	2.6	29	3.5	0.2	2.0	10.2
Sulfate (mg/L)	15.2	28	20.3	4.2	12.2	57.2
Chloride (mg/L)	23.4	29	40.6	8.9	22.9	143.0
Iron (mg/L)	0.2	25	0.2	0.0	0.1	0.7
Silicon (mg/L)	1.5	25	1.8	0.1	0.9	5.8

Utricularia purpurea (purple bladderwort)

Jesse Van Dyke

Description and distribution

Purple bladderwort has free-floating stems up to 100 mm long and no roots. Leaves are in whorls of five to seven throughout the entire plant with the nodes about 50 mm apart. Purple bladderwort has bladders at the tips of the leaves that act as traps for small aquatic insects. The inflorescence is a scape 100–500 mm long consisting of one to four purple to violet flowers about 10 mm wide. Purple bladderwort is found in the southeastern United States, west to Texas and as far north as Minnesota and southern Canada (Godfrey and Wooten 1981). The Florida distribution map shows that purple bladderwort was found primarily in northern and central Florida.

Biology

Purple bladderwort reproduces by seed germination and vegetatively through fragmentation. It grows extensively enough that, usually in association with other aquatic plants, it can impair navigational or recreational activities. It has little wildlife value but can provide refuge and habitat for invertebrates and fish populations.

Florida data

Purple bladderwort was identified in 110 lakes. The 10th and 90th percentiles for pH, alkalinity, total phosphorus, and total nitrogen values in these lakes show that 80% of the lakes with purple bladderwort had levels between 4.6 and 7.5, 0.8 and 29.4 (mg/L as $CaCO_3$), 7 and 32 (µg/L), and 260 and 1120 (µg/L), respectively. These 110 lakes also collectively averaged significantly lower pH, alkalinity, specific conductance, total phosphorus, calcium, magnesium, and potassium values than all 322 lakes. Thus while purple bladderwort can occur in a range of lake types it tends to occur in acidic, softwater, nutrient-poor lakes.

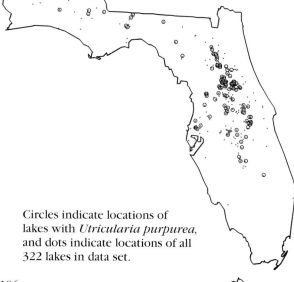

Circles indicate locations of lakes with *Utricularia purpurea,* and dots indicate locations of all 322 lakes in data set.

Utricularia purpurea: see references for
Utricularia biflora

Utricularia purpurea

Variables	Mean all lakes (n=322)	Number of lakes	Mean	10th percentile	Median	90th percentile
pH*	6.7	110	6.0	4.6	5.9	7.5
Alkalinity (mg/L as $CaCO_3$)*	23.9	110	10.3	0.8	2.3	29.4
Conductance (μS/cm @ 25°C)*	149	110	92	29	70	185
Color (Pt-Co units)	52	110	50	4	24	140
Total phosphorus (μg/L)*	45	110	18	7	12	32
Total nitrogen (μg/L)	870	110	680	260	550	1120
Chlorophyll a (μg/L)	20	110	6	1.0	3	13
Secchi (m)*	1.8	101	2.3	0.8	2.1	4.0
Calcium (mg/L)*	17.6	110	9.1	0.6	3.3	26.7
Magnesium (mg/L)*	8.2	110	5.0	0.6	2.2	11.8
Sodium (mg/L)	13.2	103	8.1	2.8	6.2	15.4
Potassium (mg/L)*	2.6	110	1.4	0.1	0.5	3.7
Sulfate (mg/L)	15.2	103	10.7	2.9	6.8	25.1
Chloride (mg/L)	23.4	110	15.0	4.7	10.6	27.5
Iron (mg/L)	0.2	65	0.2	0.0	0.10	0.4
Silicon (mg/L)	1.5	65	1.1	0.10	0.4	2.8

* Denotes a significant difference (p<0.05) from mean of all lakes.

Utricularia resupinata (resupinata bladderwort)

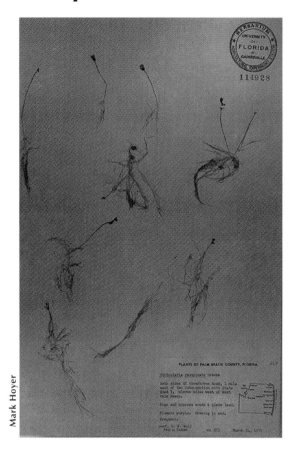

Mark Hoyer

Description and distribution

Resupinata bladderwort is an aquatic herb with a slender branch system within a wet soil substrate. Under optimal conditions resupinata bladderwort has emergent, narrowly needle-like branchlets. It rarely forms tangled floating mats, but when it does it has abundant grass-blade-like branchlets. Descending branches have claw-like structures from the base to the scape. The scape is 20–100 mm long, slender, and one-flowered. There is a bract on the scape below the flower stalk (which appears to be a continuation of the scape), and the stalk is 10–15 mm long. The flower is purple or (rarely) white, about 10 mm long, tipped backward, and facing upward. The fruit is angular and somewhat obpyramidal, and coarsely dimpled. Resupinata bladderwort is common from Nova Scotia to Quebec, New York to Delaware, northwest Pennsylvania to northwest Wisconsin, the coastal plain of Georgia to Alabama, and throughout Florida (Godfrey and Wooten 1981). The Florida distribution map shows that resupinata bladderwort was found primarily in central Florida lakes.

Biology

Utricularia species flower throughout the year in Florida (Dressler et al. 1987). They reproduce readily by fragmentation and by seed germination. Resupinata bladderwort rarely grows thick enough to cause an aquatic weed problem. It is not a major food for waterfowl in Florida, but it is a refuge and habitat for invertebrates and fish populations.

Florida data

Resupinata bladderwort was identified in only 14 lakes. The 10th and 90th percentiles for pH, alkalinity, total phosphorus, and total nitrogen values in these lakes show that 80% of the lakes with resupinata bladderwort had levels between 4.6 and 7.5, 0.0 and 26.2 (mg/L as $CaCO_3$), 3 and 18 (µg/L), and 90 and 870 (µg/L), respectively. The 14 lakes collectively averaged significantly lower total phosphorus and color values than all 322 lakes. This suggests that resupinata bladderwort tends to occur in clear, nutrient-poor lakes.

Circles indicate locations of lakes with *Utricularia resupinata,* and dots indicate locations of all 322 lakes in data set.

***Utricularia resupinata*: See selected
reference section for *Utricularia
biflora***

Utricularia resupinata

Variables	Mean all lakes (n=322)	Number of lakes	Mean	10th percentile	Median	90th percentile
pH	6.7	14	6.1	4.6	6.1	7.5
Alkalinity (mg/L as CaCO$_3$)	23.9	14	7.1	0.0	2.9	26.2
Conductance (µS/cm @ 25°C)	149	14	101	37	77	230
Color (Pt-Co units)*	52	14	9	1	7	21
Total phosphorus (µg/L)*	45	14	10	3	10	18
Total nitrogen (µg/L)	870	14	450	90	410	870
Chlorophyll a (µg/L)	20	14	5	1	2	17
Secchi (m)	1.8	14	3.0	1.3	2.4	5.7
Calcium (mg/L)	17.6	14	5.9	0.8	3.5	14.3
Magnesium (mg/L)	8.2	14	4.1	0.8	2.1	13.1
Sodium (mg/L)	13.2	12	10.2	4.1	7.9	19.6
Potassium (mg/L)	2.6	14	2.0	0.2	1.2	7.3
Sulfate (mg/L)	15.2	12	11.9	4.5	7.7	41.9
Chloride (mg/L)	23.4	14	16.7	6.1	11.8	35.7
Iron (mg/L)	0.2	12	0.0	0.0	0.0	0.1
Silicon (mg/L)	1.5	12	0.3	0.1	0.3	0.9

* Denotes a significant difference (p<0.05) from mean of all lakes.

Vallisneria americana (tape-grass, eel-grass)

Alison Fox

Kerry Dressler

Kerry Dressler

Description and distribution

Tape-grass is a submersed aquatic plant with dark green, tape-like leaves 20–50 mm wide and up to several meters long. The leaves of varying lengths are borne on short vertical stems, which arise from nodes of horizontal rhizomes. The leaves are submersed, with the longer leaves floating near the surface, and somewhat nerved, with netted veins. Numerous fibrous, unbranched roots occur about the base of the vertical shoots. Flowering occurs with the floating, pistillated flower on a long stem and the submersed staminated flower at the base of the plant. The flower consists of three sepals and three white petals. After pollen floats to the surface of the water and fertilization takes place, the stem of the pistillated flower coils and submerses the fruit to the bottom of the lake or stream. The fruit is a slender, banana-like capsule with many tiny seeds. Tape-grass is common in streams and lakes from Nova Scotia and Quebec west to North Dakota, generally south to Texas and Florida (Godfrey and Wooten 1981). The Florida distribution map shows that tape-grass was found scattered in lakes across the whole state, but primarily in central and south Florida. Lakes are progressively more alkaline and nutrient rich as one moves from northwestern to southern Florida (Canfield and Hoyer 1988). Thus the distribution of tape-grass in Florida suggests that it may tend to occur in alkaline, hardwater, nutrient-rich lakes.

Biology

Tape-grass flowers throughout the year in Florida (Dressler et al. 1987). It reproduces by seed germination and vegetatively from rhizomes. It can grow to extensive mats, impairing navigational and recreational activities in some aquatic systems. Tape-grass is a valuable plant as waterfowl food and is also used as refuge and habitat for invertebrates and fish populations.

Florida data

Tape-grass was identified in 118 lakes. The 10th and 90th percentiles for pH, alkalinity, total phosphorus, and total nitrogen values in these lakes show that

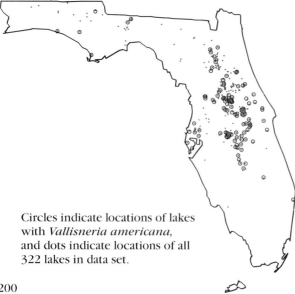

Circles indicate locations of lakes with *Vallisneria americana*, and dots indicate locations of all 322 lakes in data set.

80% of the lakes with tape-grass had levels between 6.1 and 8.8, 2.4 and 105.1 (mg/L as $CaCO_3$), 10 and 91 (µg/L), and 420 and 2170 (µg/L), respectively. These 118 lakes also collectively averaged significantly higher pH, alkalinity, specific conductance, calcium, magnesium, sodium, potassium, sulfate, and chloride values than all 322 lakes. Thus while tape-grass can occur in a range of lake types, it tends to occur in alkaline, hardwater lakes.

Selected references from a total of 530 tape-grass citations in the APIRS database:

Carter, V. and N.B. Rybicki. 1985. The effects of grazers and light penetration on the survival of transplants of *Vallisneria americana* Michx. in the tidal Potomac River, Maryland. Aquatic Botany 23(3):197-213.

Cheng, T.S. and D.N. Riemer. 1988. Allelopathy in threesquare bur-reed (*Sparganium americanum*) and American eelgrass (*Vallisneria americana*). Journal of Aquatic Plant Management 26:50-55.

Chilton, E.W. 1990. Macroinvertebrate communities associated with three aquatic macrophytes (*Ceratophyllum demersum*, *Myriophyllum spicatum*, and *Vallisneria americana*) in Lake Onalaska, Wisconsin. Journal of Freshwater Ecology 5(4):455-466.

Dawes, C.J. and J.M. Lawrence. 1989. Allocation of energy resources in the freshwater angiosperms *Vallisneria americana* Michx. and *Potamogeton pectinatus* L. in Florida. Florida Scientist 52(1):58-63.

Doust, J.L. and G. Laporte. 1991. Population sex ratios, population mixtures and fecundity in a clonal dioecious macrophyte, *Vallisneria americana*. Journal Ecology 79:477-489.

Fernald, M.L. 1918. The diagnostic character of *Vallisneria americana*. Rhodora 20:108-110.

Loczy, S., R. Carignan, and D. Planas. 1983. The role of roots in carbon uptake by the submersed macrophytes *Myriophyllum spicatum*, *Vallisneria americana*, and *Heteranthera dubia*. Hydrobiologia 98:3-7.

Overath, R.D., J.E. Titus, J.E. Hoover, and D.J. Grise. 1991. The influence of field site and natural sediments on the growth and tissue chemistry of *Vallisneria americana* Michx. Journal of Freshwater Ecology 6(2):135-145.

Wigand, C. and J.C. Stevenson. 1994. The presence and possible ecological significance of mycorrhizae of the submersed macrophyte *Vallisneria americana*. Estuaries 17(1B):206-215.

Wilder, G.J. 1974. Symmetry and development of pistillate *Vallisneria americana* (Hydrocharitaceae). American Journal of Botany 61(8):846-66.

Vallisneria americana

Variables	Mean all lakes (n=322)	Number of lakes	Mean	10th percentile	Median	90th percentile
pH*	6.7	118	7.5	6.1	7.6	8.8
Alkalinity (mg/L as $CaCO_3$)*	23.9	118	40.9	2.4	27.3	105.1
Conductance (µS/cm @ 25°C)*	149	118	239	75	177	591
Color (Pt-Co units)	52	118	46	6	25	113
Total phosphorus (µg/L)	45	118	45	10	24	91
Total nitrogen (µg/L)	870	118	1070	420	830	2170
Chlorophyll a (µg/L)	20	118	26	2	11	73
Secchi (m)	1.8	95	1.6	0.4	1.2	3.6
Calcium (mg/L)*	17.6	118	32.1	4.8	20.8	89.0
Magnesium (mg/L)*	8.2	118	15.2	2.6	10.4	39.5
Sodium (mg/L)*	13.2	114	21.7	5.8	10.8	69.1
Potassium (mg/L)*	2.6	118	4.1	0.3	2.9	10.0
Sulfate (mg/L)*	15.2	114	22.1	5.0	15.1	50.5
Chloride (mg/L)*	23.4	117	39.7	9.9	21.5	106.9
Iron (mg/L)	0.2	94	0.1	0.0	0.10	0.4
Silicon (mg/L)	1.5	94	2.2	0.1	1.0	5.9

* Denotes a significant difference (p<0.05) from mean of all lakes.

Websteria confervoides (spider-grass)

Jesse Van Dyke

Description and distribution

Spider-grass is a slender, submersed perennial plant, rooting in the mud in shallow to deep water, sometimes in floating mats. The stems are capillary, simple to the first node, terminated by a small bud with a single bract and growth point. Each terminal bud gives rise to a cluster or whorl of from 3–12 branches, each enclosed by a thin, hyaline or membranous sheath at the base. The cluster of branches elongate to 30–250 mm and may give rise to another whorl of branches, continuing to create a diffuse plant and at some time an inflorescence. The inflorescence is a solitary spike 10 mm long, on a slender stalk 10–70 mm long, held above the surface of the water. The fruit is an olive or olive-brown achene 3–4 mm long. Spider-grass occurs in Florida and tropical America (Godfrey and Wooten 1981). The Florida distribution map shows that spider-grass was found in northern and central Florida.

Biology

Spider-grass reproduces by seed germination and vegetatively. It rarely grows extensively enough to impair navigational or recreational activities and is of little importance to wildlife.

Florida data

Spider-grass was identified in only 36 lakes. The 10th and 90th percentiles for pH, alkalinity, total phosphorus, and total nitrogen values in these lakes show that 80% of the lakes with spider-grass had levels between 4.5 and 7.4, 0.9 and 21.1 (mg/L as $CaCO_3$), 7 and 42 (μg/L), and 260 and 1280 (μg/L), respectively. These 36 lakes also collectively averaged significantly lower pH, alkalinity, specific conductance, calcium, magnesium, sodium, and potassium values than all 322 lakes. Thus while spider-grass can occur in a range of lake types, it tends to occur in acidic, softwater lakes.

Circles indicate locations of lake with *Websteria confervoides,* and dots indicate locations of all 322 lakes in data set.

Selected references from a total of 7 spider-grass citations in the APIRS database:

Crisman, T.L., C.L. Clarkson, A.E. Keller, and R. A. Garren. 1986. A preliminary assessment of the importance of littoral and benthic autotrophic communities in acidic lakes. Pp. 17-27 in Impact of acid rain and deposition on aquatic biological systems, B.G. Isom, S.D. Dennis, and J.M. Bates, editors. American Society for Testing and Materials. Special Technical Publication No. 928. Philadelphia, Pa.

Ellery, K., W.N. Ellery, K.H. Rogers, and B.H. Walker. 1990. Formation, colonization and fate of floating suds in the Maunachira River system of the Okavango Delta, Botswana. Aquatic Botany 38:315-329.

Hall, J., E. Laing, M. Hossain, and G.W. Lawson. 1973. The Cyperaceae within Nigeria—distribution and habitat. Botanical Journal of the Linnean Society 66:323-346.

Ogburn, R.W. and P.L. Brezonik. 1986. Examination of the oligotrophication hypothesis. Phosphorus cycling in an acidic Florida lake. Water, Air and Soil Pollution 30(3-4):1001-1006.

Pollman, C.D. 1991. Florida overview. Pp. 365-416 in Acidic deposition and aquatic ecosystems: Regional case studies, D.F. Charles, editor. Springer-Verlag, New York.

Websteria confervoides

Variables	Mean all lakes (n=322)	Number of lakes	Mean	10th percentile	Median	90th percentile
pH*	6.7	36	5.5	4.5	5.0	7.4
Alkalinity (mg/L as CaCO$_3$)*	23.9	36	5.5	0.9	2.0	21.1
Conductance (µS/cm @ 25°C)*	149	36	63	25	45	117
Color (Pt-Co units)	52	36	50	3	19	161
Total phosphorus (µg/L)	45	36	17	7	10	42
Total nitrogen (µg/L)	870	36	690	260	550	1280
Chlorophyll a (µg/L)	20	36	5	1.0	1	16
Secchi (m)	1.8	35	2.6	0.8	2.2	4.4
Calcium (mg/L)*	17.6	36	4.7	0.6	1.5	18.2
Magnesium (mg/L)*	8.2	36	3.6	0.5	0.9	11.7
Sodium (mg/L)*	13.2	36	5.4	2.1	4.0	11.2
Potassium (mg/L)*	2.6	36	1.0	0.1	0.3	2.8
Sulfate (mg/L)	15.2	36	8.5	2.8	6.0	16.0
Chloride (mg/L)	23.4	36	10.6	4.5	8.4	21.8
Iron (mg/L)	0.2	15	0.1	0.0	0.10	0.5
Silicon (mg/L)	1.5	15	0.8	0.0	0.5	2.6

* Denotes a significant difference (p<0.05) from mean of all lakes.

Xyris spp. (yellow-eyed grass)

Kerry Dressler

Kerry Dressler

Description and distribution

Yellow-eyed grass is a perennial tufted or solitary herb coming from short fibrous or bulbous bases. The roots are fibrous but fleshy. Leaves are basal, tufted, and two-ranked, with the blades linear to laterally flattened and sword-like. The inflorescence is stalked and commonly longer than the leaves. The yellow flowers occur in a cone-like cluster, in axils of tightly clustered bracts. The 2–3 sepals are keeled and persistent. The three petals are unequal, yellow or sometimes white, with narrow bases. The fruit is a capsule with many tiny seeds. Yellow-eyed grass is common throughout the southeastern United States (Godfrey and Wooten 1981). The Florida distribution map shows that yellow-eyed grass was found in northern and central Florida.

Biology

Yellow-eyed grass reproduces by seed germination and vegetatively. It rarely grows extensively enough to impair navigational or recreational activities and is of little importance to wildlife.

Florida data

Yellow-eyed grass was identified in 66 lakes. The 10th and 90th percentiles for pH, alkalinity, total phosphorus, and total nitrogen values in these lakes show that 80% of the lakes with yellow-eyed grass had levels between 4.5 and 7.6, 0.1 and 31.1 (mg/L as $CaCO_3$), 6 and 22 (µg/L), and 150 and 1190 (µg/L), respectively. These 66 lakes also collectively averaged significantly lower pH, alkalinity, specific conductance, total phosphorus, total nitrogen, calcium, magnesium, sodium, potassium, and chloride values than all 322 lakes. Thus while yellow-eyed grass can occur in a range of lake types, it tends to occur in acidic, softwater, nutrient-poor lakes.

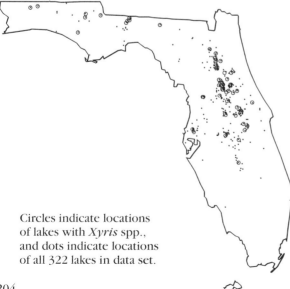

Circles indicate locations of lakes with *Xyris* spp., and dots indicate locations of all 322 lakes in data set.

Selected references from a total of 34 yellow-eyed grass citations in the APIRS database:

Botts, P.S. and B.C. Cowell. 1988. The distribution and abundance of herbaceous angiosperms in west central Florida marshes. Aquatic Botany 32:255-238.

Bryson, C.T., W. McDearman, and K.L. Gordon. 1988. *Carex exilis* Dewey (Cyperaceae) in Mississippi bogs. SIDA 1(2):171-175.

Coile, N.C. 1994. Family affiliation of species on the regulated plant index of September 1993. Palmetto 14(1):7-9.

Datta, P.C. and R.K. Maiti. 1963. Paddy fields of Midnapore District. Indian Agriculturist 7(1/2):147-165.

Duever, M.J. 1982. Hydrology-plant community relationships in the Okefenokee Swamp. Florida Scientist 45(3):171-176.

Keddy, P.A. 1989. Effects of competition from shrubs on herbaceous wetland plants: A 4-year field experiment. Canadian Journal of Botany 67(3):708-716.

Kirkman, K.L. and R.R. Sharitz, 1994 Vegetation disturbance and maintenance of diversity in intermittently flooded Carolina bays in South Carolina. Ecological Applications 4(1):177-188.

Kral, R. 1960. The genus *Xyris* in Florida. Rhodora 62:295-319.

Wheeler, G.A. and P.H. Glaser. 1979. Notable vascular plants of the Red Lake peatland, northern Michigan. The Michigan Botanist 18:137-142.

Xyris spp.

Variables	Mean all lakes (n=322)	Number of lakes	Mean	10th percentile	Median	90th percentile
pH*	6.7	66	5.7	4.5	5.3	7.6
Alkalinity (mg/L as $CaCO_3$)*	23.9	66	8.4	0.1	2.0	31.1
Conductance (µS/cm @ 25°C)*	149	66	84	26	48	143
Color (Pt-Co units)	52	66	36	2	17	127
Total phosphorus (µg/L)*	45	65	15	6	11	22
Total nitrogen (µg/L)*	870	65	620	150	490	1190
Chlorophyll a (µg/L)	20	66	8	1.0	3	14
Secchi (m)	1.8	54	2.4	0.8	2.1	4.5
Calcium (mg/L)*	17.6	65	6.5	0.7	2.5	14.6
Magnesium (mg/L)*	8.2	65	3.7	0.7	1.6	7.5
Sodium (mg/L)*	13.2	61	8.3	2.2	4.4	11.8
Potassium (mg/L)*	2.6	65	1.1	0.1	0.3	3.5
Sulfate (mg/L)	15.2	61	9.6	2.7	6.1	19.8
Chloride (mg/L)*	23.4	66	14.9	3.3	8.5	22.3
Iron (mg/L)	0.2	31	0.2	0.0	0.2	0.6
Silicon (mg/L)	1.5	31	1.1	0.1	0.5	3.4

* Denotes a significant difference (p<0.05) from mean of all lakes.

Zizaniopsis miliacea (giant cutgrass)

Kerry Dressler

Kerry Dressler

Description and distribution

Giant cutgrass is a coarse perennial plant with scaly rhizomes and stems up to 3 m tall. The stems are smooth, leafy, commonly rooting at the lower nodes, and unbranched. The leaf blades are flat, 800–1200 mm long, 10–32 mm wide, smooth on the upper and lower surfaces, but quite rough on the leaf margins. The inflorescence is a large panicle 600 mm long and 180 mm wide, with the female flowers on the terminal portions and the male flowers on the basal portions. The fruit is a long linear seed 3–5 mm long, gray-green to reddish-brown. Giant cutgrass is found from Maryland south to Florida, west to Texas, north to Kentucky, Arkansas, Oklahoma, and southeast Missouri (Godfrey and Wooten 1981). The Florida distribution map shows that giant cutgrass was found scattered throughout Florida with no apparent geographical pattern.

Biology

Giant cutgrass flowers throughout the year in Florida but primarily from June to October (Dressler et al. 1987). It reproduces by seed germination and vegetatively through rhizome growth. It grows in moist soil areas and shoreline habitats of lakes, sometimes to the extent that it impairs navigational and recreational activities. Several aquatic and songbird species use the seeds as a secondary food source and the plant as refuge and nesting habitat.

Florida data

Giant cutgrass was identified in only 18 lakes. The 10th and 90th percentiles for pH, alkalinity, total phosphorus, and total nitrogen values in these lakes show that 80% of the lakes with giant cutgrass had levels between 4.3 and 9.0, 0.0 and 116.3 (mg/L as $CaCO_3$), 8 and 132 (µg/L), and 180 and 3030 (µg/L), respectively. The water chemistry averages of the 18 lakes with giant cutgrass showed no significant differences from those for all 322 lakes. The 18 lakes also had water chemistry ranges similar to those for all 322 lakes. This suggests that giant cutgrass can occur in a wide range of aquatic systems.

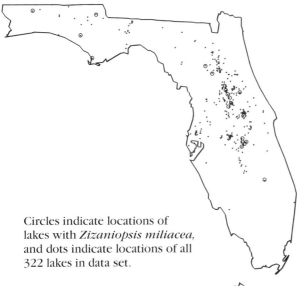

Circles indicate locations of lakes with *Zizaniopsis miliacea,* and dots indicate locations of all 322 lakes in data set.

Selected references from a total of 91 giant cutgrass citations in the APIRS database:

Birch, J.B. and J.L. Cooley. 1982. Production and standing crop patterns of giant cutgrass (*Zizaniopsis*). Oecologia 52 (2):230–235.

Birch, J.B. and J.L. Cooley. 1983. Regrowth of giant cutgrass (*Zizaniopsis miliacea*) following cutting. Aquatic Botany 15:105–111.

Fox, A.M. 1993. Giant cutgrass—an unfriendly native. Aquatics 15(4):4–9.

Holmes, W.C. and D.T. Stalling. 1990. Studies on the reproductive strategy of *Zizaniopsis miliacea*. Castanea 55(2):113–121.

Odum, E.P., J.B. Birch, and J.L. Cooley. 1983. Comparison of giant cutgrass productivity in tidal and impounded marshes with special reference to tidal subsidy and waste assimilation. Estuaries 6(2):88–94.

Smart, R.M. and J.W. Barko. 1982. Ecology of giant cutgrass (*Zizaniopsis miliacea*) in Lake Seminole. Pp. 107–109 in Proceedings of the 16th Annual Meeting of the Aquatic Plant Control Research, Planning and Operations Review. Miscellaneous Papers A-82-3. Environmental Laboratory, U.S. Army Corps of Engineers, Waterways Experiment Station. Vicksburg, Miss.

Zizaniopsis miliacea

Variables	Mean all lakes (n=322)	Number of lakes	Mean	10th percentile	Median	90th percentile
pH	6.7	18	7.2	4.3	7.3	9.0
Alkalinity (mg/L as CaCO$_3$)	23.9	18	44.7	0.0	22.5	116.3
Conductance (μS/cm @ 25°C)	149	18	146	40	95	328
Color (Pt-Co units)	52	18	66	2	46	157
Total phosphorus (μg/L)	45	18	51	8	25	132
Total nitrogen (μg/L)	870	18	1060	180	920	3030
Chlorophyll a (μg/L)	20	18	30	1.0	10	137
Secchi (m)	1.8	17	1.3	0.4	0.8	3.8
Calcium (mg/L)	17.6	18	32.0	0.7	19.6	97.7
Magnesium (mg/L)	8.2	18	14.3	0.7	8.9	53.6
Sodium (mg/L)	13.2	17	10.3	2.2	6.9	25.3
Potassium (mg/L)	2.6	18	1.9	0.2	1.2	5.3
Sulfate (mg/L)	15.2	17	12.3	3.8	10.3	30.9
Chloride (mg/L)	23.4	18	16.7	3.5	13.5	35.5
Iron (mg/L)	0.2	14	0.3	0.0	0.2	0.8
Silicon (mg/L)	1.5	14	3.2	0.5	3.1	6.7

Appendix

Table 1. Location of 322 Florida lakes used in this handbook.

County	Lake	Latitude	Longitude
Alachua	Alto	29°46′46″	82°8′52″
Alachua	Bivans Arm	29°37′38″	82°20′45″
Alachua	Little Orange	29°34′38″	82°3′25″
Alachua	Little Santa Fe	29°46′25″	82°5′46″
Alachua	Lochloosa	29°31′38″	82°8′26″
Alachua	Melrose Bay	29°43′1″	82°3′20″
Alachua	Newnan	29°39′10″	82°13′6″
Alachua	Orange	29°27′20″	82°10′20″
Alachua	Santa Fe	29°44′33″	82°4′37″
Alachua	Wauberg	29°31′32″	82°18′7″
Bay	Deer Point	30°18′26″	85°35′33″
Bradford	Crosby	29°56′38″	82°9′26″
Bradford	Hampton	29°51′37″	82°10′38″
Bradford	Rowell	29°55′24″	82°9′31″
Bradford	Sampson	29°55′40″	82°11′18″
Brevard	Fox	28°35′37″	80°52′6″
Brevard	Poinsett	28°20′24″	80°50′10″
Brevard	South Lake	28°37′12″	80°52′12″
Brevard	Washington	28°8′40″	80°44′58″
Calhoun	Turkey Pen	30°33′24″	85°17′10″
Citrus	Croft	28°52′59″	82°19′46″
Citrus	Henderson	28°50′17″	82°18′57″
Citrus	Van Ness	28°53′22″	82°19′15″
Clay	Geneva	29°45′54″	82°1′22″
Clay	Kingsley	29°57′55″	82°0′13″
Clay	Lowry	29°50′54″	82°0′29″
Clay	Magnolia	29°49′28″	82°1′7″
Collier	Trafford	26°25′30″	81°44′38″
Columbia	Alligator	30°10′8″	82°37′54″
Columbia	Watertown	30°11′34″	82°35′54″
Flagler	Disston	29°17′2″	81°23′31″
Gadsden	Talquin	30°26′23″	84°34′10″
Gulf	Wimico	29°48′16″	85°16′19″
Hernando	Lindsey	28°37′50″	82°21′59″
Hernando	Mountain	28°28′48″	82°18′46″
Highlands	Dinner	27°30′57″	81°26′49″
Highlands	Huntley	27°17′32″	81°20′44″
Highlands	Istokpoga	27°23′15″	81°18′18″
Highlands	Jackson	27°29′5″	81°27′52″
Highlands	Josephine	27°23′41″	81°26′33″
Highlands	Lotela	27°34′46″	81°29′12″
Highlands	Placid	27°14′33″	81°21′57″
Highlands	Red Beach	27°25′55″	81°24′20″
Highlands	Sebring	27°31′38″	81°29′9″
Hillsborough	Alice	28°7′56″	82°36′7″
Hillsborough	Brant	28°7′33″	82°28′5″
Hillsborough	Church	28°6′12″	82°35′59″
Hillsborough	Crenshaw	28°7′33″	82°29′34″
Hillsborough	Crescent	28°9′26″	82°35′28″

County	Lake	Latitude	Longitude
Lake	Skinny Dip	29°7'12''	81°36'51''
Lake	Susan	28°31'3''	81°45'30''
Lake	Swatara	28°52'9''	81°38'40''
Lake	Unity	28°52'18''	81°52'29''
Lake	Wildcat	29°9'43''	81°37'39''
Lake	Woodward	28°49'22''	81°40'33''
Lake	Yale	28°54'43''	81°44'8''
Leon	Blue Heron	30°36'2''	84°14'15''
Leon	Bradford	30°24'9''	84°20'29''
Leon	Carr	30°34'24''	84°17'48''
Leon	Diane	30°35'38''	84°14'21''
Leon	Hiawatha	30°24'36''	84°20'53''
Leon	Iamonia	30°38'1''	84°14'48''
Leon	Jackson	30°31'56''	84°19'44''
Leon	Loften	30°21'0''	84°23'0''
Leon	Minnehaha	30°24'50''	84°21'1''
Leon	Monkey Business	30°36'21''	84°13'56''
Leon	Moore	30°23'35''	84°24'26''
Leon	Munson	30°22'9''	84°18'30''
Madison	Mystic	30°29'0''	83°26'36''
Manatee	Manatee	27°29'3''	82°19'58''
Marion	Baptist	29°1'21''	81°40'4''
Marion	Big Bass	28°59'17''	81°46'50''
Marion	Big Steep	29°5'6''	81°49'39''
Marion	Bryant	29°8'41''	81°51'17''
Marion	Buck	29°5'33''	81°39'9''
Marion	Buckskin	29°25'35''	81°44'56''
Marion	Catherine	29°3'35''	81°49'55''
Marion	Chain-O-Lakes	29°7'16''	81°38'48''
Marion	Deer	29°11'60''	81°50'28''
Marion	Deerback	29°29'6''	81°58'0''
Marion	Delancy	29°25'40''	81°46'28''
Marion	Doe	29°2'14''	81°49'21''
Marion	Eaton	29°15'25''	81°51'57''
Marion	Echo	29°6'19''	81°38'55''
Marion	Farles	29°6'42''	81°40'23''
Marion	Fore	29°16'23''	81°54'48''
Marion	Grassy	29°3'31''	81°48'57''
Marion	Halfmoon	29°9'12''	81°49'56''
Marion	Hopkins Prairie	29°16'39''	81°42'29''
Marion	Island	29°28'36''	81°58'30''
Marion	Jumper	29°13'5''	81°51'34''
Marion	Kerr	29°21'4''	81°46'52''
Marion	Little Bryant	29°8'54''	81°54'9''
Marion	Little Weir	29°1'5''	81°58'39''
Marion	Lou	29°13'55''	81°51'36''
Marion	Mary	29°4'57''	81°49'56''
Marion	Mill Dam	29°10'54''	81°50'27''
Marion	Nicatoon	28°59'48''	81°43'32''
Marion	North	29°10'3''	81°52'47''

County	Lake	Latitude	Longitude
Hillsborough	Dead Lady	28°9'16''	82°34'11''
Hillsborough	Egypt	28°0'40''	82°29'31''
Hillsborough	Halfmoon	28°5'47''	82°32'51''
Hillsborough	Hiawatha	28°10'7''	82°34'22''
Hillsborough	Keystone	28°8'3''	82°35'23''
Hillsborough	Little Halfmoon	28°6'9''	82°32'54''
Hillsborough	Maurine	28°5'20''	82°35'6''
HIllsborough	Thonotosassa	28°3'51''	82°16'53''
Holmes	Victor	30°56'54''	85°53'54''
Indian River	Blue Cypress	27°44'0''	80°45'34''
Jackson	Compass	30°43'14''	85°23'13''
Jackson	Merritts Mill	30°46'35''	85°10'9''
Jackson	Ocheesee	30°41'16''	84°59'9''
Jackson	Round	30°39'12''	85°23'33''
Lafayette	Koon	30°2'24''	83°7'35''
Lake	Apopka	28°39'6''	81°39'29''
Lake	Beakman	29°7'17''	81°37'18''
Lake	Beauclaire	28°46'9''	81°39'36''
Lake	Boyd	29°8'7''	81°33'43''
Lake	Bunchground	29°1'50''	81°33'2''
Lake	Cherry	28°35'56''	81°48'56''
Lake	Clay	29°1'28''	81°27'10''
Lake	Clearwater	28°58'38''	81°33'19''
Lake	Cowpen	29°1'10''	81°27'24''
Lake	Crescent	28°30'20''	81°46'26''
Lake	Crooked	29°9'10''	81°36'10''
Lake	Deerhaven	29°2'34''	81°28'15''
Lake	Dora	28°47'20''	81°41'36''
Lake	Dora East	28°47'32''	81°39'24''
Lake	Dora West	28°47'8''	81°42'31''
Lake	Dorr	29°0'0''	81°37'31''
Lake	Douglas	28°33'14''	81°48'38''
Lake	Emma	28°36'55''	81°51'8''
Lake	Eustis	28°50'31''	81°43'27''
Lake	Gertrude	28°48'48''	81°39'14''
Lake	Gobbler	29°9'41''	81°36'29''
Lake	Grasshopper	29°8'20''	81°36'47''
Lake	Griffin	28°51'33''	81°50'52''
Lake	Harris	28°46'19''	81°48'50''
Lake	Idlewild	28°52'35''	81°53'2''
Lake	Kirkland	28°26'46''	81°48'23''
Lake	Lady	28°54'46''	81°53'28''
Lake	Lawbreaker	29°10'0''	81°36'60''
Lake	Little Harris	28°43'15''	81°45'15''
Lake	Louisa	28°28'45''	81°44'14''
Lake	Minnehaha	28°31'59''	81°45'56''
Lake	Minneola	28°34'37''	81°46'1''
Lake	Picciola	28°50'10''	81°52'27''
Lake	Sellers	29°6'43''	81°38'10''
Lake	Silver	28°50'3''	81°48'6''

County	Lake	Latitude	Longitude
Marion	Redwater	29°12′10″	81°53′38″
Marion	Round Lake	29°7′21″	81°54′20″
Marion	Round Pond	29°4′30″	81°48′28″
Marion	Shoesole	29°7′56″	81°54′55″
Marion	Smith	29°3′31″	81°59′31″
Marion	Sunset Harbor	28°59′39″	81°58′31″
Marion	Swim Pond	29°10′0″	81°48′60″
Marion	Tomahawk	29°8′15″	81°54′36″
Marion	Trout	29°3′2″	81°49′35″
Marion	Waldena	29°11′51″	81°56′14″
Marion	Weir	29°1′5″	81°56′12″
Marion	Wells	29°7′47″	81°50′16″
Marion	Yearling	29°6′5″	81°39′27″
Okaloosa	Karick	30°53′30″	86°38′34″
Okeechobee	Okeechobee	27°4′60″	80°49′60″
Orange	Baldwin	28°34′20″	81°19′20″
Orange	Bay	28°27′34″	81°22′17″
Orange	Butler	28°29′25″	81°33′15″
Orange	Carlton	28°45′32″	81°39′29″
Orange	Cay Dee	28°33′43″	81°20′44″
Orange	Clear	28°31′9″	81°24′37″
Orange	Concord	28°33′16″	81°23′11″
Orange	Conway	28°28′12″	81°20′58″
Orange	Down	28°30′16″	81°31′40″
Orange	Estelle	28°34′26″	81°21′56″
Orange	Fairview	28°35′34″	81°24′13″
Orange	Fredrica	28°30′20″	81°18′18″
Orange	George	28°29′55″	81°19′9″
Orange	Georgia	28°36′14″	81°14′52″
Orange	Hart	28°22′46″	81°12′41″
Orange	Hiawassee	28°31′39″	81°29′3″
Orange	Holden	28°30′12″	81°23′4″
Orange	Ivanhoe East	28°33′40″	81°22′7″
Orange	Ivanhoe Middle	28°33′36″	81°22′28″
Orange	Ivanhoe West	28°33′50″	81°22′30″
Orange	Jessamine	28°28′48″	81°23′11″
Orange	John's	28°32′6″	81°38′11″
Orange	Killarney	28°35′53″	81°22′24″
Orange	Lawne	28°33′54″	81°26′14″
Orange	Maitland	28°36′51″	81°21′5″
Orange	Marsha	28°28′32″	81°28′48″
Orange	Mary Jane	28°22′26″	81°10′44″
Orange	Ola	28°45′14″	81°38′5″
Orange	Pearl	28°36′16″	81°15′54″
Orange	Pineloch	28°30′22″	81°22′2″
Orange	Rowena	28°34′6″	81°21′25″
Orange	Silver	28°34′33″	81°23′45″
Orange	Susannah	28°33′33″	81°19′27″
Orange	Tibet	28°27′15″	81°31′28″
Orange	Underhill	28°32′16″	81°20′10″

County	Lake	Latitude	Longitude
Orange	Virginia	28°35′20′′	81°20′40′′
Osceola	Alligator	28°12′38′′	81°12′4′′
Osceola	Center	28°16′44′′	81°11′25′′
Osceola	Coon	28°15′54′′	81°10′51′′
Osceola	Cypress	28°4′40′′	81°19′36′′
Osceola	East Tohopekaliga	28°17′0′′	81°16′60′′
Osceola	Fish	28°16′12′′	81°20′13′′
Osceola	Gentry	28°8′32′′	81°14′24′′
Osceola	Kissimmee	27°56′10′′	81°17′26′′
Osceola	Live oak	28°13′54′′	81°14′2′′
Osceola	Lizzie	28°14′36′′	81°11′5′′
Osceola	Marian	27°52′44′′	81°6′21′′
Osceola	Trout	28°15′24′′	81°10′5′′
Pasco	Bass	28°10′48′′	82°35′17′′
Pasco	Bell	28°12′60′′	82°27′0′′
Pasco	Clear	28°21′46′′	82°28′46′′
Pasco	Crews	28°22′30′′	82°13′30′′
Pasco	Floyd	28°10′59′′	82°27′54′′
Pasco	Geneva	28°10′59′′	82°34′25′′
Pasco	Holiday	28°10′14′′	82°35′17′′
Pasco	Minneola	28°10′52′′	82°34′34′′
Pasco	Moon	28°17′6′′	82°36′39′′
Pasco	Parker	28°10′28′′	82°34′57′′
Pasco	Pasadena	28°19′4′′	82°13′8′′
Pasco	West Moody	28°23′60′′	82°17′60′′
Pinellas	Maggiore	27°44′20′′	82°39′18′′
Pinellas	Seminole	27°51′27′′	82°47′5′′
Pinellas	Tarpon	28°6′28′′	82°43′31′′
Polk	Agnes	28°10′6′′	81°49′6′′
Polk	Arbuckle	27°41′51′′	81°24′1′′
Polk	Ariana	28°4′58′′	81°47′59′′
Polk	Arietta	28°6′12′′	81°48′17′′
Polk	Big Bass	27°52′20′′	81°51′13′′
Polk	Boca Cove	27°52′13′′	81°51′8′′
Polk	Bonny	28°2′16′′	81°55′36′′
Polk	Buffam	27°47′54′′	81°39′51′′
Polk	Clinch	27°45′28′′	81°33′4′′
Polk	Conine	28°3′35′′	81°43′31′′
Polk	Eagle	27°58′59′′	81°45′57′′
Polk	Elbert	28°1′35′′	81°42′33′′
Polk	Fannie	28°3′42′′	81°41′27′′
Polk	Flora	27°52′10′′	81°50′58′′
Polk	Gate Lake	27°56′0′′	81°35′60′′
Polk	Haines	28°5′31′′	81°42′25′′
Polk	Hamilton	28°2′44′′	81°39′18′′
Polk	Hartridge	28°3′18′′	81°44′34′′
Polk	Hatchineha	28°0′52′′	81°24′30′′
Polk	Henry	28°5′38′′	81°40′11′′
Polk	Hollingsworth	28°1′24′′	81°56′45′′
Polk	Howard	28°1′22′′	81°44′34′′

County	Lake	Latitude	Longitude
Polk	Hunter	28°1′55″	81°57′59″
Polk	Little Bass	27°52′20″	81°51′6″
Polk	Little Spirit	27°59′40″	81°46′50″
Polk	Lowery	28°7′45″	81°40′53″
Polk	Lulu	27°59′43″	81°43′13″
Polk	Marianna	28°4′33″	81°45′55″
Polk	Marion	28°4′48″	81°31′59″
Polk	Pansy	28°4′16″	81°44′49″
Polk	Parker	28°3′54″	81°55′52″
Polk	Patrick	27°48′8″	81°30′48″
Polk	Pierce	27°58′29″	81°31′17″
Polk	Reedy	27°44′31″	81°29′58″
Polk	Rochelle	28°4′19″	81°43′21″
Polk	Rosalie	27°56′4″	81°24′18″
Polk	Smart	28°3′28″	81°42′40″
Polk	Spirit	27°59′53″	81°46′38″
Polk	Thomas	28°17′28″	81°37′43″
Polk	Tiger	27°53′34″	81°21′21″
Polk	Wales	27°54′2″	81°34′20″
Polk	Weohyakapka	27°49′6″	81°24′49″
Putnam	Barco	29°40′34″	82°0′34″
Putnam	Brim pond	29°30′60″	81°58′0″
Putnam	Broward	29°30′33″	81°35′33″
Putnam	Bull Pond	29°30′60″	81°58′0″
Putnam	Cathead	29°24′51″	81°40′29″
Putnam	Cowpen	29°36′7″	82°0′23″
Putnam	Cue	29°40′26″	82°58′19″
Putnam	Deep	29°43′12″	82°57′17″
Putnam	English	29°25′27″	81°32′1″
Putnam	Fanny	29°33′33″	81°59′23″
Putnam	Georges	29°47′15″	81°51′2″
Putnam	Gillis	29°34′10″	81°59′39″
Putnam	Grandin	29°40′33″	81°52′51″
Putnam	Hewitt	29°32′33″	81°55′51″
Putnam	Keys pond	29°31′46″	81°58′28″
Putnam	Little Fish	29°30′60″	81°59′0″
Putnam	North Estella	29°25′40″	81°36′22″
Putnam	Penner	29°29′30″	81°49′23″
Putnam	Picnic	29°30′52″	81°58′28″
Putnam	Redwater	29°33′50″	82°1′26″
Putnam	Riley	29°31′7″	82°2′19″
Putnam	Rosa	29°42′40″	82°0′34″
Putnam	Silver	29°26′37″	81°34′23″
Putnam	Star	29°31′37″	82°2′45″
Putnam	Stella	29°25′47″	81°31′7″
Putnam	Suggs	29°41′0″	82°0′60″
Putnam	Winnott	29°38′53″	82°3′3″
Santa Rosa	Bear	30°51′50″	86°49′56″
Sarasota	Upper Myakka	27°16′21″	81°17′20″
Seminole	Bear	28°39′12″	81°27′4″

County	Lake	Latitude	Longitude
Seminole	Jessup	28°43'27''	81°12'53''
Seminole	Monroe	28°49'55''	81°16'21''
Seminole	Orienta	28°39'14''	81°22'39''
Seminole	Seminary	28°38'38''	81°21'39''
Sumter	Deaton	28°50'10''	81°58'53''
Sumter	Miona	28°54'4''	82°0'40''
Sumter	Okahumpka	28°45'30''	82°5'2''
Sumter	Panasottkee	28°48'22''	82°7'26''
Suwannee	Suwannee	30°22'51''	82°57'3''
Union	Butler	30°2'6''	82°20'17''
Union	Palestine	30°7'44''	82°9'53''
Volusia	Ashby	28°55'29''	81°5'58''
Volusia	Dexter	29°6'26''	81°28'44''
Volusia	Dias	29°9'20''	81°19'7''
Volusia	Harney	28°45'16''	81°3'6''
Volusia	Spring Garden	29°7'24''	81°22'21''
Wakulla	Ellen	30°6'53''	84°22'42''
Wakulla	Otter	30°1'25''	84°23'32''
Walton	Jackson	30°59'44''	86°19'27''
Walton	Juniper	30°46'18''	86°7'54''
Walton	Stanley	30°44'16''	86°8'14''
Washington	Gap	30°33'2''	85°34'18''
Washington	Pate	30°41'44''	85°44'33''

Table 2. Summary statistics for lake water chemistry.

Variables	Number of Lakes	Min	Mean	Max
pH	322	4.1	6.7	9.7
Total alkalinity (mg/L as $CaCO_3$)	322	0.0	23.9	130.6
Specific conductance (µS/cm@25°C)	322	12	149	1008
Color (Pt-Co units)	322	0	52	700
Total Phosphorus (µg/L)	321	2	45	834
Total Nitrogen (µg/L)	321	80	866	4118
Chlorophyll a (µg/L)	322	0	20	252
Secchi (m)	277	0.2	1.8	6.2
Calcium (mg/L)	321	0.3	17.6	215.4
Magnesium (mg/L)	321	0.1	8.2	66.8
Sodium (mg/L)	292	1.2	13.2	141.3
Potassium (mg/L)	321	0.0	2.6	14.5
Sulfate (mg/l)	292	0.0	15.2	106.8
Chloride (mg/L)	321	2.0	23.4	275.2
Iron (mg/L)	209	0.0	0.2	1.2
Silicon (mg/L)	209	0.0	1.5	12.6
Surface Area (hectares)	283	1.6	1243.0	181305.6

Table 3. Scientific and common names for aquatic plants identified in 10 or more of the 322 Florida lakes sampled.

Scientific names	Common name	Number of lakes
Alternanthera philoxeroides	alligator-weed	181
Azolla caroliniana	azolla	63
Baccharis spp.	salt bush	24
Bacopa caroliniana	lemon bacopa	102
Bacopa monnieri	bacopa	59
Bidens spp.	bur marigold	70
Brachiaria mutica	paragrass	162
Brasenia schreberi	water shield	43
Cabomba caroliniana	fanwort	49
Canna spp.	golden canna	24
Cephalanthus occidentalis	buttonbush	193
Ceratophyllum demersum	coontail	93
Ceratopteris thalictroides	water horn fern	22
Chara spp.	muskgrass	107
Cicuta mexicana	water hemlock	37
Cladium jamaicense	saw grass	143
Colocasia esculenta	wild taro	126
Crinum americanum	swamp lily	24
Cyperus alternifolius	umbrella flat sedge	28
Cyperus articulatus	umbrella sedge	15
Cyperus odoratus	flat sedge	18
Decodon verticillatus	swamp loosestrife	30
Echinochloa spp.	water grasses	36
Egeria densa	common waterweed, Brazilian elodea	19
Eichhornia crassipes	water hyacinth	192
Eleocharis baldwinii	road-grass	136
Eleocharis cellulosa	club-rush	61
Eleocharis elongata	water spikerush	14
Eleocharis interstincta	giant-spikerush	51
Eriocaulon spp.	hat-pins, pipeworts	57
Fontinalis spp.	water-moss	32
Fuirena scirpoidea	rush fuirena	109
Fuirena squarrosa	lake-rush, umbrella-grass	98
Habenaria repens	water spider orchid	38
Hydrilla verticillata	hydrilla	159
Hydrocotyle umbellata	water pennywort	275
Hypericum spp.	St. John's-wort	95
Juncus effusus	soft rush	89
Lachnanthes caroliana	redroot	63
Leersia hexandra	southern cutgrass	104
Lemna minor	common duckweed	125
Limnobium spongia	frog's-bit	52
Ludwigia arcuata	long-stalked ludwigia	19
Ludwigia octovalvis	water primrose	226
Ludwigia repens	red ludwigia	114
Luziola fluitans	southern water-grass	87
Mayaca fluviatilis	bog moss	83
Melaleuca quinquenervia	melaleuca	27
Micranthemum glomeratum	hemianthus	32

Micranthemum umbrosum	baby-tears	38
Mikania scandens	climbing hempvine, hempweed	98
Myrica cerifera	wax myrtle	47
Myriophyllum aquaticum	parrot feather	28
Myriophyllum heterophyllum	variable-leaf milfoil	51
Najas guadalupensis	southern naiad	113
Nelumbo lutea	American lotus	63
Nitella spp.	stonewort	64
Nuphar luteum	spatterdock	263
Nymphaea mexicana	yellow water lily	30
Nymphaea odorata	fragrant water lily	195
Nymphoides aquatica	banana lily	144
Panicum hemitomon	maidencane	301
Panicum repens	torpedograss	215
Paspalidium geminatum	Egyptian paspalidium	108
Paspalum distichum	knotgrass	36
Paspalum repens	water paspalum	34
Peltandra virginica	arrow arum	30
Pennisetum purpureum	napier grass	16
Phragmites australis	common reed	32
Pistia stratiotes	water lettuce	85
Polygonum hydropiperoides	smartweed	54
Pontederia cordata	pickerelweed	255
Potamogeton diversifolius	variable-leaf pondweed	40
Potamogeton illinoensis	Illinois pondweed	47
Potamogeton pectinatus	sago pondweed	26
Rhynchospora inundata	inundated beak-rush	15
Rhynchospora tracyi	Tracy's beak-rush	28
Sacciolepis striata	American cupscalegrass	107
Sagittaria kurziana	strap-leaf sagittaria	15
Sagittaria lancifolia	duck potato	178
Sagittaria latifolia	common arrowhead	68
Sagittaria subulata	dwarf arrowhead	73
Salix spp.	willow	207
Salvinia spp.	water fern	137
Sambucus canadensis	elderberry	22
Saururus cernuus	lizard's tail	41
Scirpus californicus	giant bulrush	30
Scirpus cubensis	burhead sedge	92
Spartina bakeri	cordgrass	64
Spirodela polyrhiza	giant duckweed	37
Thalia geniculata	fire flag	25
Typha spp.	cattail	236
Utricularia biflora	tangled bladderwort	90
Utricularia floridana	Florida bladderwort	90
Utricularia foliosa	bladderwort	101
Utricularia gibba	cone-spur bladderwort	33
Utricularia inflata	big floating bladderwort	29
Utricularia purpurea	purple bladderwort	110
Utricularia resupinata	resupinata bladderwort	14
Vallisneria americana	tape-grass, eel-grass	119
Websteria confervoides	spider-grass	37
Xyris spp.	yellow-eyed grass	66
Zizaniopsis miliacea	giant cutgrass	18

Table 4.1 Statistics for pH values from 322 Florida lakes (in bold type) compared to the same statistics for pH values from lakes in which individual plant species were identified. The plant species are sorted by the median pH values.

Plant Species	Number of Lakes	pH Mean	10.0%	Median	90.0%
Rhynchospora tracyi	28	5.4	4.4	4.9	7.0
Fontinalis spp.	32	5.2	4.5	5.0	6.7
Websteria confervoides	36	5.5	4.5	5.0	7.4
Eriocaulon spp.	57	5.4	4.5	5.1	7.0
Rhynchospora inundata	15	5.7	4.4	5.1	8.0
Xyris spp.	66	5.7	4.5	5.4	7.6
Leersia hexandra	104	5.9	4.5	5.5	7.8
Hypericum spp.	95	5.7	4.6	5.6	7.0
Utricularia floridana	90	5.8	4.5	5.6	7.2
Eleocharis elongata	14	5.8	4.5	5.7	7.4
Fuirena scirpoidea	109	5.9	4.5	5.8	7.7
Lachnanthes caroliana	63	5.9	4.5	5.8	7.4
Mayaca fluviatilis	83	5.9	4.6	5.8	7.2
Brasenia schreberi	43	5.9	4.7	5.9	7.2
Myriophyllum heterophyllum	51	6.0	4.7	5.9	7.5
Utricularia purpurea	110	6.0	4.6	5.9	7.5
Nymphoides aquatica	144	6.1	4.6	6.1	7.6
Eleocharis baldwinii	136	6.1	4.6	6.1	7.7
Utricularia resupinata	14	6.1	4.6	6.1	7.5
Ludwigia arcuata	19	6.3	5.8	6.2	7.1
Ludwigia repens	114	6.3	4.7	6.2	8.3
Potamogeton diversifolius	40	6.3	5.2	6.3	7.7
Habenaria repens	38	6.7	5.5	6.4	8.3
Utricularia gibba	33	6.3	4.7	6.4	8.1
Cabomba caroliniana	49	6.6	5.3	6.5	8.3
Decodon verticillatus	30	6.6	4.9	6.5	8.6
Sagittaria subulata	73	6.6	4.8	6.6	8.3
Bacopa caroliniana	102	6.6	4.9	6.6	8.4
Luziola fluitans	87	6.7	5.3	6.6	8.4
Panicum hemitomon	300	6.6	4.7	6.7	8.6
Nuphar luteum	262	6.6	4.8	6.7	8.5
Melaleuca quinquenervia	27	6.8	5.3	6.7	8.4
Nymphaea odorata	194	6.7	4.9	6.7	8.5
Cladium jamaicense	141	6.8	4.9	6.8	8.6
All Lakes	**322**	**6.7**	**4.7**	**6.8**	**8.6**
Cephalanthus occidentalis	193	6.8	4.9	6.8	8.6
Pontederia cordata	254	6.9	5.0	6.9	8.7
Eleocharis interstincta	51	6.9	5.3	7.0	8.5
Baccharis spp.	24	7.1	5.6	7.0	8.9
Sagittaria kurziana	15	6.9	4.4	7.0	8.7
Sacciolepis striata	106	6.9	5.3	7.0	8.6
Hydrocotyle umbellata	273	6.9	5.0	7.0	8.7
Nitella spp.	64	7.0	5.9	7.0	8.2
Fuirena squarrosa	98	6.9	5.1	7.0	8.5
Utricularia biflora	89	7.0	5.4	7.0	8.6
Utricularia foliosa	101	6.9	5.5	7.0	8.5
Eichhornia crassipes	190	7.0	5.2	7.0	8.7
Micranthemum umbrosum	38	7.0	5.4	7.0	8.2
Cyperus odoratus	18	7.2	6.3	7.0	8.3

Bidens spp.	70	6.9	5.0	7.0	8.6
Limnobium spongia	52	7.1	5.6	7.1	8.6
Juncus effusus	87	7.2	5.6	7.1	8.8
Saururus cernuus	41	7.2	5.4	7.1	8.7
Hydrilla verticillata	157	7.1	5.4	7.1	8.6
Nelumbo lutea	62	7.2	5.8	7.1	8.7
Panicum repens	213	7.1	5.3	7.1	8.7
Salvinia spp.	136	7.2	5.5	7.1	8.8
Potamogeton pectinatus	26	7.0	5.8	7.1	8.4
Spartina bakeri	63	7.0	5.0	7.1	8.6
Peltandra virginica	29	7.1	5.0	7.1	8.8
Najas guadalupensis	112	7.2	5.9	7.2	8.6
Alternanthera philoxeroides	180	7.2	5.3	7.2	8.8
Scirpus cubensis	91	7.2	5.7	7.2	8.6
Chara spp.	106	7.1	5.4	7.2	8.5
Eleocharis cellulosa	61	7.2	5.8	7.2	8.8
Typha spp.	234	7.2	5.6	7.2	8.7
Sagittaria lancifolia	176	7.2	5.3	7.3	8.7
Ludwigia octovalvis	225	7.2	5.6	7.3	8.8
Zizaniopsis miliacea	18	7.2	4.3	7.3	9.0
Brachiaria mutica	161	7.1	5.3	7.3	8.8
Azolla caroliniana	62	7.3	5.7	7.3	8.7
Sagittaria latifolia	67	7.3	5.5	7.3	8.9
Utricularia inflata	29	7.3	5.5	7.3	8.6
Pistia stratiotes	84	7.3	5.5	7.3	8.8
Polygonum hydropiperoides	54	7.3	5.8	7.4	8.8
Ceratopteris thalictroides	21	7.5	6.6	7.4	8.6
Salix spp.	207	7.3	5.5	7.4	8.8
Mikania scandens	98	7.3	5.8	7.4	8.7
Myrica cerifera	47	7.3	5.4	7.4	9.1
Micranthemum glomeratum	32	7.4	6.4	7.4	8.6
Paspalidium geminatum	108	7.4	5.8	7.4	8.8
Ceratophyllum demersum	92	7.3	6.0	7.4	8.6
Egeria densa	19	7.4	6.0	7.4	8.7
Myriophyllum aquaticum	28	7.6	6.8	7.5	8.8
Lemna minor	124	7.4	5.6	7.5	8.8
Bacopa monnieri	57	7.4	6.1	7.6	8.7
Paspalum repens	34	7.5	6.4	7.6	8.6
Vallisneria americana	118	7.5	6.1	7.6	8.8
Echinochloa spp.	36	7.6	6.3	7.6	8.8
Spirodela polyrhiza	37	7.4	5.5	7.7	8.6
Paspalum distichum	36	7.5	5.7	7.7	8.9
Colocasia esculenta	125	7.5	5.8	7.7	8.8
Scirpus californicus	30	7.6	5.8	7.8	8.9
Cyperus alternifolius	27	7.4	5.1	7.8	8.8
Crinum americanum	23	7.5	5.3	7.8	8.9
Canna spp.	24	7.7	5.5	7.8	8.9
Potamogeton illinoensis	47	7.8	6.8	7.9	8.7
Nymphaea mexicana	30	7.6	6.0	7.9	8.8
Cyperus articulatus	15	7.8	6.3	7.9	8.9
Thalia geniculata	25	7.7	5.5	7.9	8.8
Phragmites australis	30	7.9	6.9	7.9	8.7
Cicuta mexicana	37	7.8	6.8	7.9	8.9
Pennisetum purpureum	15	7.8	6.0	8.2	8.7
Sambucus canadensis	22	7.9	6.4	8.2	8.9

Table 4.2 Statistics for total alkalinity (mg/L as CaCO$_3$) values from 322 Florida lakes (in bold type) compared to the same statistics for total alkalinity (mg/L as CaCO$_3$) values from lakes in which individual plant species were identified. The plant species are sorted by the median total alkalinity (mg/L as CaCO$_3$) values.

Plant Species	Number of Lakes	Total alkalinity (mg/L as CaCO$_3$)			
		Mean	10.0%	Median	90.0%
Fontinalis spp.	32	2.3	0.0	1.5	7.8
Rhynchospora tracyi	28	5.9	0.10	1.5	20.8
Eriocaulon spp.	57	4.3	0.2	1.8	19.2
Rhynchospora inundata	15	12.1	0.3	1.8	50.0
Xyris spp.	66	8.4	0.1	2.0	31.1
Fuirena scirpoidea	109	11.2	0.3	2.0	33.0
Hypericum spp.	95	5.3	0.3	2.0	17.4
Websteria confervoides	36	5.5	0.9	2.0	21.1
Leersia hexandra	104	12.3	0.0	2.0	45.1
Lachnanthes caroliana	63	8.1	0.0	2.1	25.1
Mayaca fluviatilis	83	7.5	0.2	2.1	26.2
Eleocharis elongata	14	7.2	0.7	2.1	33.9
Utricularia floridana	90	8.0	0.8	2.2	22.3
Myriophyllum heterophyllum	51	9.8	1.0	2.3	41.4
Eleocharis baldwinii	136	11.6	0.1	2.3	36.2
Utricularia purpurea	110	10.3	0.8	2.3	29.4
Nymphoides aquatica	144	9.5	1.0	2.5	26.5
Brasenia schreberi	43	7.7	1.1	2.5	23.4
Ludwigia arcuata	19	6.3	1.6	2.8	19.8
Utricularia resupinata	14	7.1	0.0	2.9	26.2
Ludwigia repens	114	17.2	0.9	3.0	50.9
Potamogeton diversifolius	40	11.6	1.3	3.6	43.5
Sagittaria subulata	73	18.5	0.4	4.3	56.4
Melaleuca quinquenervia	27	19.1	1.0	4.6	53.9
Habenaria repens	38	16.5	1.5	5.6	50.0
Luziola fluitans	87	18.9	1.3	6.0	51.7
Decodon verticillatus	30	25.8	0.5	6.2	100.4
Bacopa caroliniana	102	18.8	1.4	6.4	49.6
Utricularia gibba	33	19.4	0.4	7.3	52.3
Cabomba caroliniana	49	16.0	1.6	7.3	40.0
Panicum hemitomon	300	22.7	0.8	7.3	67.0
Nuphar luteum	262	21.7	1.0	7.7	61.8
Nymphaea odorata	194	21.8	1.2	9.1	61.6
All Lakes	**322**	**23.9**	**0.8**	**9.3**	**68.7**
Fuirena squarrosa	98	22.6	1.3	9.5	62.6
Cephalanthus occidentalis	193	25.4	1.0	10.2	74.0
Sacciolepis striata	106	27.6	1.5	10.7	83.5
Eleocharis interstincta	51	20.0	1.5	10.7	52.4
Pontederia cordata	254	25.5	1.2	11.1	69.0
Cladium jamaicense	141	28.3	1.2	11.5	100.2
Utricularia biflora	89	27.0	1.6	11.5	97.1
Hydrocotyle umbellata	273	26.6	1.2	11.8	72.8
Baccharis spp.	24	32.4	0.7	12.2	122.5
Bidens spp.	70	30.0	1.0	12.4	97.0
Utricularia foliosa	101	26.2	1.4	12.5	74.1
Nitella spp.	64	23.0	2.0	13.7	60.8
Micranthemum umbrosum	38	22.3	1.9	14.0	58.7
Potamogeton pectinatus	26	25.4	2.3	15.1	80.7
Eichhornia crassipes	190	28.8	1.5	15.7	77.6

Panicum repens	213	29.2	1.5	16.7	74.7
Spartina bakeri	63	31.7	1.5	17.0	102.3
Scirpus cubensis	91	28.6	2.2	17.0	74.6
Nelumbo lutea	62	27.9	2.1	17.7	88.7
Limnobium spongia	52	29.9	2.1	17.7	90.3
Sagittaria kurziana	15	36.2	0.8	18.6	106.4
Salvinia spp.	136	31.3	1.9	18.7	97.9
Hydrilla verticillata	157	29.9	1.7	18.8	77.6
Juncus effusus	87	27.1	2.1	18.8	61.1
Cyperus odoratus	18	19.4	2.3	19.3	48.2
Brachiaria mutica	161	32.1	1.2	19.4	87.9
Alternanthera philoxeroides	180	31.1	1.6	19.6	77.1
Ludwigia octovalvis	225	31.2	1.6	20.5	75.9
Azolla caroliniana	62	28.1	2.2	20.8	65.7
Typha spp.	234	31.2	1.6	20.9	76.2
Najas guadalupensis	112	31.4	2.3	20.9	94.0
Saururus cernuus	41	34.7	1.9	21.3	102.9
Chara spp.	106	32.0	1.9	21.5	96.8
Myrica cerifera	47	30.2	0.2	21.7	72.4
Eleocharis cellulosa	61	27.5	2.1	21.7	66.7
Sagittaria latifolia	67	34.2	1.8	21.7	101.2
Sagittaria lancifolia	176	32.9	1.6	21.8	92.4
Salix spp.	207	32.6	1.6	22.0	80.2
Peltandra virginica	29	34.6	1.3	22.0	110.8
Egeria densa	19	38.2	2.3	22.4	108.9
Zizaniopsis miliacea	18	44.7	0.0	22.5	116.3
Paspalidium geminatum	108	34.7	2.3	22.7	103.6
Pistia stratiotes	84	33.8	2.2	22.7	98.4
Polygonum hydropiperoides	54	30.0	1.9	23.0	68.7
Ceratophyllum demersum	92	36.2	2.6	23.5	100.1
Utricularia inflata	29	35.5	1.7	23.9	99.6
Lemna minor	124	36.3	2.2	24.1	100.0
Myriophyllum aquaticum	28	33.6	8.2	24.1	70.8
Mikania scandens	98	36.2	2.4	24.9	100.3
Spirodela polyrhiza	37	39.7	2.3	25.5	96.5
Micranthemum glomeratum	32	29.5	2.8	26.5	55.2
Paspalum repens	34	34.9	5.3	27.1	70.2
Vallisneria americana	118	40.9	2.4	27.3	105.1
Paspalum distichum	36	42.8	1.4	27.8	115.9
Ceratopteris thalictroides	21	36.8	4.0	28.6	100.4
Bacopa monnieri	57	37.6	2.3	30.8	92.4
Colocasia esculenta	125	40.6	1.8	36.0	100.4
Echinochloa spp.	36	41.6	4.9	36.5	93.4
Nymphaea mexicana	30	43.1	2.3	37.1	100.3
Potamogeton illinoensis	47	49.4	10.6	40.0	104.6
Pennisetum purpureum	15	50.7	5.6	44.8	101.7
Cyperus articulatus	15	41.7	7.2	44.8	88.2
Cicuta mexicana	37	53.9	10.0	44.8	111.8
Phragmites australis	30	51.9	10.8	45.9	108.4
Canna spp.	24	53.0	1.5	46.8	121.4
Crinum americanum	23	52.3	2.0	47.0	122.5
Scirpus californicus	30	44.4	1.6	47.1	119.4
Sambucus canadensis	22	45.0	1.6	47.9	106.4
Cyperus alternifolius	27	46.1	1.6	48.8	105.9
Thalia geniculata	25	50.0	2.0	49.3	114.5

Table 4.3. Statistics for specific conductance (µS/cm@25°C) values from 322 Florida lakes (in bold type) compared to the same statistics for specific conductance (µS/cm@25°C) values from lakes in which individual plant species were identified. The plant species are sorted by the median specific conductance (µS/cm@25°C) values.

Plant species	Number of Lakes	Specific conductance (µS/cm@°C)			
		Mean	10.0%	Median	90.0%
Brasenia schreberi	43	56	17	40	116
Rhynchospora tracyi	28	65	31	44	138
Rhynchospora inundata	15	70	30	45	153
Websteria confervoides	36	63	25	45	117
Eriocaulon spp.	57	67	20	46	145
Xyris spp.	66	84	26	48	143
Utricularia floridana	90	71	20	48	151
Fontinalis spp.	32	58	31	53	98
Hypericum spp.	95	80	20	55	146
Eleocharis elongata	14	79	34	55	169
Myriophyllum heterophyllum	51	112	27	57	204
Leersia hexandra	104	127	31	60	290
Mayaca fluviatilis	83	102	23	70	189
Utricularia purpurea	110	92	29	70	185
Sagittaria kurziana	15	263	36	70	878
Fuirena scirpoidea	109	106	34	71	244
Nymphoides aquatica	144	89	28	71	183
Utricularia gibba	33	141	30	71	334
Lachnanthes caroliana	63	98	40	73	179
Decodon verticillatus	30	101	20	74	260
Utricularia resupinata	14	101	37	77	230
Eleocharis baldwinii	136	110	34	80	211
Cabomba caroliniana	49	94	19	83	204
Ludwigia repens	114	130	34	86	246
Potamogeton diversifolius	40	96	18	89	182
Bacopa caroliniana	102	142	32	93	260
Zizaniopsis miliacea	18	146	40	95	328
Ludwigia arcuata	19	93	42	96	134
Habenaria repens	38	101	28	99	184
Luziola fluitans	87	145	28	100	288
Sagittaria subulata	73	147	35	100	297
Panicum hemitomon	300	143	32	100	286
Sacciolepis striata	106	177	36	100	422
Nuphar luteum	262	146	34	100	295
Eleocharis interstincta	51	146	21	101	309
Peltandra virginica	29	153	35	101	347
Bidens spp.	70	162	23	105	420
Nymphaea odorata	194	157	28	106	310
All Lakes	**322**	**149**	**33**	**106**	**295**
Utricularia biflora	89	175	40	106	384
Cephalanthus occidentalis	193	158	32	106	309
Fuirena squarrosa	98	140	49	106	262
Eleocharis cellulosa	61	176	59	107	387
Limnobium spongia	52	205	44	109	693
Sagittaria latifolia	67	156	27	111	356
Egeria densa	19	184	20	111	663
Nelumbo lutea	62	168	33	112	321
Nitella spp.	64	134	44	112	257
Eichhornia crassipes	190	172	32	113	346

Cladium jamaicense	141	181	42	113	400
Juncus effusus	87	145	32	113	280
Azolla caroliniana	62	204	69	113	550
Potamogeton pectinatus	26	238	68	115	789
Utricularia foliosa	101	193	49	115	561
Pontederia cordata	254	161	39	116	311
Scirpus cubensis	91	182	63	116	317
Hydrocotyle umbellata	273	164	39	117	312
Saururus cernuus	41	156	36	117	335
Melaleuca quinquenervia	27	174	59	117	304
Najas guadalupensis	112	191	50	117	421
Salvinia spp.	136	199	56	118	422
Spirodela polyrhiza	37	237	26	118	734
Micranthemum umbrosum	38	157	54	122	285
Myriophyllum aquaticum	28	233	66	126	677
Spartina bakeri	63	233	57	128	708
Hydrilla verticillata	157	183	27	128	355
Alternanthera philoxeroides	180	182	43	130	346
Mikania scandens	98	204	58	131	430
Paspalidium geminatum	108	211	63	133	459
Baccharis spp.	24	188	68	133	412
Pistia stratiotes	84	214	58	134	519
Brachiaria mutica	161	189	55	135	365
Polygonum hydropiperoides	54	172	53	136	323
Panicum repens	213	182	41	137	344
Cyperus odoratus	18	151	63	137	260
Sagittaria lancifolia	176	190	46	140	390
Lemna minor	124	213	59	140	436
Paspalum distichum	36	206	60	141	407
Salix spp.	207	186	54	143	348
Typha spp.	234	184	54	145	340
Ludwigia octovalvis	225	187	57	147	343
Myrica cerifera	47	202	58	154	342
Chara spp.	106	201	53	162	354
Utricularia inflata	29	230	57	165	613
Ceratophyllum demersum	92	224	55	170	608
Echinochloa spp.	36	258	49	171	715
Bacopa monnieri	57	233	59	173	627
Paspalum repens	34	283	64	174	762
Nymphaea mexicana	30	288	50	174	841
Vallisneria americana	118	239	75	177	591
Colocasia esculenta	125	202	60	178	392
Micranthemum glomeratum	32	249	75	179	762
Cyperus alternifolius	27	227	69	180	475
Potamogeton illinoensis	47	238	99	183	473
Scirpus californicus	30	241	62	183	566
Sambucus canadensis	22	202	79	189	295
Cicuta mexicana	37	252	66	200	676
Ceratopteris thalictroides	21	294	86	201	773
Thalia geniculata	25	334	74	204	818
Crinum americanum	23	274	61	214	723
Cyperus articulatus	15	400	69	225	878
Phragmites australis	30	316	83	241	790
Pennisetum purpureum	15	315	80	244	818
Canna spp.	24	289	79	246	705

Table 4.4   Statistics for color (Pt-Co units) values from 322 Florida lakes (in bold type) compared to the same statistics for color (Pt-Co units) values from lakes in which individual plant species were identified. The plant species are sorted by the median color (Pt-Co units) values.

| Plant species | Number of lakes | Color (Pt-Co units) | | | |
		Mean	10.0%	Median	90.0%
Utricularia resupinata	14	9	1	7	21
Eriocaulon spp.	57	39	2	12	161
Hypericum spp.	95	40	2	13	136
Fuirena scirpoidea	109	35	4	13	101
Rhynchospora tracyi	28	42	3	14	161
Mayaca fluviatilis	83	38	3	14	103
Sagittaria subulata	73	34	4	14	98
Potamogeton diversifolius	40	41	6	15	121
Eleocharis elongata	14	19	2	16	50
Cyperus odoratus	18	28	4	16	86
Utricularia floridana	90	36	3	16	108
Nitella spp.	64	36	4	17	93
Sambucus canadensis	22	24	7	17	50
Xyris spp.	66	36	2	17	127
Potamogeton illinoensis	47	30	4	17	94
Baccharis spp.	24	28	6	18	76
Chara spp.	106	41	5	18	101
Nymphoides aquatica	144	41	4	19	105
Websteria confervoides	36	50	3	19	161
Eleocharis baldwinii	136	43	4	20	125
Myrica cerifera	47	39	7	20	116
Leersia hexandra	104	46	4	20	129
Ludwigia repens	114	45	5	22	121
Fuirena squarrosa	98	43	4	22	101
Canna spp.	24	30	4	23	88
Scirpus californicus	30	45	6	23	130
Melaleuca quinquenervia	27	50	4	23	145
Myriophyllum heterophyllum	51	45	6	23	150
Polygonum hydropiperoides	54	49	9	24	102
Colocasia esculenta	125	42	6	24	103
Panicum hemitomon	300	51	5	24	127
Juncus effusus	87	45	6	24	93
Nymphaea odorata	194	46	5	24	112
Utricularia purpurea	110	50	4	24	140
Brasenia schreberi	43	36	5	24	82
All Lakes	**322**	**52**	**5**	**24**	**129**
Paspalum distichum	36	58	6	24	137
Hydrocotyle umbellata	273	47	5	24	111
Panicum repens	213	46	5	24	112
Lachnanthes caroliana	63	50	4	24	166
Utricularia gibba	33	62	7	24	147
Bacopa monnieri	57	41	6	25	111
Micranthemum umbrosum	38	48	6	25	135
Bacopa caroliniana	102	44	5	25	111
Decodon verticillatus	30	39	9	25	90
Vallisneria americana	118	46	6	25	113
Nuphar luteum	262	57	5	25	133
Utricularia inflata	29	38	4	25	91
Fontinalis spp.	32	67	3	25	213

Typha spp.	234	47	7	25	111
Pontederia cordata	254	51	6	26	125
Ludwigia octovalis	225	46	6	26	107
Cladium jamaicense	141	68	5	26	174
Hydrilla verticillata	157	48	5	26	103
Salix spp.	207	52	7	27	129
Sagittaria lancifolia	176	61	7	29	154
Rhynchospora inundata	15	49	5	29	162
Eleocharis interstincta	51	41	4	29	104
Saururus cernuus	41	53	13	29	109
Cephalanthus occidentalis	193	54	6	29	131
Utricularia foliosa	101	56	5	29	133
Najas guadalupensis	112	49	7	30	110
Brachiaria mutica	161	51	7	31	126
Bidens spp.	70	62	4	31	161
Eleocharis cellulosa	61	50	5	32	112
Ludwigia arcuata	19	52	6	32	101
Cabomba caroliniana	49	48	8	32	101
Eichhornia crassipes	190	57	6	32	132
Alternanthera philoxeroides	180	61	7	34	137
Mikania scandens	98	60	6	35	152
Peltandra virginica	29	58	8	36	129
Nymphaea mexicana	30	49	5	37	112
Utricularia biflora	89	62	6	37	133
Ceratophyllum demersum	92	57	6	37	112
Cyperus alternifolius	27	68	4	37	197
Habenaria repens	38	58	7	38	154
Scirpus cubensis	91	59	7	38	131
Sacciolepis striata	106	68	8	39	166
Lemna minor	124	62	7	39	135
Sagittaria latifolia	67	57	9	39	112
Paspalidium geminatum	108	61	7	40	132
Salvinia spp.	136	63	7	41	135
Egeria densa	19	45	9	41	132
Potamogeton pectinatus	26	59	4	41	147
Spartina bakeri	63	57	4	42	151
Pistia stratiotes	84	66	5	44	121
Crinum americanum	23	76	6	45	183
Zizaniopsis miliacea	18	66	2	46	157
Pennisetum purpureum	15	49	3	47	97
Sagittaria kurziana	15	54	2	47	143
Spirodela polyrhiza	37	63	5	47	131
Cicuta mexicana	37	73	14	48	140
Luziola fluitans	87	67	8	49	154
Nelumbo lutea	62	55	10	50	113
Ceratopteris thalictroides	21	59	4	50	112
Echinochloa spp.	36	62	16	51	130
Thalia geniculata	25	72	4	53	120
Micranthemum glomeratum	32	60	4	53	132
Paspalum repens	34	72	5	56	121
Myriophyllum aquaticum	28	66	9	56	131
Limnobium spongia	52	84	13	56	190
Azolla caroliniana	62	80	20	56	160
Phragmites australis	30	66	14	58	127
Cyperus articulatus	15	112	48	102	247

Table 4.5 Statistics for total phosphorus (μg/L) values from 321 Florida lakes (in bold type) compared to the same statistics for color total phosphorus (μg/L) values from lakes in which individual plant species were identified. The plant species are sorted by the median total phosphorus (μg/L) values.

		Total Phosphorus (μg/L)			
Plant species	Number of lakes	Mean	10.0%	Median	90.0%
Rhynchospora tracyi	27	12	6	10	20
Eriocaulon spp.	56	11	5	10	19
Eleocharis elongata	14	11	2	10	21
Fuirena scirpoidea	108	14	6	10	23
Utricularia resupinata	14	10	3	10	18
Fontinalis spp.	32	14	5	10	28
Websteria confervoides	36	17	7	10	42
Xyris spp.	65	15	6	11	22
Utricularia floridana	89	16	7	11	27
Hypericum spp.	94	14	5	11	27
Mayaca fluviatilis	82	17	6	11	27
Utricularia gibba	32	23	8	11	54
Utricularia purpurea	110	18	7	12	32
Lachnanthes caroliana	62	21	6	12	45
Leersia hexandra	104	22	7	12	42
Myriophyllum heterophyllum	51	22	7	13	21
Nymphoides aquatica	143	19	8	13	37
Eleocharis baldwinii	135	20	7	13	34
Brasenia schreberi	43	17	9	13	30
Rhynchospora inundata	14	17	7	13	36
Potamogeton diversifolius	40	21	9	14	40
Ludwigia repens	113	31	9	14	63
Baccharis spp.	23	25	5	14	50
Bacopa caroliniana	102	23	9	14	50
Sagittaria subulata	72	24	7	15	52
Nymphaea odorata	193	29	9	15	58
Cabomba caroliniana	49	23	10	16	44
Ludwigia arcuata	19	29	10	16	63
Nitella spp.	64	24	9	16	42
Decodon verticillatus	30	35	9	17	79
Potamogeton illinoensis	47	30	10	17	76
Utricularia inflata	29	28	10	17	52
Eleocharis interstincta	51	29	9	17	78
Panicum hemitomon	299	40	9	17	82
Utricularia foliosa	101	36	10	18	80
Nuphar luteum	261	38	10	18	80
Cladium jamaicense	141	32	10	19	73
Fuirena squarrosa	98	29	10	19	61
Cephalanthus occidentalis	192	35	10	19	83
Chara spp.	105	35	10	19	79
All Lakes	**321**	**45**	**9**	**19**	**90**
Luziola fluitans	87	38	11	20	90
Sagittaria kurziana	15	34	7	20	86
Hydrocotyle umbellata	272	45	10	20	92
Pontederia cordata	253	44	10	20	92
Micranthemum umbrosum	38	53	10	21	112
Bidens spp.	70	53	9	22	108
Hydrilla verticillata	156	49	10	22	106
Spartina bakeri	63	37	10	22	89

Habenaria repens	38	36	12	22	87
Melaleuca quinquenervia	27	35	10	22	106
Panicum repens	212	53	10	22	112
Sagittaria lancifolia	176	44	10	22	108
Utricularia biflora	89	37	11	22	82
Typha spp.	233	55	10	22	112
Ludwigia octovalvis	224	56	10	23	113
Potamogeton pectinatus	26	38	12	23	52
Eichhornia crassipes	190	56	10	23	122
Myrica cerifera	46	64	9	23	178
Cyperus odoratus	17	25	9	23	47
Paspalum distichum	36	46	7	23	110
Najas guadalupensis	111	44	10	23	85
Egeria densa	19	68	12	23	126
Scirpus cubensis	90	42	12	24	103
Vallisneria americana	118	45	10	24	91
Eleocharis cellulosa	61	40	10	24	102
Sacciolepis striata	106	46	12	24	108
Salix spp.	206	59	10	24	116
Colocasia esculenta	125	64	10	25	127
Mikania scandens	98	55	11	25	114
Zizaniopsis miliacea	18	51	8	25	132
Sambucus canadensis	22	34	6	26	106
Polygonum hydropiperoides	53	59	10	26	121
Brachiaria mutica	161	51	12	26	113
Juncus effusus	87	43	10	26	86
Saururus cernuus	41	53	12	26	120
Ceratophyllum demersum	92	64	11	27	129
Salvinia spp.	136	56	12	28	124
Alternanthera philoxeroides	180	61	11	28	125
Bacopa monnieri	57	43	12	28	84
Peltandra virginica	29	42	10	28	105
Sagittaria latifolia	67	59	12	28	124
Paspalidium geminatum	108	55	12	29	112
Scirpus californicus	30	43	12	30	113
Limnobium spongia	51	56	13	30	107
Lemna minor	123	69	12	30	129
Pistia stratiotes	84	68	10	31	129
Pennisetum purpureum	15	57	7	31	201
Crinum americanum	23	85	11	31	152
Nelumbo lutea	62	61	10	33	111
Cyperus alternifolius	27	45	14	35	91
Myriophyllum aquaticum	28	82	14	36	138
Nymphaea mexicana	30	51	12	36	126
Micranthemum glomeratum	32	80	10	39	152
Canna spp.	24	48	10	39	122
Spirodela polyrhiza	37	80	12	42	234
Thalia geniculata	25	64	16	42	139
Azolla caroliniana	62	66	15	44	119
Ceratopteris thalictroides	21	64	11	44	186
Paspalum repens	34	63	14	44	119
Phragmites australis	30	68	15	45	169
Cicuta mexicana	37	76	15	49	155
Cyperus articulatus	15	80	19	52	217
Echinochloa spp.	36	94	16	57	168

Table 4.6 Statistics for total nitrogen (µg/L) values from 321 Florida lakes (in bold type) compared to the same statistics for total nitrogen (µg/L) values from lakes in which individual plant species were identified. The plant species are sorted by the median total nitrogen (µg/L) values.

Plant species	Number of lakes	Total Nitrogen (µg/L)			
		Mean	10.0%	Median	90.0%
Eriocaulon spp.	56	509	148	402	1114
Mayaca fluviatilis	82	547	155	405	1089
Utricularia resupinata	14	453	87	411	874
Fontinalis spp.	32	436	141	422	692
Hypericum spp.	94	516	156	440	1110
Utricularia floridana	89	600	184	455	1112
Leersia hexandra	104	589	156	471	1156
Potamogeton diversifolius	40	542	275	482	899
Xyris spp.	65	621	153	488	1189
Brasenia schreberi	43	583	210	490	1080
Fuirena scirpoidea	108	629	189	491	1253
Sagittaria subulata	72	698	161	498	1447
Ludwigia arcuata	19	658	223	527	1110
Myriophyllum heterophyllum	51	666	236	528	1318
Nymphoides aquatica	143	664	245	528	1242
Rhynchospora tracyi	27	696	201	541	1426
Eleocharis elongata	14	634	183	544	1196
Lachnanthes caroliana	62	663	178	550	1169
Utricularia purpurea	110	682	261	551	1121
Websteria confervoides	36	693	255	551	1277
Nitella spp.	64	676	265	567	1275
Eleocharis baldwinii	135	679	266	593	1148
Ludwigia repens	113	747	288	598	1461
Cabomba caroliniana	49	736	320	601	1276
Decodon verticillatus	30	881	316	611	1921
Bacopa caroliniana	102	738	302	613	1275
Utricularia gibba	32	853	381	617	1714
Micranthemum umbrosum	38	688	315	625	1100
Nymphaea odorata	193	802	306	630	1524
Panicum hemitomon	299	832	277	640	1708
Eleocharis interstincta	51	753	251	640	1509
Nuphar luteum	261	828	302	643	1562
Fuirena squarrosa	98	794	271	652	1716
All Lakes	**321**	**866**	**286**	**658**	**1788**
Cephalanthus occidentalis	192	877	313	661	1754
Habenaria repens	38	809	298	667	1294
Bidens spp.	70	873	225	674	1915
Potamogeton pectinatus	26	865	374	677	1618
Melaleuca quinquenervia	27	803	321	680	1806
Cladium jamaicense	141	927	311	680	1806
Pontederia cordata	253	871	311	680	1783
Hydrocotyle umbellata	272	884	311	683	1786
Hydrilla verticillata	156	903	313	689	1816
Luziola fluitans	87	817	313	690	1375
Cyperus odoratus	17	769	351	693	1203
Micranthemum glomeratum	32	923	406	693	1813
Chara spp.	105	878	327	694	1634
Eichhornia crassipes	190	938	310	707	1878
Egeria densa	19	996	455	710	1708

Baccharis spp.	23	1003	323	710	2657
Saururus cernuus	41	1058	394	710	2376
Brachiaria mutica	161	951	391	710	1854
Sacciolepis striata	106	907	332	712	1734
Najas guadalupensis	111	920	373	714	1800
Panicum repens	212	950	317	715	1929
Rhynchospora inundata	14	845	310	724	1725
Typha spp.	233	965	358	729	1945
Myrica cerifera	46	1005	398	745	2221
Bacopa monnieri	57	944	406	747	1899
Eleocharis cellulosa	61	919	311	747	1827
Utricularia biflora	89	916	320	747	1836
Nelumbo lutea	62	970	327	765	1914
Ludwigia octovalvis	224	980	372	771	1963
Juncus effusus	87	949	325	780	1874
Salix spp.	206	1013	391	789	1989
Utricularia foliosa	101	883	324	796	1691
Spartina bakeri	63	917	309	796	1715
Utricularia inflata	29	951	337	796	2013
Salvinia spp.	136	1005	376	802	1958
Potamogeton illinoensis	47	1014	431	808	1899
Colocasia esculenta	125	1073	396	815	2197
Scirpus cubensis	90	919	372	815	1784
Sagittaria lancifolia	176	1021	391	817	1958
Alternanthera philoxeroides	180	998	358	819	1933
Cyperus alternifolius	27	1035	434	822	2182
Ceratophyllum demersum	92	1017	382	830	1867
Vallisneria americana	118	1070	417	830	2174
Sagittaria kurziana	15	862	235	838	1595
Myriophyllum aquaticum	28	902	447	839	1580
Mikania scandens	98	1048	334	843	1983
Paspalum repens	34	927	424	855	1310
Spirodela polyrhiza	37	1045	430	863	1764
Limnobium spongia	51	991	454	863	1812
Ceratopteris thalictroides	21	952	329	863	1847
Paspalidium geminatum	108	1094	404	890	2028
Nymphaea mexicana	30	976	388	891	1876
Polygonum hydropiperoides	53	1078	472	897	1962
Zizaniopsis miliacea	18	1061	178	916	3032
Peltandra virginica	29	1049	301	920	2013
Sagittaria latifolia	67	1137	381	920	2471
Azolla caroliniana	62	992	444	927	1797
Scirpus californicus	30	1098	405	938	2481
Pistia stratiotes	84	1029	277	965	1964
Lemna minor	123	1099	410	994	1977
Pennisetum purpureum	15	1031	308	994	2162
Sambucus canadensis	22	1071	376	1015	1967
Crinum americanum	23	1255	402	1034	3232
Cicuta mexicana	37	1228	464	1056	2880
Paspalum distichum	36	1309	384	1076	3230
Phragmites australis	30	1186	502	1083	2385
Echinochloa spp.	36	1250	485	1101	2464
Thalia geniculata	25	1164	478	1111	2091
Canna spp.	24	1420	280	1185	3497
Cyperus articulatus	15	1275	743	1263	2078

Table 4.7 Statistics for chlorophyll *a* (µg/L) values from 321 Florida lakes (in bold type) compared to the same statistics for chlorophyll *a* (µg/L) values from lakes in which individual plant species were identified. The plant species are sorted by the median chlorophyll *a* (µg/L) values.

Plant species	Number of lakes	Chlorophyll a (µg/L)			
		Mean	10.0%	Median	90.0%
Websteria confervoides	36	5	1.0	1	16
Rhynchospora tracyi	28	3	1.0	1	13
Eriocaulon spp.	57	3	1.0	2	6
Utricularia resupinata	14	5	1	2	17
Eleocharis elongata	14	4	1.0	2	11
Fontinalis spp.	32	4	1.0	3	9
Utricularia floridana	90	7	1.0	3	13
Fuirena scirpoidea	109	6	1.0	3	12
Xyris spp.	66	8	1.0	3	14
Myriophyllum heterophyllum	51	7	1.0	3	10
Hypericum spp.	95	4	1.0	3	10
Utricularia purpurea	110	6	1.0	3	13
Mayaca fluviatilis	83	7	1.0	3	11
Leersia hexandra	104	8	1.0	3	17
Utricularia gibba	33	11	1	3	21
Brasenia schreberi	43	7	1.0	4	19
Nymphoides aquatica	144	7	1.0	4	17
Rhynchospora inundata	15	9	1.0	4	25
Eleocharis baldwinii	136	8	1	4	20
Ludwigia repens	114	11	1.0	4	30
Lachnanthes caroliana	63	6	1	4	11
Bacopa caroliniana	102	10	1	4	26
Nitella spp.	64	9	2	5	22
Potamogeton diversifolius	40	7	2	5	19
Nymphaea odorata	194	14	1	5	32
Ludwigia arcuata	19	8	2	5	31
Sagittaria subulata	73	12	1	5	34
Melaleuca quinquenervia	27	13	2	6	37
Nuphar luteum	262	16	1	6	37
Fuirena squarrosa	98	14	2	6	37
Cladium jamaicense	141	17	1	6	39
Cabomba caroliniana	49	11	2	6	30
Utricularia foliosa	101	14	2	6	36
Panicum hemitomon	300	17	1	6	39
Potamogeton pectinatus	26	15	2	6	40
All Lakes	**322**	**20**	**1**	**6**	**47**
Utricularia biflora	89	18	3	7	40
Chara spp.	106	16	1	7	40
Cephalanthus occidentalis	193	18	2	7	41
Bidens spp.	70	19	2	7	60
Crinum americanum	23	31	3	7	118
Pontederia cordata	254	19	2	7	45
Habenaria repens	38	11	2	7	29
Spartina bakeri	63	20	2	7	57
Hydrilla verticillata	157	20	2	7	62
Luziola fluitans	87	13	3	8	32
Hydrocotyle umbellata	273	20	2	8	58
Limnobium spongia	52	18	3	8	42
Decodon verticillatus	30	20	2	8	61

Eleocharis interstincta	51	13	2	8	33
Baccharis spp.	24	26	2	8	119
Eichhornia crassipes	190	23	2	8	66
Eleocharis cellulosa	61	21	2	8	64
Potamogeton illinoensis	47	18	2	8	52
Ceratopteris thalictroides	21	21	2	8	66
Utricularia inflata	29	16	3	8	42
Scirpus cubensis	91	17	3	8	37
Ceratophyllum demersum	92	23	2	8	66
Najas guadalupensis	112	18	2	8	41
Sacciolepis striata	106	20	3	9	44
Sagittaria lancifolia	176	23	2	9	67
Egeria densa	19	24	3	9	62
Micranthemum umbrosum	38	13	3	9	21
Salvinia spp.	136	24	3	9	68
Panicum repens	213	25	2	9	67
Nelumbo lutea	62	25	2	9	73
Sagittaria kurziana	15	17	1.0	10	59
Typha spp.	234	25	3	10	67
Mikania scandens	98	25	2	10	73
Saururus cernuus	41	28	3	10	84
Brachiaria mutica	161	24	3	10	66
Myriophyllum aquaticum	28	19	3	10	62
Zizaniopsis miliacea	18	30	1.0	10	137
Salix spp.	207	27	2	11	73
Juncus effusus	87	23	2	11	63
Ludwigia octovalvis	225	26	2	11	69
Alternanthera philoxeroides	180	25	2	11	67
Peltandra virginica	29	23	2	11	62
Pistia stratiotes	84	24	2	11	66
Nymphaea mexicana	30	22	3	11	66
Vallisneria americana	118	26	2	11	73
Sagittaria latifolia	67	30	3	11	89
Azolla caroliniana	62	20	3	11	47
Paspalidium geminatum	108	27	3	11	74
Myrica cerifera	47	30	2	12	80
Micranthemum glomeratum	32	21	2	12	58
Bacopa monnieri	57	21	3	13	52
Spirodela polyrhiza	37	24	3	13	62
Cyperus odoratus	18	15	3	13	31
Lemna minor	124	27	3	13	75
Scirpus californicus	30	25	3	14	74
Polygonum hydropiperoides	54	28	2	14	73
Paspalum repens	34	20	3	14	41
Cicuta mexicana	37	33	3	14	129
Cyperus alternifolius	27	28	3	14	83
Thalia geniculata	25	29	3	15	99
Colocasia esculenta	125	32	2	15	91
Pennisetum purpureum	15	27	3	15	96
Paspalum distichum	36	43	2	15	166
Phragmites australis	30	29	4	15	85
Cyperus articulatus	15	33	3	19	99
Echinochloa spp.	36	38	4	21	133
Sambucus canadensis	22	29	2	23	73
Canna spp.	24	44	2	30	156

Table 4.8 Statistics for Secchi depth (m) values from 322 Florida lakes (in bold type) compared to the same statistics for Secchi depth (m) values from lakes in which individual plant species were identified. The plant species are sorted by the median Secchi depth (m) values.

Plant species	Number of lakes	Secchi depth (m) Mean	10.0%	Median	90.0%
Cyperus articulatus	15	0.6	0.4	0.6	0.9
Phragmites australis	29	0.8	0.4	0.7	1.3
Pennisetum purpureum	13	1.0	0.4	0.7	2.6
Thalia geniculata	24	1.0	0.4	0.7	1.8
Echinochloa spp.	34	1.0	0.4	0.7	1.6
Crinum americanum	22	1.1	0.4	0.8	2.9
Nymphaea mexicana	26	1.3	0.4	0.8	2.8
Sambucus canadensis	12	0.9	0.3	0.8	1.6
Zizaniopsis miliacea	17	1.3	0.4	0.8	3.8
Myriophyllum aquaticum	26	1.2	0.5	0.8	3.1
Paspalum distichum	29	1.1	0.3	0.8	2.6
Cicuta mexicana	35	0.9	0.4	0.8	1.5
Egeria densa	13	1.2	0.5	0.8	2.6
Micranthemum glomeratum	30	1.6	0.4	0.8	4.9
Spirodela polyrhiza	33	1.4	0.5	0.8	3.4
Limnobium spongia	45	1.2	0.5	0.8	2.8
Azolla caroliniana	56	1.1	0.5	0.8	2.4
Paspalum repens	33	1.4	0.4	0.8	3.8
Nelumbo lutea	57	1.5	0.5	0.8	3.9
Peltandra virginica	27	1.3	0.4	0.9	2.8
Lemna minor	108	1.3	0.4	0.9	2.9
Pistia stratiotes	76	1.4	0.4	0.9	3.6
Sagittaria latifolia	62	1.4	0.4	1.0	2.9
Paspalidium geminatum	98	1.3	0.4	1.0	2.9
Ceratopteris thalictroides	21	1.5	0.4	1.0	3.6
Scirpus californicus	20	1.4	0.3	1.0	2.9
Salvinia spp.	123	1.5	0.4	1.0	3.1
Mikania scandens	87	1.5	0.4	1.0	3.4
Sacciolepis striata	95	1.4	0.4	1.1	3.0
Brachiaria mutica	142	1.4	0.4	1.1	2.9
Salix spp.	169	1.5	0.4	1.1	3.3
Scirpus cubensis	81	1.5	0.4	1.1	2.9
Eleocharis cellulosa	56	1.5	0.4	1.1	3.4
Micranthemum umbrosum	31	1.6	0.5	1.1	3.2
Alternanthera philoxeroides	159	1.5	0.4	1.1	3.0
Cyperus alternifolius	22	1.5	0.4	1.1	3.4
Melaleuca quinquenervia	23	1.7	0.4	1.1	4.3
Ceratophyllum demersum	81	1.5	0.4	1.1	3.5
Utricularia biflora	79	1.5	0.4	1.1	3.4
Saururus cernuus	38	1.3	0.4	1.2	2.7
Colocasia esculenta	109	1.5	0.4	1.2	3.5
Luziola fluitans	81	1.6	0.5	1.2	3.6
Vallisneria americana	95	1.6	0.4	1.2	3.6
Myrica cerifera	18	1.5	0.5	1.2	3.7
Sagittaria kurziana	15	1.7	0.5	1.2	3.8
Bacopa monnieri	52	1.5	0.4	1.2	3.5
Canna spp.	21	1.9	0.4	1.2	5.6
Najas guadalupensis	98	1.6	0.5	1.2	3.5
Spartina bakeri	56	1.6	0.5	1.2	3.6

Sagittaria lancifolia	157	1.5	0.4	1.3	3.2
Ludwigia octovalvis	187	1.6	0.4	1.3	3.0
Eichhornia crassipes	172	1.6	0.4	1.3	3.6
Typha spp.	194	1.5	0.4	1.3	2.9
Juncus effusus	75	1.5	0.4	1.3	3.5
Baccharis spp.	13	1.4	0.3	1.3	2.7
Panicum repens	182	1.7	0.4	1.3	3.6
Habenaria repens	34	1.7	0.6	1.4	3.6
Potamogeton pectinatus	19	1.7	0.5	1.4	3.6
Decodon verticillatus	28	1.6	0.5	1.4	3.3
Cephalanthus occidentalis	169	1.7	0.4	1.4	3.4
Utricularia foliosa	86	1.7	0.5	1.4	3.7
Bidens spp.	62	1.7	0.5	1.4	3.7
Hydrilla verticillata	143	1.7	0.4	1.4	3.7
Potamogeton illinoensis	39	1.7	0.5	1.4	3.6
Utricularia inflata	26	1.7	0.5	1.4	3.6
Pontederia cordata	221	1.7	0.4	1.4	3.6
Cladium jamaicense	121	1.7	0.4	1.4	3.6
Hydrocotyle umbellata	234	1.7	0.5	1.4	3.6
Polygonum hydropiperoides	43	1.4	0.4	1.4	2.2
All Lakes	**277**	**1.8**	**0.4**	**1.5**	**3.7**
Nuphar luteum	233	1.8	0.5	1.5	3.7
Panicum hemitomon	265	1.8	0.5	1.5	3.9
Fuirena squarrosa	90	1.9	0.5	1.5	3.8
Ludwigia arcuata	18	1.9	0.8	1.6	3.7
Cabomba caroliniana	44	1.9	0.7	1.6	3.6
Rhynchospora inundata	12	2.0	0.8	1.6	4.1
Chara spp.	90	1.9	0.5	1.6	3.7
Cyperus odoratus	15	1.9	0.9	1.6	3.7
Eleocharis interstincta	49	1.8	0.5	1.6	3.6
Nymphaea odorata	166	2.0	0.6	1.6	3.9
Bacopa caroliniana	91	2.1	0.6	1.7	4.1
Ludwigia repens	100	2.1	0.6	1.8	4.1
Sagittaria subulata	63	2.3	0.6	1.9	5.2
Eleocharis baldwinii	112	2.1	0.7	1.9	3.8
Utricularia gibba	28	1.8	0.6	1.9	2.9
Nitella spp.	59	2.3	0.7	2.0	4.3
Lachnanthes caroliana	51	2.2	0.8	2.0	4.2
Nymphoides aquatica	134	2.2	0.7	2.0	4.1
Leersia hexandra	96	2.3	0.6	2.1	4.3
Xyris spp.	54	2.4	0.8	2.1	4.5
Mayaca fluviatilis	75	2.4	0.8	2.1	4.6
Utricularia purpurea	101	2.3	0.8	2.1	4.0
Brasenia schreberi	41	2.3	1.0	2.1	4.2
Myriophyllum heterophyllum	46	2.4	0.8	2.1	4.2
Fuirena scirpoidea	93	2.5	0.9	2.2	4.4
Websteria confervoides	35	2.6	0.8	2.2	4.4
Potamogeton diversifolius	37	2.3	0.8	2.2	3.9
Utricularia floridana	84	2.6	0.8	2.3	4.5
Utricularia resupinata	14	3.0	1.3	2.4	5.7
Fontinalis spp.	29	2.5	0.5	2.4	5.2
Eriocaulon spp.	55	2.8	1.2	2.5	4.9
Hypericum spp.	86	2.7	0.8	2.5	5.0
Eleocharis elongata	12	2.9	1.5	2.5	5.3
Rhynchospora tracyi	26	2.7	1.0	2.6	4.6

Table 4.9 Statistics for calcium (mg/L) values from 277 Florida lakes (in bold type) compared to the same statistics for calcium (mg/L) values from lakes in which individual plant species were identified. The plant species are sorted by the median calcium (mg/L) values.

		Calcium (mg/L)			
Plant name	Number of lakes	Mean	10.0%	Median	90.0%
Rhynchospora tracyi	28	4.4	0.6	1.2	16.8
Rhynchospora inundata	15	6.3	0.6	1.5	26.6
Websteria confervoides	36	4.7	0.6	1.5	18.2
Fontinalis spp.	32	3.3	0.6	1.6	9.2
Eriocaulon spp.	57	3.8	0.6	2.0	12.9
Eleocharis elongata	14	4.1	0.4	2.2	12.8
Xyris spp.	65	6.5	0.7	2.5	14.6
Hypericum spp.	94	6.3	0.7	2.5	15.4
Leersia hexandra	104	13.6	0.6	2.8	40.1
Brasenia schreberi	43	6.6	0.7	2.9	21.4
Utricularia floridana	90	7.0	0.7	3.0	18.6
Utricularia purpurea	110	9.1	0.6	3.3	26.7
Fuirena scirpoidea	109	6.6	0.6	3.4	16.0
Utricularia resupinata	14	5.9	0.8	3.5	14.3
Eleocharis baldwinii	135	7.2	0.7	3.5	15.8
Mayaca fluviatilis	82	8.8	0.9	3.7	18.3
Nymphoides aquatica	144	9.0	0.7	4.0	23.7
Myriophyllum heterophyllum	51	11.0	0.7	4.5	22.4
Lachnanthes caroliana	63	7.8	0.7	4.6	16.1
Ludwigia repens	114	15.3	0.8	5.4	43.7
Potamogeton diversifolius	40	11.8	2.1	6.3	39.5
Utricularia gibba	33	10.2	0.8	6.8	22.8
Sagittaria subulata	73	16.3	1.3	6.8	39.0
Ludwigia arcuata	19	9.2	3.0	7.3	22.4
Decondon verticillatus	30	16.7	1.6	7.6	51.7
Baccharis spp.	24	15.0	2.7	7.7	44.6
Myrica cerifera	46	14.8	2.5	7.7	36.4
Panicum hemitomon	299	16.9	0.9	8.0	46.0
Cabomba caroliniana	49	13.3	1.5	8.2	26.8
Nuphar luteum	262	16.9	1.1	8.5	47.2
All Lakes	**321**	**17.6**	**0.9**	**8.6**	**46.5**
Bacopa caroliniana	101	17.9	1.1	8.7	47.3
Nymphaea odorata	194	18.0	1.2	9.0	50.8
Habenaria repens	38	17.2	2.4	9.0	45.6
Melaleuca quinquenervia	27	17.4	3.9	9.2	36.1
Cyperus odoratus	18	12.0	3.0	9.6	25.4
Luziola fluitans	87	20.2	2.8	9.6	52.9
Cephalanthus occidentalis	193	20.5	1.7	9.8	57.9
Cladium jamaicense	141	21.9	1.8	10.1	66.9
Polygonum hydropiperoides	54	15.9	2.0	10.1	37.7
Hydrocotyle umbellata	272	19.9	1.6	10.1	51.5
Pontederia cordata	254	19.2	1.6	10.2	50.8
Micranthemum umbrosum	37	16.3	3.0	10.3	39.5
Potamogeton pectinatus	26	23.5	4.4	11.2	72.5
Fuirena squarrosa	98	20.2	2.0	12.6	51.5
Panicum repens	213	22.8	2.5	13.2	61.2
Sacciolepis striata	106	24.8	2.8	13.2	83.2
Eleocharis interstincta	51	20.9	1.9	13.2	68.6
Eichhornia crassipes	190	24.3	2.4	13.2	67.2

Juncus effusus	86	19.5	2.8	13.3	47.8
Typha spp.	234	23.0	2.8	13.4	59.7
Scirpus cubensis	91	28.4	4.6	13.7	85.0
Ludwigia octovalvis	225	23.1	2.7	13.7	59.6
Paspalum distichum	36	20.2	3.3	13.8	41.5
Chara spp.	105	26.5	3.0	14.0	70.3
Alternanthera philoxeroides	180	25.4	2.5	14.0	70.5
Utricularia foliosa	101	23.9	2.1	14.3	66.9
Nitella spp.	64	21.1	4.0	14.5	53.5
Salix spp.	207	24.3	2.8	14.7	65.0
Brachiaria mutica	161	26.3	2.5	14.8	71.6
Saururus cernuus	41	25.6	2.6	14.8	63.6
Sagittaria lancifolia	176	23.9	2.5	14.8	68.3
Utricularia biflora	89	23.8	3.2	14.9	60.3
Hydrilla verticillata	157	26.6	2.4	14.9	73.7
Bidens spp.	70	28.7	1.3	15.4	91.8
Salvinia spp.	136	28.7	3.8	16.0	77.4
Najas guadalupensis	112	28.0	4.1	16.0	80.1
Sagittaria kurziana	15	39.1	1.2	17.3	101.0
Peltandra virginica	29	26.3	0.9	17.3	73.3
Scirpus californicus	30	19.5	3.6	17.6	39.0
Sambucus canadensis	21	19.2	5.3	18.0	37.6
Limnobium spongia	52	29.7	3.9	18.0	87.9
Azolla caroliniana	62	30.8	5.3	18.0	91.3
Egeria densa	19	28.2	2.4	18.3	85.7
Eleocharis cellulosa	61	26.8	3.1	18.3	86.1
Nelumbo lutea	62	26.5	2.9	18.9	76.1
Pistia stratiotes	84	30.4	3.6	19.0	90.6
Lemna minor	124	30.9	4.0	19.0	87.2
Mikania scandens	98	30.0	4.6	19.1	86.0
Zizaniopsis miliacea	18	32.0	0.7	19.6	97.7
Sagittaria latifolia	67	29.0	2.3	19.9	82.9
Colocasia esculenta	125	28.7	3.4	19.9	72.4
Utricularia inflata	29	28.3	4.6	19.9	85.7
Bacopa monnieri	57	33.4	4.4	20.0	89.6
Paspalidium geminatum	108	31.5	4.1	20.1	86.0
Spartina bakeri	63	29.9	2.9	20.2	91.9
Ceratophyllum demersum	92	32.9	6.0	20.6	91.3
Vallisneria americana	118	32.1	4.8	20.8	89.1
Micranthemum glomeratum	32	34.0	8.2	22.8	96.2
Cyperus alternifolius	27	39.3	3.1	25.0	93.6
Echinochloa spp.	36	39.9	7.1	25.1	98.1
Myriophyllum aquaticum	28	40.2	8.3	25.3	98.0
Canna spp.	24	38.3	2.5	26.7	94.7
Potamogeton illinoensis	47	38.7	7.7	26.8	93.0
Spirodela polyrhiza	37	38.6	2.5	29.6	94.2
Ceratopteris thalictroides	21	42.8	10.1	31.8	98.0
Nymphaea mexicana	30	48.9	4.2	35.3	97.5
Cicuta mexicana	37	47.0	10.1	35.8	98.0
Paspalum repens	34	45.5	5.1	38.3	98.1
Crinum americanum	23	43.3	5.2	38.5	100.0
Phragmites australis	30	49.3	9.7	40.1	98.2
Thalia geniculata	25	51.6	8.6	44.4	99.4
Pennisetum purpureum	15	55.1	7.3	51.0	102.9
Cyperus articulatus	15	60.7	12.1	82.2	102.9

Table 4.10 Statistics for magnesium (mg/L) values from 321 Florida lakes (in bold type) compared to the same statistics for magnesium (mg/L) values from lakes in which individual plant species were identified. The plant species are sorted by the median magnesium (mg/L) values.

Plant name	Number of lakes	Magnesium (mg/L) Mean	10.0%	Median	90.0%
Websteria confervoides	36	3.6	0.5	0.9	11.7
Rhynchospora inundata	15	1.9	0.5	0.9	6.0
Rhynchospora tracyi	28	2.7	0.6	0.9	8.3
Eleocharis elongata	14	1.5	0.6	1.0	3.7
Fontinalis spp.	32	2.3	0.5	1.1	7.4
Eriocaulon spp.	57	2.5	0.6	1.1	6.8
Xyris spp.	65	3.7	0.7	1.6	7.5
Hypericum spp.	94	4.6	0.6	1.8	10.9
Brasenia schreberi	43	3.3	0.6	1.9	8.8
Leersia hexandra	104	7.7	0.7	1.9	29.4
Utricularia floridana	90	4.1	0.6	2.0	10.5
Eleocharis baldwinii	135	3.7	0.7	2.0	8.5
Utricularia resupinata	14	4.1	0.8	2.1	13.1
Fuirena scirpoidea	109	3.6	0.7	2.1	9.7
Myriophyllum heterophyllum	51	7.1	0.7	2.1	23.1
Utricularia gibba	33	5.4	0.7	2.1	15.5
Utricularia purpurea	110	5.0	0.6	2.2	11.8
Mayaca fluviatilis	82	6.2	0.8	2.4	12.4
Nymphoides aquatica	144	5.6	0.7	2.5	12.4
Lachnanthes caroliana	63	4.3	0.8	2.7	11.0
Ludwigia repens	114	7.9	0.8	2.9	22.3
Potamogeton diversifolius	40	6.8	1.2	3.0	14.6
Sagittaria subulata	73	8.6	0.9	3.2	24.1
Baccharis spp.	24	6.9	1.5	3.4	16.9
Decodon verticillatus	30	7.4	1.2	3.5	18.1
Polygonum hydropiperoides	54	6.2	1.0	3.6	13.9
Panicum hemitomon	299	8.2	0.8	3.7	21.3
Cyperus odoratus	18	4.9	1.5	3.9	11.4
Nuphar luteum	262	8.5	0.8	4.0	21.5
All Lakes	**321**	**8.2**	**0.8**	**4.0**	**19.4**
Myrica cerifera	46	6.8	1.7	4.2	13.9
Scirpus californicus	30	8.4	2.4	4.7	17.0
Nymphaea odorata	194	9.3	0.8	4.8	27.8
Hydrocotyle umbellata	272	9.3	1.0	4.8	22.9
Pontederia cordata	254	9.3	1.0	5.2	23.7
Sambucus canadensis	21	6.4	2.7	5.2	11.6
Cabomba caroliniana	49	7.5	0.9	5.6	14.8
Sagittaria kurziana	15	18.4	0.7	5.8	59.7
Bacopa caroliniana	101	9.4	0.8	5.8	20.9
Cephalanthus occidentalis	193	9.5	1.0	5.8	22.8
Paspalum distichum	36	8.3	1.3	6.1	16.5
Cladium jamaicense	141	11.3	1.0	6.3	32.3
Micranthemum umbrosum	37	8.8	1.4	6.3	24.0
Eleocharis interstincta	51	11.5	1.6	6.5	31.7
Panicum repens	213	11.0	1.7	6.7	29.6
Ludwigia arcuata	19	7.0	2.6	6.8	11.8
Typha spp.	234	10.8	2.0	6.8	27.8
Ludwigia octovalvis	225	10.9	1.8	6.9	28.1
Chara spp.	105	12.6	1.7	7.0	35.0

Nitella spp.	64	10.6	2.1	7.0	28.1
Hydrilla verticillata	157	12.3	1.5	7.1	33.1
Colocasia esculenta	125	12.4	2.0	7.1	33.7
Bidens spp.	70	12.6	1.0	7.1	34.9
Juncus effusus	86	10.5	1.9	7.1	23.2
Luziola fluitans	87	11.2	2.1	7.1	31.8
Habenaria repens	38	7.2	2.1	7.1	12.1
Alternanthera philoxeroides	180	11.8	1.2	7.2	32.4
Eichhornia crassipes	190	11.5	1.2	7.2	31.6
Salix spp.	207	11.1	1.7	7.3	28.0
Egeria densa	19	9.5	2.1	7.4	17.0
Saururus cernuus	41	11.9	2.1	7.4	32.3
Utricularia foliosa	101	12.6	1.5	7.4	34.6
Sagittaria lancifolia	176	11.6	1.5	7.5	32.1
Brachiaria mutica	161	12.8	1.5	7.8	34.7
Nelumbo lutea	62	12.3	2.0	7.8	34.2
Fuirena squarrosa	98	11.9	1.5	7.9	31.8
Cyperus alternifolius	27	14.7	2.2	8.1	44.2
Sacciolepis striata	106	13.0	1.8	8.2	35.2
Sagittaria latifolia	67	12.3	1.7	8.2	31.8
Najas guadalupensis	112	12.8	2.2	8.2	32.5
Lemna minor	124	14.4	2.3	8.6	39.2
Bacopa monnieri	57	15.0	2.5	8.8	46.5
Zizaniopsis miliacea	18	14.3	0.7	9.0	53.6
Echinochloa spp.	36	17.6	2.9	9.3	53.3
Melaleuca quinquenervia	27	13.1	2.6	9.3	29.4
Scirpus cubensis	91	13.7	2.7	9.4	34.7
Salvinia spp.	136	14.6	2.7	9.5	39.1
Spirodela polyrhiza	37	15.6	2.1	9.6	46.5
Limnobium spongia	52	13.9	2.2	9.6	34.2
Mikania scandens	98	14.2	2.9	9.7	35.6
Potamogeton pectinatus	26	14.3	2.5	9.7	39.6
Utricularia biflora	89	12.9	2.3	9.7	31.8
Peltandra virginica	29	12.0	0.8	9.7	32.0
Paspalidium geminatum	108	15.8	2.9	9.7	43.4
Pistia stratiotes	84	15.0	2.2	10.1	40.2
Eleocharis cellulosa	61	14.1	2.6	10.2	32.3
Ceratophyllum demersum	92	15.3	2.9	10.2	41.5
Azolla caroliniana	62	14.3	3.7	10.3	34.4
Vallisneria americana	118	15.2	2.6	10.4	39.5
Spartina bakeri	63	16.5	1.9	10.4	49.6
Utricularia inflata	29	16.3	3.4	10.4	44.9
Myriophyllum aquaticum	28	17.9	3.3	10.6	52.9
Phragmites australis	30	23.7	6.6	10.7	55.5
Paspalum repens	34	20.8	3.0	10.8	53.7
Micranthemum glomeratum	32	19.2	3.8	10.8	54.0
Thalia geniculata	25	23.4	2.8	11.3	55.0
Potamogeton illinoensis	47	17.5	2.5	11.8	46.0
Cicuta mexicana	37	20.5	5.7	12.0	53.1
Nymphaea mexicana	30	20.3	2.7	12.1	55.3
Cyperus articulatus	15	27.4	6.3	12.1	59.7
Crinum americanum	23	20.0	4.4	13.7	51.9
Canna spp.	24	22.0	2.0	16.5	57.9
Ceratopteris thalictroides	21	24.9	7.3	17.0	54.2
Pennisetum purpureum	15	26.5	3.4	17.0	59.1

Table 4.11 Statistics for sodium (mg/L) values from 292 Florida lakes (in bold type) compared to the same statistics for sodium (mg/L) values from lakes in which individual plant species were identified. The plant species are sorted by the median sodium (mg/L) values.

Plant species	Number of lakes	Sodium (mg/L)			
		Mean	10.0%	Median	90.0%
Brasenia schreberi	43	4.9	1.8	3.7	8.8
Websteria confervoides	36	5.4	2.1	4.0	11.2
Rhynchospora inundata	14	5.3	2.1	4.1	10.5
Rhynchospora tracyi	28	5.4	2.4	4.1	11.7
Eriocaulon spp.	53	5.5	2.3	4.2	10.6
Xyris spp.	61	8.3	2.2	4.4	11.8
Utricularia floridana	85	6.4	1.9	4.4	11.5
Fontinalis spp.	29	5.8	3.1	4.7	9.5
Hypericum spp.	86	8.1	2.2	5.1	12.8
Myriophyllum heterophyllum	48	12.2	2.5	5.2	14.4
Leersia hexandra	95	13.9	2.8	5.5	21.3
Eleocharis elongata	10	8.0	3.2	5.6	19.9
Utricularia purpurea	103	8.2	2.8	6.2	15.4
Cabomba caroliniana	47	7.5	1.8	6.4	14.5
Utricularia gibba	31	11.5	2.8	6.4	14.7
Zizaniopsis miliacea	17	10.4	2.2	6.9	25.3
Nymphoides aquatica	137	7.7	2.7	7.0	13.8
Decodon verticillatus	30	7.8	2.0	7.0	19.5
Mayaca fluviatilis	79	10.4	2.6	7.0	16.7
Fuirena scirpoidea	97	8.6	3.5	7.0	16.1
Sagittaria kurziana	15	31.7	2.8	7.1	130.6
Eleocharis baldwinii	123	9.5	3.2	7.1	16.2
Lachnanthes caroliana	63	9.1	3.5	7.1	16.9
Ludwigia repens	107	12.5	3.2	7.5	18.7
Eleocharis interstincta	48	14.1	2.1	7.6	18.7
Bidens spp.	70	15.0	2.0	7.7	42.6
Panicum hemitomon	275	12.8	2.9	7.7	19.8
Ludwigia arcuata	19	8.4	4.9	7.7	11.8
Nuphar luteum	243	13.5	3.3	7.7	20.3
All Lakes	**292**	**13.2**	**2.9**	**7.7**	**19.9**
Bacopa caroliniana	98	14.2	2.8	7.8	20.1
Habenaria repens	38	8.6	2.1	7.8	16.2
Peltandra virginica	29	12.5	3.4	7.9	20.4
Utricularia resupinata	12	10.2	4.1	7.9	19.6
Cephalanthus occidentalis	181	14.2	2.6	8.0	19.6
Sacciolepis striata	104	17.2	3.4	8.2	42.4
Utricularia biflora	84	16.9	3.7	8.3	32.8
Nymphaea odorata	186	14.8	2.7	8.3	21.2
Sagittaria subulata	68	14.3	3.3	8.3	17.3
Eichhornia crassipes	182	16.0	2.7	8.3	25.9
Luziola fluitans	86	14.9	2.7	8.4	20.2
Saururus cernuus	39	12.6	3.1	8.5	20.1
Pontederia cordata	237	14.2	3.6	8.5	20.9
Sagittaria latifolia	65	12.4	2.1	8.6	17.8
Eleocharis cellulosa	57	17.2	4.3	8.6	38.5
Egeria densa	19	16.2	1.9	8.6	82.3
Hydrocotyle umbellata	251	14.6	3.5	8.6	21.6
Potamogeton diversifolius	40	8.8	1.8	8.7	17.0
Juncus effusus	80	11.2	2.4	8.7	16.9

Myriophyllum aquaticum	27	26.9	5.5	8.8	100.3
Hydrilla verticillata	147	17.4	2.5	8.8	33.3
Spirodela polyrhiza	37	25.3	2.1	8.8	89.6
Brachiaria mutica	148	17.3	4.9	8.8	35.5
Nitella spp.	62	9.8	4.0	8.8	16.3
Limnobium spongia	50	22.6	4.1	8.8	85.6
Alternanthera philoxeroides	170	17.0	3.9	8.8	32.0
Polygonum hydropiperoides	49	14.3	3.6	8.8	25.7
Micranthemum umbrosum	33	13.6	5.0	8.8	24.5
Fuirena squarrosa	96	11.0	4.1	8.8	16.4
Nelumbo lutea	58	16.0	2.7	8.8	33.7
Najas guadalupensis	109	18.2	3.9	8.9	45.1
Cladium jamaicense	133	16.7	3.8	8.9	32.0
Cyperus odoratus	17	11.6	6.1	9.0	20.1
Paspalum distichum	31	16.4	4.5	9.0	26.0
Azolla caroliniana	60	21.8	5.2	9.0	84.7
Scirpus cubensis	87	16.8	5.6	9.2	28.1
Utricularia foliosa	100	19.5	4.6	9.4	54.9
Mikania scandens	94	19.0	4.4	9.4	45.7
Salix spp.	195	16.3	4.1	9.5	25.8
Panicum repens	202	16.4	3.7	9.5	25.9
Salvinia spp.	132	19.5	5.0	9.5	43.5
Nymphaea mexicana	30	31.3	5.2	9.6	120.9
Sagittaria lancifolia	163	17.2	3.9	9.6	30.5
Micranthemum glomeratum	31	26.9	6.2	9.6	116.6
Typha spp.	217	16.1	4.3	9.6	23.5
Cicuta mexicana	36	22.9	5.1	9.7	90.8
Melaleuca quinquenervia	26	16.6	5.4	9.8	31.9
Ludwigia octovalvis	210	16.5	5.0	9.9	25.7
Paspalum repens	34	32.3	5.3	10.0	108.5
Potamogeton pectinatus	25	28.5	4.6	10.0	102.9
Cyperus alternifolius	25	19.8	5.8	10.0	65.0
Baccharis spp.	24	13.6	7.0	10.0	17.0
Chara spp.	100	18.0	4.1	10.3	22.8
Lemna minor	118	20.9	5.0	10.3	49.9
Spartina bakeri	60	25.1	5.0	10.3	91.7
Pistia stratiotes	82	21.6	5.0	10.4	71.5
Paspalidium geminatum	104	20.5	5.6	10.4	64.3
Ceratophyllum demersum	90	22.0	4.4	10.4	85.6
Colocasia esculenta	114	17.0	5.0	10.5	33.9
Potamogeton illinoensis	45	20.1	4.9	10.5	50.1
Pennisetum purpureum	15	34.8	5.6	10.5	122.7
Echinochloa spp.	33	29.0	3.8	10.5	111.2
Sambucus canadensis	20	12.9	6.5	10.7	25.6
Vallisneria americana	114	21.7	5.8	10.8	69.1
Myrica cerifera	44	18.2	6.5	10.9	21.3
Scirpus californicus	24	23.3	6.6	11.4	69.1
Bacopa monnieri	51	24.3	5.5	11.4	90.8
Utricularia inflata	28	23.5	5.2	12.3	89.8
Ceratopteris thalictroides	21	32.8	6.5	13.5	116.0
Canna spp.	22	25.9	5.2	14.5	111.2
Crinum americanum	23	26.3	6.3	14.7	89.9
Phragmites australis	29	34.9	6.9	14.7	122.0
Thalia geniculata	24	38.4	6.7	15.0	122.9
Cyperus articulatus	15	52.4	6.8	15.8	130.6

Table 4.12 Statistics for potassium (mg/L) values from 321 Florida lakes (in bold type) compared to the same statistics for potassium (mg/L) values from lakes in which individual plant species were identified. The plant species are sorted by the median potassium (mg/L) values.

Plant name	Number of lakes	Potassium (mg/L) Mean	10.0%	Median	90.0%
Brasenia schreberi	43	0.9	0.10	0.3	2.0
Websteria confervoides	36	1.0	0.1	0.3	2.8
Rhynchospora inundata	15	0.9	0.10	0.3	2.7
Rhynchospora tracyi	28	0.9	0.2	0.3	2.6
Eleocharis elongata	14	1.0	0.1	0.3	3.5
Eriocaulon spp.	57	1.3	0.2	0.3	4.0
Utricularia floridana	90	1.0	0.1	0.3	2.5
Xyris spp.	65	1.2	0.1	0.3	3.5
Myriophyllum heterophyllum	51	1.5	0.1	0.3	5.8
Hypericum spp.	94	1.4	0.2	0.4	3.6
Fontinalis spp.	32	0.7	0.1	0.4	1.8
Utricularia purpurea	110	1.4	0.1	0.5	3.7
Leersia hexandra	104	1.7	0.1	0.5	4.9
Utricularia gibba	33	2.9	0.1	0.5	11.1
Decodon verticillatus	30	1.3	0.2	0.8	3.5
Cabomba caroliniana	49	1.5	0.2	0.8	4.5
Lachnanthes caroliana	63	1.6	0.2	0.9	3.7
Fuirena scirpoidea	109	2.1	0.2	0.9	6.7
Mayaca fluviatilis	82	1.8	0.2	0.9	5.3
Nymphoides aquatica	144	1.7	0.2	0.9	3.8
Eleocharis baldwinii	135	2.2	0.2	1.0	6.2
Sagittaria kurziana	15	2.3	0.2	1.0	6.1
Ludwigia repens	114	2.0	0.2	1.0	5.2
Habenaria repens	38	1.7	0.2	1.2	3.9
Bacopa caroliniana	101	2.3	0.2	1.2	6.7
Utricularia resupinata	14	2.0	0.2	1.2	7.3
Bidens spp.	70	1.8	0.2	1.2	4.8
Potamogeton diversifolius	40	1.7	0.2	1.2	3.7
Zizaniopsis miliacea	18	1.9	0.2	1.2	5.3
Eleocharis interstincta	51	2.2	0.2	1.3	6.5
Luziola fluitans	87	2.0	0.2	1.4	5.2
Nuphar luteum	262	2.6	0.2	1.4	6.7
Sagittaria subulata	73	2.4	0.2	1.5	6.4
Peltandra virginica	29	2.2	0.2	1.5	5.1
Panicum hemitomon	299	2.5	0.2	1.6	6.8
Nelumbo lutea	62	2.6	0.2	1.6	7.7
Egeria densa	19	1.8	0.1	1.6	4.2
Cephalanthus occidentalis	193	2.7	0.2	1.7	6.9
Saururus cernuus	41	2.6	0.2	1.7	7.7
All Lakes	**321**	**2.6**	**0.2**	**1.7**	**6.8**
Sacciolepis striata	106	2.8	0.2	1.7	7.1
Spirodela polyrhiza	37	2.3	0.2	1.7	5.5
Utricularia biflora	89	2.6	0.2	1.7	6.6
Nymphaea odorata	194	2.6	0.2	1.7	6.8
Limnobium spongia	52	2.2	0.2	1.8	5.1
Myriophyllum aquaticum	28	2.3	0.2	1.8	5.3
Ludwigia arcuata	19	2.1	0.2	1.9	3.0
Utricularia foliosa	101	2.6	0.2	1.9	6.6
Sagittaria latifolia	67	2.6	0.2	1.9	6.4

Nitella spp.	64	2.8	0.3	1.9	7.5
Eichhornia crassipes	190	2.9	0.2	1.9	8.0
Najas guadalupensis	112	2.7	0.3	1.9	6.6
Potamogeton pectinatus	26	2.8	0.6	2.0	7.2
Hydrilla verticillata	157	2.9	0.2	2.0	7.0
Hydrocotyle umbellata	272	2.9	0.2	2.0	7.8
Cladium jamaicense	141	3.1	0.2	2.0	8.5
Fuirena squarrosa	98	2.7	0.2	2.0	6.7
Pontederia cordata	254	2.9	0.2	2.0	8.1
Eleocharis cellulosa	61	2.7	0.2	2.0	6.6
Alternanthera philoxeroides	180	3.0	0.2	2.0	8.0
Utricularia inflata	29	3.5	0.2	2.0	10.2
Polygonum hydropiperoides	54	3.4	0.2	2.1	9.3
Juncus effusus	86	3.1	0.3	2.1	8.1
Azolla caroliniana	62	2.7	0.3	2.1	5.9
Echinochloa spp.	36	3.1	0.3	2.1	7.1
Salix spp.	207	3.3	0.3	2.2	8.6
Paspalum distichum	36	3.7	0.3	2.2	10.0
Scirpus cubensis	91	3.0	0.6	2.2	6.7
Typha spp.	234	3.3	0.3	2.2	8.6
Panicum repens	213	3.3	0.3	2.2	8.4
Salvinia spp.	136	3.2	0.3	2.3	8.4
Ceratophyllum demersum	92	3.3	0.3	2.3	8.2
Pistia stratiotes	84	3.3	0.2	2.3	8.8
Paspalum repens	34	3.0	0.3	2.3	6.7
Brachiaria mutica	161	3.2	0.3	2.3	8.2
Sagittaria lancifolia	176	3.4	0.2	2.3	8.8
Paspalidium geminatum	108	3.3	0.4	2.3	8.5
Ludwigia octovalvis	225	3.4	0.3	2.3	8.4
Nymphaea mexicana	30	2.9	0.2	2.3	6.1
Spartina bakeri	63	3.4	0.2	2.3	8.4
Lemna minor	124	3.5	0.3	2.3	8.8
Mikania scandens	98	3.4	0.3	2.4	8.8
Bacopa monnieri	57	3.5	0.8	2.4	8.2
Cyperus odoratus	18	4.0	1.1	2.4	11.2
Pennisetum purpureum	15	3.2	0.6	2.5	6.6
Myrica cerifera	46	3.5	0.5	2.5	7.4
Baccharis spp.	24	3.8	0.4	2.5	11.7
Cyperus articulatus	15	3.4	0.8	2.5	6.6
Micranthemum umbrosum	37	3.5	0.6	2.5	9.2
Colocasia esculenta	125	3.7	0.3	2.5	9.2
Cyperus alternifolius	27	3.5	0.7	2.5	8.5
Chara spp.	105	3.7	0.3	2.6	8.9
Thalia geniculata	25	3.6	1.0	2.6	7.4
Melaleuca quinquenervia	27	3.4	1.0	2.6	7.0
Cicuta mexicana	37	3.5	0.2	2.6	9.7
Vallisneria americana	118	4.1	0.3	2.9	10.0
Micranthemum glomeratum	32	4.0	1.0	3.1	8.0
Crinum americanum	23	3.5	0.7	3.2	8.4
Ceratopteris thalictroides	21	4.5	0.6	3.3	12.5
Potamogeton illinoensis	47	3.5	0.2	3.3	7.4
Phragmites australis	30	3.9	1.2	3.4	8.1
Scirpus californicus	30	4.3	0.6	3.7	9.5
Sambucus canadensis	21	4.8	1.7	4.4	8.8
Canna spp.	24	5.9	0.2	5.1	12.5

Table 4.13 Statistics for sulfate (mg/L) values from 292 Florida lakes (in bold type) compared to the same statistics for sulfate (mg/L) values from lakes in which individual plant species were identified. The plant species are sorted by the median sulfate (mg/L) values.

Plant species	Number of lakes	Mean	10.0%	Median	90.0%
Rhynchospora inundata	14	6.2	0.6	5.0	13.2
Rhynchospora tracyi	28	7.3	2.6	5.2	13.0
Brasenia schreberi	43	6.6	2.8	5.5	10.6
Decodon verticillatus	30	6.1	3.2	5.6	11.6
Utricularia floridana	85	8.6	3.0	5.8	13.5
Websteria confervoides	36	8.5	2.8	6.0	16.0
Eriocaulon spp.	53	9.3	3.0	6.1	19.2
Xyris spp.	61	9.6	2.7	6.1	19.8
Eleocharis elongata	10	7.9	0.5	6.4	23.1
Cabomba caroliniana	47	9.6	2.9	6.4	20.8
Fontinalis spp.	29	7.0	0.6	6.4	11.5
Utricularia purpurea	103	10.7	2.9	6.8	25.1
Myriophyllum heterophyllum	48	12.0	3.1	6.8	29.4
Leersia hexandra	95	14.1	2.8	7.0	48.1
Sagittaria kurziana	15	21.9	3.2	7.0	74.9
Hypericum spp.	86	11.5	3.5	7.1	24.2
Nymphoides aquatica	137	11.0	3.0	7.2	24.2
Utricularia gibba	31	13.5	1.4	7.4	40.6
Fuirena scirpoidea	97	12.0	3.2	7.5	28.3
Eleocharis baldwinii	123	12.3	2.8	7.5	32.5
Utricularia resupinata	12	11.9	4.5	7.7	41.9
Lachnanthes caroliana	63	11.4	2.9	7.8	25.8
Polygonum hydropiperoides	49	14.4	0.7	7.8	25.3
Mayaca fluviatilis	79	13.3	4.0	7.8	27.7
Peltandra virginica	29	13.0	3.0	7.8	26.4
Ludwigia repens	107	13.8	3.3	7.9	32.6
Bacopa caroliniana	98	16.1	3.0	7.9	44.3
Saururus cernuus	39	13.8	2.5	8.2	47.2
Potamogeton diversifolius	40	10.9	3.6	8.2	18.0
Egeria densa	19	11.6	2.4	8.3	25.7
Luziola fluitans	86	14.8	3.4	8.3	44.9
Bidens spp.	70	14.7	3.3	9.2	43.3
Sagittaria latifolia	65	13.6	3.1	9.2	28.4
Habenaria repens	38	10.9	3.4	9.3	22.0
All Lakes	**292**	**15.2**	**3.3**	**9.4**	**36.7**
Panicum hemitomon	275	14.8	3.3	9.7	34.7
Nuphar luteum	243	15.1	3.5	9.7	37.4
Cladium jamaicense	133	16.5	3.7	10.0	46.6
Cephalanthus occidentalis	181	15.0	3.3	10.0	33.5
Paspalum distichum	31	16.2	1.0	10.0	34.2
Nymphaea odorata	186	15.9	3.2	10.2	41.4
Zizaniopsis miliacea	17	12.3	3.8	10.3	30.9
Ludwigia arcuata	19	13.0	3.3	10.6	31.8
Eichhornia crassipes	182	17.3	4.1	10.7	47.1
Nelumbo lutea	58	19.2	3.0	10.7	56.8
Hydrocotyle umbellata	251	16.6	4.2	10.9	39.7
Sagittaria subulata	68	16.4	5.0	11.0	50.2
Pontederia cordata	237	16.4	4.2	11.0	39.7
Hydrilla verticillata	147	18.3	3.6	11.1	48.6

Limnobium spongia	50	18.8	3.2	11.1	56.1
Spirodela polyrhiza	37	20.9	3.2	11.2	60.2
Alternanthera philoxeroides	170	17.5	4.0	11.3	44.7
Utricularia foliosa	100	18.0	3.3	11.3	47.7
Eleocharis interstincta	48	17.5	3.4	11.3	49.3
Sacciolepis striata	104	17.4	4.0	11.5	46.0
Sagittaria lancifolia	163	17.1	3.7	11.5	43.6
Cicuta mexicana	36	20.4	4.0	11.5	54.4
Najas guadalupensis	109	17.7	3.3	11.5	48.5
Nitella spp.	62	16.9	4.0	11.5	45.9
Juncus effusus	80	14.3	3.2	11.6	30.5
Fuirena squarrosa	96	16.7	5.1	11.6	41.4
Crinum americanum	23	20.4	3.7	11.6	53.3
Utricularia biflora	84	17.1	3.5	11.6	44.4
Echinochloa spp.	33	24.2	3.2	11.7	67.3
Typha spp.	217	18.2	4.4	11.7	44.1
Salix spp.	195	17.8	4.2	11.7	43.4
Eleocharis cellulosa	57	18.6	5.6	11.8	49.5
Panicum repens	202	18.1	4.7	11.8	42.3
Salvinia spp.	132	19.7	4.7	12.0	48.6
Pistia stratiotes	82	20.3	3.5	12.2	50.6
Azolla caroliniana	60	20.3	4.3	12.2	51.1
Utricularia inflata	28	20.3	4.2	12.2	57.2
Mikania scandens	94	18.1	5.1	12.3	42.3
Chara spp.	100	20.5	5.1	12.3	54.6
Ludwigia octovalvis	210	18.5	4.7	12.3	43.8
Scirpus cubensis	87	19.3	5.1	12.4	47.9
Cyperus odoratus	17	19.9	3.3	12.4	49.2
Lemna minor	118	19.7	4.3	12.5	48.5
Potamogeton pectinatus	25	18.9	4.2	12.7	56.9
Brachiaria mutica	148	19.5	4.4	12.7	47.8
Paspalidium geminatum	104	20.6	5.1	12.7	50.0
Myriophyllum aquaticum	27	22.1	3.1	12.7	56.4
Spartina bakeri	60	21.3	5.4	12.8	56.6
Cyperus alternifolius	25	16.7	5.4	13.0	37.4
Bacopa monnieri	51	22.7	4.5	13.0	60.4
Myrica cerifera	44	17.1	2.8	13.0	35.3
Colocasia esculenta	114	18.6	4.4	13.2	46.7
Ceratophyllum demersum	90	21.7	3.3	13.4	54.6
Thalia geniculata	24	26.9	7.0	13.7	69.8
Phragmites australis	29	25.7	6.4	13.7	56.7
Scirpus californicus	24	20.4	5.9	14.0	38.6
Baccharis spp.	24	16.9	2.5	15.0	35.3
Vallisneria americana	114	22.1	5.0	15.1	50.6
Potamogeton illinoensis	45	21.0	3.2	15.5	48.0
Sambucus canadensis	20	17.4	7.3	15.7	32.5
Nymphaea mexicana	30	27.2	3.2	16.0	72.6
Micranthemum umbrosum	33	20.5	4.3	16.3	47.0
Paspalum repens	34	29.6	4.5	18.4	67.9
Melaleuca quinquenervia	26	21.9	9.0	19.4	43.3
Pennisetum purpureum	15	27.8	7.8	20.3	63.8
Canna spp.	22	27.4	4.3	23.0	64.2
Micranthemum glomeratum	31	28.4	6.7	27.0	64.5
Cyperus articulatus	15	30.9	4.2	27.6	74.9
Ceratopteris thalictroides	21	31.0	8.1	27.6	60.8

Table 4.14 Statistics for chloride (mg/L) values from 321 Florida lakes (in bold type) compared to the same statistics for chloride (mg/L) values from lakes in which individual plant species were identified. The plant species are sorted by the median chloride (mg/L) values.

Plant name	Number of lakes	Chloride (mg/L) Mean	10.0%	Median	90.0%
Brasenia schreberi	43	8.9	2.8	7.6	17.8
Eleocharis elongata	14	14.1	5.8	8.1	35.0
Eriocaulon spp.	57	10.8	3.1	8.2	21.8
Rhynchospora tracyi	28	10.8	6.0	8.3	21.8
Rhynchospora inundata	15	10.1	5.2	8.3	20.8
Websteria confervoides	36	10.6	4.5	8.4	21.8
Xyris spp.	66	14.9	3.3	8.5	22.4
Utricularia floridana	90	11.7	2.9	8.5	22.9
Fontinalis spp.	32	10.7	6.0	8.5	18.2
Hypericum spp.	95	14.5	3.1	8.7	25.1
Myriophyllum heterophyllum	51	22.3	4.1	9.3	28.1
Leersia hexandra	104	24.7	5.8	10.0	33.2
Utricularia purpurea	110	15.0	4.7	10.6	27.5
Utricularia resupinata	14	16.7	6.1	11.8	35.7
Decodon verticillatus	30	13.3	3.2	12.1	25.9
Mayaca fluviatilis	83	18.6	4.2	12.1	27.5
Sagittaria kurziana	15	57.6	4.1	12.2	235.7
Utricularia gibba	33	22.1	6.2	12.3	33.4
Fuirena scirpoidea	109	16.2	6.6	12.3	30.5
Nymphoides aquatica	144	14.4	4.3	12.5	25.8
Lachnanthes caroliana	63	16.7	7.1	12.5	31.9
Eleocharis baldwinii	135	17.8	6.6	12.5	31.0
Cabomba caroliniana	49	13.8	2.9	12.5	27.6
Habenaria repens	38	15.2	3.3	13.5	28.1
Zizaniopsis miliacea	18	16.7	3.5	13.5	35.5
Ludwigia arcuata	19	16.1	7.0	13.6	27.7
Bidens spp.	70	27.1	3.3	13.8	67.4
Panicum hemitomon	299	22.4	5.8	14.0	36.0
Ludwigia repens	113	22.6	6.5	14.0	34.6
Bacopa caroliniana	101	25.3	4.8	14.1	34.4
All Lakes	**321**	**23.4**	**5.8**	**14.2**	**36.0**
Nuphar luteum	262	23.8	6.6	14.3	36.9
Eleocharis interstincta	51	24.9	3.2	14.4	28.7
Peltandra virginica	29	22.2	6.0	14.4	37.0
Sacciolepis striata	106	30.9	6.4	14.6	54.8
Limnobium spongia	52	39.1	5.3	14.9	155.8
Sagittaria subulata	73	25.5	6.2	15.2	35.2
Eichhornia crassipes	190	28.5	4.4	15.2	42.1
Nelumbo lutea	61	28.2	4.4	15.2	46.7
Sagittaria latifolia	67	22.7	3.2	15.2	38.1
Egeria densa	19	29.4	3.3	15.2	161.3
Spirodela polyrhiza	37	43.7	3.3	15.3	171.1
Cephalanthus occidentalis	193	25.7	5.5	15.3	37.0
Micranthemum umbrosum	38	22.6	8.7	15.4	36.8
Nitella spp.	64	17.1	5.8	15.5	28.2
Myriophyllum aquaticum	28	47.2	8.9	15.5	177.8
Luziola fluitans	87	27.1	4.3	15.5	36.0
Paspalum repens	34	57.9	8.3	15.6	201.9
Nymphaea mexicana	30	57.6	8.4	15.7	219.3

Nymphaea odorata	193	27.0	4.5	15.8	38.3
Eleocharis cellulosa	61	30.8	8.6	15.8	61.9
Utricularia biflora	89	30.3	6.8	15.8	42.4
Pontederia cordata	254	25.3	7.0	15.8	39.4
Hydrocotyle umbellata	272	25.9	6.9	15.9	39.5
Hydrilla verticillata	157	30.7	4.1	15.9	44.7
Brachiaria mutica	160	30.3	8.7	15.9	44.4
Alternanthera philoxeroides	180	30.0	8.0	15.9	44.0
Potamogeton diversifolius	40	15.7	2.9	15.9	28.0
Fuirena squarrosa	98	20.0	7.9	16.0	28.3
Najas guadalupensis	111	32.9	7.3	16.0	69.9
Juncus effusus	86	20.1	4.5	16.0	31.1
Saururus cernuus	40	21.7	6.0	16.1	36.5
Micranthemum glomeratum	32	47.5	11.8	16.1	207.9
Echinochloa spp.	36	48.6	7.9	16.2	187.9
Azolla caroliniana	62	39.2	8.9	16.7	149.3
Cyperus odoratus	18	20.3	11.7	16.9	33.4
Melaleuca quinquenervia	27	29.3	9.8	17.1	49.4
Salix spp.	206	29.1	8.2	17.1	41.3
Cladium jamaicense	141	30.7	7.9	17.3	43.5
Ceratophyllum demersum	92	39.0	8.2	17.4	155.8
Salvinia spp.	136	34.8	8.5	17.4	67.7
Lemna minor	123	36.9	8.6	17.4	86.4
Scirpus cubensis	91	30.9	10.1	17.4	43.0
Typha spp.	233	28.7	8.3	17.4	40.5
Panicum repens	213	29.3	6.9	17.4	42.7
Mikania scandens	98	33.8	8.3	17.4	73.4
Sagittaria lancifolia	176	30.8	8.0	17.4	43.8
Utricularia foliosa	101	35.6	8.5	17.5	97.6
Polygonum hydropiperoides	53	25.8	8.2	17.8	42.9
Ludwigia octovalvis	224	29.4	8.9	17.9	41.6
Pistia stratiotes	84	38.0	8.4	18.0	129.0
Paspalum distichum	36	29.1	10.6	18.0	41.3
Cicuta mexicana	37	41.3	8.7	18.2	174.4
Paspalidium geminatum	108	36.8	9.8	18.7	101.4
Colocasia esculenta	125	29.0	9.0	18.7	43
Potamogeton illinoensis	47	35.3	9.0	19.1	76.2
Spartina bakeri	63	45.3	9.3	19.7	171.2
Pennisetum purpureum	15	63.2	10.2	19.7	223.2
Sambucus canadensis	22	22.5	11.8	19.7	39.9
Bacopa monnieri	57	41.3	8.7	19.7	148.1
Baccharis spp.	24	27.1	12.0	20.0	41.3
Chara spp.	106	32.4	7.9	20.0	41.1
Myrica cerifera	46	33.8	12.0	20.4	37.0
Vallisneria americana	117	39.7	9.9	21.5	106.9
Scirpus californicus	30	37.1	10.1	22.1	92.8
Potamogeton pectinatus	26	51.5	9.1	22.1	187.3
Utricularia inflata	29	40.6	8.9	22.9	143.0
Cyperus alternifolius	27	36.6	10.0	23.7	112.0
Crinum americanum	23	48.4	12.3	24.2	168.2
Ceratopteris thalictroides	21	59.1	12.6	24.9	212.7
Canna spp.	24	46.0	9.4	26.3	183.0
Thalia geniculata	25	69.2	13.9	26.5	223.2
Phragmites australis	30	62.4	12.6	26.7	218.7
Cyperus articulatus	15	96.9	12.8	27.1	235.7

Table 4.15 Statistics for iron (mg/L) values from 209 Florida lakes (in bold type) compared to the same statistics for iron (mg/L) values from lakes in which individual plant species were identified. The plant species are sorted by the median iron (mg/L) values.

Plant species	Number of lakes	Iron (mg/L) Mean	10.0%	Median	90.0%
Utricularia resupinata	12	0.03	0.00	0.02	0.09
Rhynchospora inundata	2	0.02	0.00	0.02	0.04
Cyperus odoratus	14	0.06	0.00	0.03	0.15
Fuirena scirpoidea	49	0.10	0.00	0.04	0.28
Baccharis spp.	12	0.08	0.00	0.05	0.29
Chara spp.	78	0.12	0.00	0.05	0.35
Eleocharis baldwinii	71	0.11	0.00	0.05	0.32
Mayaca fluviatilis	60	0.15	0.00	0.05	0.42
Eleocharis elongata	4	0.06	0.00	0.05	0.15
Potamogeton illinoensis	40	0.11	0.01	0.05	0.23
Polygonum hydropiperoides	36	0.14	0.00	0.05	0.27
Myrica cerifera	15	0.09	0.00	0.05	0.29
Sambucus canadensis	11	0.07	0.00	0.05	0.29
Eriocaulon spp.	30	0.12	0.00	0.06	0.32
Paspalum distichum	23	0.11	0.00	0.06	0.31
Canna spp.	18	0.10	0.00	0.06	0.38
Sagittaria subulata	54	0.15	0.00	0.06	0.37
Nitella spp.	57	0.17	0.01	0.07	0.53
Vallisneria americana	94	0.14	0.00	0.07	0.35
Cladium jamaicense	102	0.14	0.00	0.08	0.32
Nymphaea odorata	137	0.16	0.00	0.08	0.36
Lachnanthes caroliana	38	0.13	0.00	0.08	0.38
Potamogeton diversifolius	37	0.18	0.00	0.08	0.62
Colocasia esculenta	97	0.14	0.00	0.08	0.33
Hydrocotyle umbellata	195	0.15	0.00	0.08	0.35
Rhynchospora tracyi	7	0.10	0.00	0.08	0.24
Websteria confervoides	15	0.14	0.03	0.08	0.50
Utricularia floridana	53	0.15	0.01	0.08	0.40
Fuirena squarrosa	82	0.14	0.01	0.08	0.35
Cyperus alternifolius	19	0.13	0.00	0.08	0.35
Panicum repens	168	0.16	0.00	0.08	0.38
Typha spp.	179	0.16	0.00	0.09	0.38
Sagittaria lancifolia	133	0.17	0.00	0.09	0.43
Spartina bakeri	52	0.18	0.01	0.09	0.46
Bacopa caroliniana	79	0.20	0.00	0.09	0.60
Panicum hemitomon	202	0.15	0.00	0.09	0.36
Utricularia purpurea	65	0.16	0.01	0.09	0.37
Nuphar luteum	178	0.15	0.00	0.09	0.35
All Lakes	**209**	**0.15**	**0.00**	**0.09**	**0.38**
Ludwigia octovalvis	170	0.15	0.00	0.09	0.35
Mikania scandens	81	0.16	0.01	0.09	0.41
Pontederia cordata	184	0.15	0.00	0.09	0.35
Nymphoides aquatica	94	0.17	0.01	0.09	0.44
Utricularia gibba	15	0.21	0.00	0.09	0.94
Hypericum spp.	54	0.20	0.00	0.09	0.67
Decodon verticillatus	27	0.16	0.05	0.10	0.35
Leersia hexandra	57	0.18	0.00	0.10	0.40
Ludwigia repens	72	0.19	0.00	0.10	0.55
Salix spp.	155	0.17	0.00	0.10	0.42

Hydrilla verticillata	130	0.17	0.01	0.10	0.42
Brasenia schreberi	31	0.20	0.02	0.10	0.62
Cephalanthus occidentalis	149	0.18	0.01	0.10	0.40
Fontinalis spp.	18	0.19	0.00	0.10	0.41
Brachiaria mutica	125	0.18	0.01	0.10	0.41
Bacopa monnieri	45	0.14	0.00	0.10	0.31
Scirpus californicus	15	0.16	0.00	0.10	0.54
Utricularia inflata	25	0.18	0.01	0.10	0.66
Melaleuca quinquenervia	20	0.16	0.01	0.10	0.49
Eleocharis cellulosa	51	0.18	0.02	0.11	0.37
Eichhornia crassipes	158	0.18	0.01	0.11	0.42
Utricularia foliosa	80	0.19	0.01	0.11	0.50
Pistia stratiotes	72	0.17	0.02	0.11	0.35
Pennisetum purpureum	14	0.20	0.02	0.11	0.68
Bidens spp.	59	0.20	0.02	0.11	0.60
Juncus effusus	69	0.21	0.01	0.11	0.63
Ceratophyllum demersum	80	0.17	0.01	0.11	0.35
Alternanthera philoxeroides	140	0.18	0.01	0.11	0.43
Crinum americanum	21	0.21	0.02	0.11	0.75
Paspalidium geminatum	92	0.18	0.02	0.11	0.37
Saururus cernuus	36	0.18	0.03	0.11	0.42
Scirpus cubensis	77	0.20	0.02	0.12	0.53
Utricularia biflora	74	0.21	0.03	0.13	0.63
Eleocharis interstincta	43	0.22	0.01	0.13	0.68
Ludwigia arcuata	18	0.17	0.02	0.13	0.41
Najas guadalupensis	94	0.20	0.02	0.13	0.47
Ceratopteris thalictroides	21	0.17	0.01	0.13	0.37
Sacciolepis striata	92	0.23	0.03	0.14	0.63
Lemna minor	104	0.19	0.02	0.14	0.43
Micranthemum umbrosum	26	0.23	0.00	0.14	0.75
Salvinia spp.	116	0.20	0.02	0.14	0.50
Myriophyllum heterophyllum	31	0.21	0.00	0.14	0.72
Sagittaria kurziana	13	0.13	0.01	0.15	0.25
Paspalum repens	33	0.20	0.01	0.15	0.52
Xyris spp.	31	0.22	0.00	0.15	0.63
Cicuta mexicana	35	0.19	0.05	0.16	0.40
Phragmites australis	28	0.26	0.05	0.16	0.74
Habenaria repens	33	0.22	0.02	0.16	0.56
Sagittaria latifolia	59	0.24	0.02	0.17	0.63
Potamogeton pectinatus	19	0.29	0.01	0.17	0.87
Peltandra virginica	24	0.21	0.05	0.17	0.53
Nymphaea mexicana	26	0.17	0.02	0.18	0.31
Limnobium spongia	45	0.27	0.05	0.19	0.69
Nelumbo lutea	53	0.25	0.02	0.19	0.63
Luziola fluitans	80	0.26	0.03	0.19	0.70
Cabomba caroliniana	40	0.26	0.03	0.19	0.70
Spirodela polyrhiza	33	0.24	0.02	0.19	0.63
Micranthemum glomeratum	28	0.23	0.01	0.19	0.52
Azolla caroliniana	54	0.26	0.05	0.21	0.57
Thalia geniculata	23	0.25	0.00	0.21	0.74
Echinochloa spp.	31	0.25	0.05	0.21	0.59
Zizaniopsis miliacea	14	0.32	0.03	0.21	0.80
Cyperus articulatus	15	0.28	0.13	0.23	0.63
Egeria densa	15	0.24	0.05	0.23	0.51
Myriophyllum aquaticum	26	0.28	0.03	0.23	0.70

Table 4.16 Statistics for silicon (mg/L) values from 209 Florida lakes (in bold type) compared to the same statistics for silicon (mg/L) values from lakes in which individual plant species were identified. The plant species are sorted by the median silicon (mg/L) values.

Plant species	Number of lakes	Silicon (mg/L)			
		Mean	10.0%	Median	90.0%
Eleocharis elongata	4	0.3	0.1	0.2	0.5
Eriocaulon spp.	30	0.5	0.10	0.3	1.2
Utricularia resupinata	12	0.3	0.1	0.3	0.9
Utricularia floridana	53	0.7	0.10	0.3	1.6
Fuirena scirpoidea	49	0.6	0.10	0.3	1.3
Fontinalis spp.	18	1.0	0.0	0.3	3.6
Brasenia schreberi	31	0.9	0.10	0.3	3.4
Mayaca fluviatilis	60	0.9	0.10	0.3	3.4
Cyperus odoratus	14	0.7	0.2	0.3	2.3
Hypericum spp.	54	0.8	0.10	0.3	2.4
Nymphoides aquatica	94	0.9	0.1	0.4	2.6
Myriophyllum heterophyllum	31	1.0	0.10	0.4	3.5
Utricularia purpurea	65	1.1	0.10	0.4	2.9
Potamogeton diversifolius	37	0.8	0.1	0.4	1.9
Myrica cerifera	15	1.1	0.1	0.4	3.6
Eleocharis baldwinii	71	0.7	0.1	0.4	1.8
Rhynchospora tracyi	7	0.4	0.10	0.4	0.9
Utricularia gibba	15	2.2	0.10	0.5	10.1
Polygonum hydropiperoides	36	1.8	0.1	0.5	7.7
Lachnanthes caroliana	38	1.0	0.1	0.5	3.5
Sagittaria subulata	54	1.2	0.10	0.5	3.8
Nitella spp.	57	1.1	0.1	0.5	3.6
Leersia hexandra	57	1.4	0.1	0.5	4.0
Ludwigia arcuata	18	1.0	0.1	0.5	3.6
Xyris spp.	31	1.2	0.1	0.5	3.4
Nymphaea odorata	137	1.4	0.1	0.5	3.7
Bacopa caroliniana	79	1.4	0.1	0.5	3.8
Websteria confervoides	15	0.9	0.0	0.5	2.6
Ludwigia repens	72	1.4	0.1	0.5	3.8
Nuphar luteum	178	1.4	0.1	0.5	3.7
Cabomba caroliniana	40	1.3	0.10	0.5	3.6
Pontederia cordata	184	1.5	0.1	0.6	3.8
Baccharis spp.	12	2.2	0.2	0.6	9.4
Chara spp.	78	1.8	0.1	0.6	5.2
Panicum hemitomon	202	1.5	0.1	0.6	3.7
All Lakes	**209**	**1.5**	**0.1**	**0.6**	**3.8**
Fuirena squarrosa	82	1.2	0.1	0.6	3.5
Hydrocotyle umbellata	195	1.6	0.2	0.6	3.8
Juncus effusus	69	1.2	0.1	0.7	3.5
Eleocharis interstincta	43	1.3	0.2	0.7	3.8
Typha spp.	179	1.7	0.2	0.7	4.2
Cyperus alternifolius	19	1.7	0.2	0.7	5.3
Panicum repens	168	1.6	0.1	0.7	3.9
Hydrilla verticillata	130	1.7	0.1	0.7	4.4
Rhynchospora inundata	2	0.7	0.2	0.7	1.3
Cladium jamaicense	102	1.8	0.1	0.8	5.1
Ludwigia octovalvis	170	1.7	0.2	0.8	3.9
Bacopa monnieri	45	1.6	0.2	0.8	4.1
Micranthemum umbrosum	26	1.5	0.10	0.8	3.4

Colocasia esculenta	97	1.9	0.1	0.9	5.3
Cephalanthus occidentalis	149	1.7	0.2	0.9	3.8
Eichhornia crassipes	158	1.7	0.1	0.9	3.9
Decodon verticillatus	27	1.1	0.10	0.9	2.9
Sagittaria lancifolia	133	1.9	0.1	0.9	5.0
Salix spp.	155	1.9	0.2	0.9	5.0
Najas guadalupensis	94	1.9	0.2	0.9	5.0
Alternanthera philoxeroides	140	1.8	0.1	0.9	4.4
Utricularia inflata	25	1.8	0.1	0.9	5.8
Habenaria repens	33	1.3	0.1	1.0	3.4
Potamogeton pectinatus	19	1.7	0.1	1.0	5.1
Scirpus californicus	15	1.7	0.1	1.0	4.5
Brachiaria mutica	125	1.7	0.2	1.0	3.8
Scirpus cubensis	77	1.7	0.2	1.0	3.7
Utricularia foliosa	80	1.8	0.1	1.0	4.4
Vallisneria americana	94	2.2	0.1	1.0	5.9
Paspalum distichum	23	2.2	0.2	1.0	7.9
Eleocharis cellulosa	51	1.6	0.2	1.0	3.8
Saururus cernuus	36	1.8	0.2	1.0	5.1
Sagittaria latifolia	59	2.2	0.1	1.1	7.0
Mikania scandens	81	2.0	0.1	1.1	4.4
Luziola fluitans	80	1.7	0.1	1.1	3.8
Salvinia spp.	116	2.0	0.2	1.1	5.0
Egeria densa	15	2.6	0.1	1.1	8.1
Utricularia biflora	74	1.8	0.1	1.1	3.9
Melaleuca quinquenervia	20	1.7	0.3	1.1	3.9
Ceratophyllum demersum	80	2.1	0.1	1.2	5.9
Spartina bakeri	52	1.7	0.1	1.2	4.1
Sacciolepis striata	92	1.9	0.2	1.3	4.4
Bidens spp.	59	2.3	0.1	1.3	6.4
Lemna minor	104	2.1	0.2	1.3	5.2
Paspalidium geminatum	92	2.1	0.2	1.3	5.1
Canna spp.	18	2.1	0.1	1.3	5.5
Nymphaea mexicana	26	2.7	0.2	1.3	7.8
Limnobium spongia	45	2.3	0.1	1.3	7.0
Pistia stratiotes	72	2.2	0.2	1.5	4.8
Potamogeton illinoensis	40	2.3	0.2	1.6	5.8
Nelumbo lutea	53	2.1	0.1	1.6	5.2
Spirodela polyrhiza	33	2.5	0.1	1.6	7.0
Micranthemum glomeratum	28	2.0	0.1	1.7	4.1
Sambucus canadensis	11	1.8	0.3	1.7	4.1
Peltandra virginica	24	2.4	0.3	1.9	5.0
Azolla caroliniana	54	2.6	0.4	1.9	6.5
Echinochloa spp.	31	2.7	0.4	2.1	7.0
Sagittaria kurziana	13	2.1	0.1	2.1	6.0
Myriophyllum aquaticum	26	2.6	0.2	2.1	7.0
Paspalum repens	33	2.7	0.1	2.4	6.6
Crinum americanum	21	3.0	0.3	2.5	6.8
Ceratopteris thalictroides	21	2.5	0.1	2.6	5.0
Pennisetum purpureum	14	3.0	0.2	2.6	8.3
Cicuta mexicana	35	3.3	0.4	2.6	7.1
Phragmites australis	28	3.0	0.4	2.6	6.0
Thalia geniculata	23	2.7	0.3	3.1	5.2
Cyperus articulatus	15	2.9	0.8	3.1	5.0
Zizaniopsis miliacea	14	3.2	0.5	3.1	6.7

Glossary

Terms in definitions that are in bold type are also found in the glossary.

Acaulescent. Either having no **stem** or appearing to have none.

Achene. A hard, dry **indehiscent**, one-seeded **fruit** with a single cavity.

Adnate. Said of plant **organs** that are organically fused not just closely adjacent.

Alternate. Said of leaves that occur one at successive **nodes** forming a definite sequence around the **stem**; said also of members of adjacent **whorls** in the **flower** when any member of one whorl is in front of or behind the junction of two adjacent members of the succeeding whorl.

Annual. A plant that completes its life history within a year. Compare **biennial** and **perennial**.

Anther. The **pollen**-bearing part of a **stamen**.

Apical. At the apex or tip.

Aquatic. Living in water.

Asexual. Characterized by reproduction that does not involve the fusion of a sperm and an egg.

Axil. The upper angle between an organ and the **axis** that bears it, such as the angle between the leaf and the **stem** bearing that leaf.

Axillary. Growing in an **axil**.

Axis. The main stem of a plant or the main line of development of a plant part.

Barb. A reflexed projection. Compare **spur**.

Berry. A fleshy, few- to many-seeded **fruit**.

Biennial. A plant that requires two years complete its life history; in the first year the vegetative growth occurs, and in the second it flowers, seeds, and dies.

Bisexual. Having both sexes on the same individual; a hermaphrodite.

Blade. The **lamina** or expanded part of a leaf.

Bract. A reduced or modified leaf, particularly the scale-like leaves in a **flower cluster**. Also said of any bract-like emergence.

Bractlet. A small **bract**; sometimes applied to bracts in secondary positions.

Bristle. A stiff, sharp hair.

Bulb. A short, rounded underground stem covered by overlapping leaf bases or scales. Compare with **corm**, **rhizome**, and **tuber**.

Calcareous. Containing an excess of available calcium, usually in the form of the compound calcium carbonate (mineral form: limestone); "limy."

Calyx. The outermost **whorl** of the **floral envelopes**, composed of separate or united **sepals**.

Capillary. Very slender, thread-like.

Capsule. A dry, **dehiscent fruit** originating from two or more **carpels**.

Carpel. The ovule-bearing structure. It consists of the ovary, the **style**, and the **stigma**. A **flower** may have one or many carpels.

Catkin. A **deciduous** spike, either erect or lax, that consists of **unisexual flowers** that lack **petals**.

Compound. Formed of several similar parts united in one common whole, as a compound **pistil**, or of **leaves** composed of two or more distinct **leaflets**.

Compressed. Flattened laterally.

Cordate. Entirely heart-shaped or bilobed at the base, as the base of a leaf.

Corm. A solid, **bulb**-like **stem**, usually found underground.

Corolla. The inner **whorl** or whorls of the **perianth**. Usually differentiated, often by color.

Culm. The aboveground **stem** of **grasses** or grass-like plants.

Cyme. A form of **inflorescence** in which the main **axis** terminates in a single **flower** that opens before the lateral flowers arising beneath.

Deciduous. Losing **leaves** seasonally.

Decumbent. Reclining on the ground, with ascending **distal** portions.

Dehiscent. Said of stamens and fruits that open and shed their contents.

Dimorphic, dimorphous. In general, having two forms. Specifically, the difference in appearance between male and female structures, as **flowers** with short **stamens** and long **styles** or vice versa.

Distal. Farthest away from the center, the point of attachment, or the origin. The opposite is **proximal**.

Dorsal. The upper side of a surface, for example, of a leaf. The opposite is **ventral**.

Drupe. Any fleshy **indehiscent fruit** that contains one stone with a kernel, e.g., a plum.

Drupelet. A diminutive **drupe**.

Elliptic. In the form of an elongated circle, usually more than twice as long as broad. Compare **obovate**.

Ellipsoidal. Shaped like an ellipsoid which is an elliptic solid. Compare **ovoid**.

Emersed, emergent. Said of aquatic plants whose upper parts are held above the water, in contrast to **submersed** or floating plants.

Entire. Having a **margin** devoid of any indentations, lobes, or teeth; said of the margin of appendages such as **leaves**, **bracts**, **stipules**, **sepals**, and **petals**.

Exotic. Introduced from another country. The opposite is **native**. Compare **naturalized**.

Floret. One of the **flowers** in an **inflorescence** of small flowers, such as in the **spikelet** of a **grass**.

Flower. An **axis** bearing either functional **stamens** or **pistils** or both, these either naked or subtended by a **perianth**.

Frond. Leaf of a fern, including the **stipe** and **blade**.

Fruit. The matured **pistil** or pistils and accessory structures, bearing the ripened seeds.

Fusiform. Tapering at both ends; applied to any structure.

Glabrous. Smooth without **pubescence** of any kind.

Glaucous. Having a frosted or whitish waxy appearance from a waxy bloom or powdery coating.

Glume. A member of a pair of **bracts** (often chaffy) subtending the **spikelet** of the **grasses**.

Grass. Any plant of the family, Gramineae. Very common and possessing characteristic structures.

Head. A dense globular cluster of **sessile** or **subsessile flowers** arising essentially from the same point on the **peduncle**.

Herb. An **annual**, **perennial**, or **biennial** plant with aboveground parts that are not **woody**.

Herbaceous. Having the structure or texture of an **herb**; not **woody**.

Indehiscent. Opposite of **dehiscent**; remains closed at maturity.

Inferior. Occurring below; said of the **ovary** when it occurs so as to appear to be below the other **flower** parts.

Inflorescence. A cluster of **flowers** on a floral axis; usually characteristic of a given plant.

Internode. A component of a plant **stem**. The portions of a stem between the **nodes**; they can be quite short.

Irregular. Said of structures when they are unlike in shape or size, such as the unequal lobes of a **corolla**.

Joint. The **internodes** of a **culm**; the space between two **nodes** on a **grass stem**.

Keel. The ridge of any structure formed by a fold, alluding to its resemblance to the keel of a boat; the two united front **petals** characteristic of Papilionoideae; for example, in bean plants.

Lamina. Synonymous with **blade**.

Lanceolate. Shaped like the head of a spear or lance; much longer than broad, and tapering from a broad base to a fairly pointed apex.

Leaflet. A discrete segment of a **compound** leaf.

Ligule. An elongated, flattened structure; specifically, in **monocotyledons**, especially **grasses**, the **bract**-like emergence from the top of the leaf sheath at the base of the **blade**; in Compositae, a strap-shaped **corolla**. (All corollas are ligules in the tribe Cichoriaceae; in many other Compositae only the marginal ray corollas are ligules.)

Lobe. An outward projection from the **margin** of an **organ**, usually with the margin indented on either side of the projection, as in leaves.

Margin. The edge of a structure.

Marsh. A tract of wet or periodically inundated treeless land, usually characterized by **grasses**, cattails, or other **monocotyledons**.

Midrib. The conspicuous central vein in the **vascular system** of an appendage.

Native. An original or indigenous inhabitant.

Naturalized. Exotic, but established and reproducing itself as though **native**.

Node. The region on the **stem** where a leaf or leaves occur.

Nut. An **indehiscent**, one-seeded **fruit** from more than one **carpel** and having a **woody** coat.

Nutlet. A diminutive **nut**; loosely applied to any small, dry, nut-like **fruit**.

Oblanceolate. The opposite of **lanceolate**; the broadest part is near the apex and tapers back to the base.

Oblong. Longer than broad, the sides nearly parallel for most of their length.

Obovate. The reverse of **ovate**: The broadest part is near the **distal** end.

Obovoid. Inversely **ovoid**.

Obpyramidal. In the shape of an inverted pyramid.

Obtuse. Having a blunt or rounded terminal part.

Opposite. Leaves occurring two at a **node** on opposite sides of the **stem**. Or of **flower** parts, when one part occurs in front of another.

Organ. A plant part or structure composed of specific tissues and with specific functions. Many organs are visually distinctive, such as leaves, **stems**, and **roots**.

Ovate. Said of a plane structure that has the shape of an egg's outline; the broadest part is closer to the base or **proximal** end. The reverse is **obovate**.

Ovoid. An egg-shaped solid.

Palmate. Having three or more lobes radiating from a common base like the fingers from the palm of the hand.

Panicle. A **compound inflorescence**, that is, one in which the **axis** is branched one or more times.

Pappus. The chaffy, scaly, bristle-like, or **plumose** structure at the junction of the **achene** and the **corolla** in Compositae.

Pedicel. **Stalk** or **stem** of a **flower** in a flower cluster.

Peduncle. The **stem** of a solitary **flower** or the main **stem** of a flower cluster.

Peltate. Said of a plane structure that is attached at a point on its surface instead of at the **margin**.

Perennial. Living three or more years. Compare **annual** and **biennial**.

Persistent. Said of an **organ** that remains attached after ceasing to perform its usual biological function.

Petal. A unit segment of the **corolla** presumed to be homologous with a leaf.

Petiole. The **stem** or **stalk** of a leaf.

Pinnate. Having a common elongated **rachis** or **axis**, with segments arranged either oppositely or alternately along either side.

Pinnately compound. Said of structures with discrete lateral segments arranged along a common **axis**.

Pistil. One of the essential **organs** of a **flower**, consisting usually of **stigma**, **style**, and **ovary**, which contains the **ovule** or ovules.

Pistillate. Said of a **flower** that has one or more **carpels** but no **stamens**.

Plumose. With hair-like branches; feathery.

Pollen. The powdery grains that bear the sperm nuclei and are contained in the **anther**.

Proximal. The opposite of **distal**. Close to the center, point of attachment, or origin.

Pubescent. A general term meaning hairy. The opposite is **glabrous**. Compare **scabrous**.

Raceme. An **inflorescence** with a single **axis**; the **flowers** arranged along it on **pedicels**.

Rachis. The central prolongation of the **stalk** (**peduncle**) through an **inflorescence**, or of a leaf stalk (**petiole**) through a **compound** leaf.

Rhizome. A horizontal underground **stem**. Compare corm and tuber.

Runner. A horizontal **stem** with long **internodes** that trails along the surface of the ground.

Scabrous. Rough to the touch because of short stiff hairs. Compare **glabrous** and **pubescent**.

Scape. An erect, naked **peduncle** of an **acaulescent** plant arising at the surface or from below the surface of the ground.

Sepal. One of the segments of the **calyx**.

Serrate. Having teeth on the **margin** pointing forward.

Sessile. Joined directly to the base without a **stalk**, **pedicel**, or **petiole**.

Sheath. The basal part of a lateral **organ** that closely surrounds or invests the **stem**.

Simple. Neither branched nor otherwise **compound**.

Smooth. Not rough to the touch; compare **glabrous**, hairless, which may be either smooth or **scabrous**.

Spathe. A sheathing lateral **organ** or pair of organs usually open on one side and enclosing an **inflorescence**.

Spatulate. Shaped like a spatula, i.e., gradually widening **distally** and with a round tip.

Spike. A type of **inflorescence** in which the **axis** is somewhat elongated and the **flowers** are numerous and **sessile**.

Spikelet. The segment of the **inflorescence** of **grasses** enclosed by a pair of **glumes**.

Spine. A rigid, sharp-pointed structure usually modified from a **stem**. Compare barb.

Spore. The reproductive body of pteridophytes (e.g., ferns) and lower plants, analogous to the seed.

Spur. Any hollow, elongated, pointed or blunt outgrowth of the **corolla** or **calyx**, as in *Delphinium*.

Stalk. A short or elongated structure bearing or supporting another structure.

Stamen. The **pollen**-bearing **organ**; usually consisting of the **stalk** or **filament** and the **anther** containing the pollen.

Staminate. Said of plants or structures bearing **stamens** and not bearing **pistils**.

Stem. The part of the plant bearing the foliar and floral **organs** and composed of **nodes** and **internodes**, or the latter much reduced.

Stigma. That part of the **pistil** that receives the **pollen** and in which pollination is effected.

Stipule. An appendage frequently occurring at the base of a leaf.

Stolon. A **stem** with elongated **internodes** that trails along the surface of the ground, often rooting at the **nodes**.

Style. The slender extension of the **pistil** that connects **ovary** and **stigma**.

Submerged, submersed. Growing under water.

Subsessile. Not quite **sessile**, i.e., joined very closely to the base but not directly.

Succulent. Fleshy; composed of soft, watery tissue.

Superior. Wholly above and not **adnate** to other **organs,** e.g., a superior ovary.

Tuber. An enlarged, fleshy, reproductive structure produced on an underground **stem**, such as the potato.

Turion. A scaly, often thick and fleshy, winter bud that detaches and allows a plant to survive the cold weather.

Umbel. An **inflorescence** of few to many **flowers** on **stalks** of approximately equal length arising from the top of a **scape** or **peduncle**.

Unisexual. In flowering plants, said of a plant or flower that bears **stamens** or **pistils**, but not both.

Utricle. A usually one-seeded, **indehiscent fruit** with a thin, **bladdery**, persistent ovary wall.

Veins. The ultimate branches or divisions of the **vascular system;** they are found in leaves or **petals**.

Vascular system. The network of structures in a plant through which materials are distributed.

Whorl. A ring of leaves, **flower** parts, or flowers occurring at a single **node**.

Woody. Said of plants that possess secondary tissues which are hard and lignified. Compare **herbaceous**.

Index of Common Names of Aquatic Weeds

About the Authors

L to R: Mark V. Hoyer, Christine A. Horsburgh, Karen Brown, Daniel E. Canfield, Jr.   Photo: Tom Wright

Mark V. Hoyer is Scientific Research Manager in the University of Florida's Department of Fisheries and Aquatic Sciences. He received a Bachelor of Science in Fisheries and Wildlife Biology from Iowa State University; his Master of Science in Limnology is from the University of Missouri, Columbia. He has worked extensively on the interrelationships of water chemistry, aquatic macrophyte communities, fish populations, and aquatic bird populations. In Iowa and Missouri, his primary interest was lake eutrophication, including nutrient loading models and the relationship between in-lake nutrients and chlorophyll *a*. Mark came to the University of Florida in 1983; the vast range of aquatic systems he has encountered in Florida has made him aware of the state's great resources. During this time, Mark has authored many technical publications; his previous book was "Handbook of Common Freshwater Fish in Florida Lakes," also with Daniel E. Canfield, Jr.

Dr. Daniel E. Canfield, Jr. is a Professor of Limnology in the University of Florida's Department of Fisheries and Aquatic Sciences. His specialty is the management of aquatic ecosystems. A native of Connecticut, he obtained a Bachelor of Science in 1973 from Bates College in Lewiston, Maine. He obtained both a Master of Science and a doctoral degree from Iowa State University in Ames. Dr. Canfield has served as President of the North American Lake Management Society (NALMS), and he is a recipient of its prestigious Secchi Disk Award for his many contributions to the preservation of America's lakes. He is founder of Florida LAKEWATCH, a pioneering citizen-volunteer water quality monitoring program involving over 500 lakes statewide, and now being emulated across the United States.

Christine A. Horsburgh is a Biological Scientist in the Department of Fisheries and Aquatic Sciences at the University of Florida. For the past 11 years, she has studied Florida's lakes and rivers. As a native Floridian, she has a deep appreciation for Florida's unique aquatic habitats. Christy has been involved in several studies of relationships between aquatic macrophytes, water chemistry and fish in Florida's lakes. As a limnologist, Ms. Horsburgh specializes in aquatic macrophytes; she has surveyed the aquatic plant communities of many Florida lakes. For her Master of Science thesis project, she investigates environmental influences on lake biomass and cover of submersed aquatic macrophytes. Ms. Horsburgh holds a Bachelor of Science in Wildlife Ecology from the University of Florida.

Karen Brown is Coordinator for Educational Media and a specialist in the Aquatic Plant Information Retrieval System at the University of Florida's Center for Aquatic Plants. She began part-time at the Center in 1983, while a student at the University of Florida, and joined the full-time staff after completion of her Bachelor of Arts in English. She says that she had never noticed aquatic plants before coming to Gainesville, but has now developed keen interest in them through her work. She has contributed extensively to videotapes from the Center for Aquatic Plants' Information Office, especially the Aquatic Plants Identification videotape series.

261

Florida Freshwater Plants

Ian Breheny, designer
Composed in ITC Garamond and Optima using Pagemaker 6.0
Printed direct-to-press and bound in 8 pt Carolina C1S by Warecraft Press, Inc.
on 70 lb Patina Matte